THE
DOCTOR
LOOKS AT LIFE

THE
DOCTOR
LOOKS AT LIFE

By

PETER J. STEINCROHN
M.D., F.A.C.P.

GREYSTONE PRESS
NEW YORK

Published By
THE GREYSTONE PRESS
100 Sixth Avenue
New York 13, N. Y.

Manufactured in the United States of America

For

Patti and Barbara

"I expect to pass through this life but once. If, therefore, there be any kindness I can show or any good thing I can do to my fellow human beings, let me do it now. Let me not defer it or neglect it, for I shall not pass this way again."

EDMUND COURTENAY, EARL OF DEVON

Contents

Part Three

THE DOCTOR LOOKS AT
SEX, LOVE, AND MARRIAGE

Part Four

THE DOCTOR CONSIDERS
WORK AND PLAY

Part Five

THE DOCTOR DISCUSSES
SOME OLD-OLD PROBLEMS

THE DOCTOR LOOKS
AT LIFE

Prologue:

The Good Old Days

DO WE NEED MORE THAN THE PRETZEL to prove that man goes about making life unnecessarily complicated? He is a strange mixture, man. He sighs for the good old days yet goes busily about inventing new contraptions; these often ensnare and enslave rather than release him.

It is difficult to say which evokes more nostalgia, an old horse hitched to a wagon or a Model T Ford. Both turn our thoughts to things that are no more. We fondly remember the desk without the irritating ring of the telephone; the home not yet blasted by radio and television; the fireplace that was for use and not for adornment; the stereopticon and its natural views, so much more inspiring than today's technicolor inanities—in short, the pleasant, quiet days when life, we suppose, was music in the major key, even, placid, and enjoyable.

But a voice of the 1950's asks: "And do you pine, too, for the endless hours of doing the wash by hand; or perhaps for the blisters you raised cutting the grass with a scythe? Do you have any idea, for example, what the mortality from pneumonia and tuberculosis used to be, compared to today's?"

The answer is obvious. Man does not resent—as much as he tries to convince you—all the comforting inventions of the twentieth century. Nor does he decry the new vaccinations, injec-

3

tions, and drugs that have been decimating the agents of smallpox, typhoid, yellow fever, pneumonia, diphtheria, malaria and
other infections. He will swallow a vitamin capsule with com-
posure, and make a face if you force sulphur and molasses down
his throat.

The good old horse-and-buggy days? Just drive up to any
man's front door with a live horse and polished buggy and say:
"Here, they're yours." Watch him throw up his hands. What man,
in his right mind, will surrender one inch in the long road of
progress?

Man yearns for the olden days only because of his ever-present
state of unrest and uneasiness. He has a vague yet persistent
sense of impending catastrophe. He is not dissatisfied with today
as much as he is with himself. But he prefers to blame the times,
rather than the sense of insecurity that is his human heritage

The good old days are here—now. They are here to be enjoyed
for the asking. Perhaps they are darker than the past. But, in the
final analysis, they are no blacker than you paint them. It's what
you make of them that counts.

Once, years ago, I held and played a Stradivarius. It was a
great thrill—and a great lesson. As I ran the bow over the strings
and fingered a few notes, I was disappointed at the sounds it
produced because I played it amateurishly; yet I felt that wonderful fiddle's potentialities for making exceptionally fine music.

Then its owner tucked my relatively cheap instrument under
his chin and played. By some stroke of luck I was hearing a private recital by an artist who was to perform before a packed
house that evening. As I listened to him play on my fiddle, I
learned this lesson I shall never forget: It's not the tools, so much
as what you *do* with them.

When men fail, they blame their helpless inanimate assistants.
An inefficient surgeon who gets into difficulty will damn everyone
and everything within reach. Most often, however, he will condemn his instruments and berate the surgical nurse for not putting
out better ones. When a clamp slips off an artery, he blames the
clamp and not how it was applied.

So it is with most of us. Modern existence gives us every material opportunity to enjoy life as man could never before in the history of the race. What do we do? We botch our job. We complain about the inconveniences of the modern world and its insecurity.

There used to be a time when people expected every muscle and bone in their back to ache after a full day's work. They accepted it as part of existence. But, these days, they complain of push-button thumbs and "wrist-flick."

Electricity washes, dries and presses our laundry; automatic ovens can almost talk. Machines now do the dishes. Cook books have popularized the most secret recipes Grandma used to keep to herself. Refrigerators and freezing units have made shopping less of a chore. Physical labor in the house has been approaching the vanishing point. Yet woman is "tired." (But it isn't physical work that causes her to wilt.)

What about man? A telephone call or a wire will save him a two-mile walk or a hundred-mile business trip. He has dictaphones, typewriters and other short-cuts for his correspondence. In a physical sense, his life is relatively easy. Yet he, too, is discontented.

Charge it up to emotional tension. Life seems so full of problems and unhappiness that we can't help longing for the quiet old days when life, we suppose, was lived slowly and enjoyed to the utmost. If Great-grandfather could only see us now, I have small doubt he would take us over his knee, let us have it, and then tell us a thing or two.

He would tell us we are being as ungrateful as a spoiled child with a room chuck-full of new toys. He would remind us there's no such thing as the good old days—there's only today.

The good old days we long for were only his todays. And his life, in general, was no different from ours except that he lived it slower. He was scared, too. How do you think he felt during the Revolution or during the Civil War? He didn't think there were going to be many tomorrows either. And don't think his world didn't have its share of thievery, hate, envy, laziness, dishonesty, and cruelty. Men and women were much the same in the good old days—no better, no worse. There were happy ones and sad ones, too. Despair and tension are not the exclusive property of any one age.

The good old days—like the wonderful new days in the offing —are, for all practical purposes, mirages. They exist only in your imagination.

In this life, you are a one-way passenger. You can't turn back. The train only goes forward. Sometimes, to be sure, the track winds along high, dangerous mountainsides or plunges precipitously into deep valleys. Sometimes it halts for a while in black tunnels. But most of the going is smooth and easy, across sunlit landscapes.

Of the passengers on the train, two kinds stand out. One expects the worst all along the way. Forebodings of disaster plague him constantly. He is so preoccupied dreading the catastrophe which may be ahead that he misses the pleasant, even ride that stretches most of the way. The other kind of passenger is exactly the opposite. When the train shoots downward at a dizzy pace, he exclaims: "But there's a lovely valley just below." He is always looking forward to the good things before him.

Which kind of passenger are you? If you are like most human beings, part of the time you are the first kind, part of the time the second. You swing back and forth between despair and happiness—without knowing why. You spend too much of today wishing for yesterday or waiting for tomorrow. You have forgotten—or perhaps have never learned—that you have only one life to live and that you can live it only in the present.

If you don't like the present—your life as it is—you can sometimes change it. Even if you are relatively contented, there is still room for the improvement. If men did not feel that way about life and the world, we would still be where we were fifty thousand years ago.

If you are to live fully and happily in the present, your head must catch up with your heart. You must realize you possess a powerful heritage of primitive emotion. Within your breast you carry an animal, a savage, a child. They do not think—they only feel. If the world does not give them what they want, they strike out against it blindly; they rage, they wail, or they flee. They shout hysterical commands at you, and too often you obey them.

Your feelings must be taught to take orders, not give them. They must learn to toe the mark. Until you make your wishes, impulses, instincts, and habits your servants instead of your masters, you will not be a well-rounded, mature human being. You will always be a fugitive from the present, a mourner of the past.

To help you to see your emotions for what they are—to teach you to make head and heart to work together—is one of the purposes of this book. It will hold a mirror up to life. It will show you to yourself as you are—and as you can be.

Sometimes your reflection in the mirror will be very much to your liking. Don't feel complacent—you may be deceiving yourself. Sometimes the image may displease you. Don't refuse to recognize it—you will be denying you are human, and therefore imperfect.

Whatever you find in the mirror, take it as a challenge. Ask yourself: What can I do about it? Until you ask questions, you cannot find answers. For my part, I will give you the solutions that I, as a physician, have found, and will strive to point the way to the rest. And let me reassure you in advance—none of the images you will see is really hopeless or fearful—not even the first, which is fear itself.

Part One

———

THE DOCTOR LOOKS
AT FEAR

Chapter 1

Admit It—You're Afraid

I HAVE YET TO MEET my first human being who has never been, isn't at present, or won't be sometime in the future, neurotic. Sweeping? Too all-inclusive? I think not. As a doctor I have observed human beings in every conceivable tilt with fortune—good or bad. Nobody, in my experience, is free from anxiety. If you accept that premise, then everyone has the seeds of neurosis within him.

There is fear in every infant as soon as the cord is cut and the fetus is no more. The sudden thrust into a new and strange environment is necessarily a fearful experience.

Fear is inevitable because life itself depends on tension, and tension easily becomes anxiety. Even the primitive one-celled amoeba, which doesn't give birth, but splits in two, does so only when the increasing tension within its membrane starts a chain of nuclear changes that cause the splitting of the cell.

But the amoeba doesn't worry; man does. The child does. The question is not: Does the human worry? Rather: What can he do about it?

Our job as one-way passengers is to enjoy life as much as we can. This is impossible unless we cast out much of fear. But the doing is not simple. Our trouble has a long history. With each one of us it goes back at least to that first moment when we are on our own.

The life-giving placenta (for months the nourishing center in the mother's uterus) is now a discarded encumbrance. If the seeds of fear in us are many; if the soil of environment is warm and moist; if we are born into a family of neurotics who water our inherited fears so that they grow into poison ivy and ragweed plants rather than into rosebushes, then we necessarily become neurotics—spending our lives in trying to adjust to ourselves and to others.

Birth, then, is more than the thrill-producing event in the life of the young mother and father. Birth is a challenge—all around. The child challenges his environment each hour and day of growth; and how often life slaps him down I need not remind you. And his birth is a challenge to the former marital equilibrium of the parents. And the environment challenges all three and bends them, on occasion, to its will.

But fear, it seems to me, is even older than the beginning of life. Remember that birth is not the beginning; it is the continuation. Each new life is only one pearl on a multi-billioned string. If you think of it that way, both you and later the infant will find less reason to suffer fear. You will accept it as part of your heritage, handed down by those who have gone before.

Fear is bred in your bones—and your bones go back millions of years. Think for a moment of what man and his ancestors have experienced and have had to overcome—in all the days of those years.

Man in the beginning was an angry and hostile creature, but he had little time in which to turn his anger and hostility toward his neighbor. Most of his life was taken up in finding food and shelter, and in combatting forces of destruction. He vented his disappointments and rages upon nature, and directed his questionings at it.

A bolt of lightning seeks out, of all things, his mate beside him; he looks up at the skies, shakes his clenched fist at them, and runs to hide. A flood destroys his home; he curses the waters as he swims to safety. A tornado rips apart his hut: he flails the unfriendly wind with grunts, wails and old-world epithets.

These manifestations of anger reflect his inner fear. The skies, the winds, the waters frighten him; he cannot possibly understand them, newcomer on earth that he is. He cannot combat them. Only fright—and consequent flight—save his life. Fear helps him to survive.

With tens of thousands of years of facing the threats of nature, man learns how to combat its destructiveness: with lightning rods, dikes, and shelter against windstorms. These failing, he resorts to artificial resuscitation if someone is struck; he can expertly rebuild his dikes and shelters. As quickly as they are brought down, they begin to rise up again.

Man wastes no time now, except momentarily, shaking his fists at heaven. He has come to grips with his environment and has overcome it to the extent necessary for him to be able to survive. But his anxieties—the protective devices of yesteryear—remain. They have been too long with him to be easily discarded.

It is only our table manners that make us control our urge to reach out first and get our share of the food before the next fellow does; we grudgingly allow him to be served first. But you must admit that the hungrier you are the more impatient you become. (Have you ever sat with waiter-baiters?) The ancient animal within you goads you on to get your sustenance while the getting is good. We suffer from the fear of starvation in the twentieth century as we did when we swayed to the breeze in the topmost branches.

We mistrust our neighbor, not in superficial matters of self-interest, but in the deeper urges. Consciously or subconsciously we know, if it came to a showdown, he would kill us to take our food for himself and his family. He might even kill us to make us his food. The realization of this fundamental truth—that we live in a world of potential enemies—is one of the forces which prevent the plant of fear from withering entirely.

Fear and insecurity are the mother and father of man's worst

behavior. **Competition** often plays the role of the midwife. In its
best sense, competition denotes a fair fight for the prize, whether
it be in love, battle, or business. We deny it on Sunday but the
week has six other days. Cutthroat competition raises its ugly head
more often than businessmen—to mention only one group—like
to admit. Even the multi-million-dollar corporations are afraid of
one another.

Not a cigarette company and a drug company, for instance.
They get along famously with one another. Why? Because fear
does not enter to mar their relationship. Let the one sell billions
of pills and the other its billions of cigarettes as long as they do
not invade each other's fields.

You would think that the "top" cigarette company would be
content, but it never is. In its advertising, it will suggest that the
other cigarette companies are making false claims—that no cigarette can compare with its own brand. Low, cheap, cutthroat
attitudes are not, you see, confined to occasional little businessmen. That is so because the men who direct large corporations
are also human beings. They are weak and frightened; therefore,
they, too, become cannibalistic. If they can't outdo a competitor,
they will often swallow him in a merger.

Although you may—being human—react against the man who
is greedy, avaricious, jealous, envious, cruel, dishonest and selfish,
you should not maintain, for long, your feelings of condemnation
against him. You should realize that at the root of it all is the fact
that he is a frightened human being. Men don't go out of their
way to be mean. They are driven to it by fear and insecurity.

Deep down, most of us want to be kind, considerate and helpful
to the next fellow. Not being saints, we strike out at real or
imagined dangers. Sometimes, our judgment being beclouded, we
ride off in all directions at once to combat imagined aggressors.

Think of your friends and your enemies. What makes one an
enemy, the other a friend? The friend is the one who brings you
gifts. When you are ill he comforts you. When you need money
he gives it gladly. Most likely, he is not an active business com-

petitor of yours, or engaged in the same type of work. He is not
only always reliable and entertaining as a social partner; he can
be counted on whenever you are in trouble. These attributes go
to make a friend—a person who, in a world of insecurity, offers
you some security. We love people because we need them.

What, then, causes such a friendship to break apart? Often it
is money. Let's say, for example, you have loaned your best friend
a thousand dollars. He has deliberately absconded with it. This
was perhaps the first real test of your friendship. You have become
bitter enemies.

Both you and he have now forgotten how much you meant to
each other in the past. Hatred reigns now because each has become
more insecure. Each is frightened. And each will deny it. Yet fear
is the real basis for their enmity.

Call it disappointment, chagrin, loss of respect for the man
who has run off with your money; but the fact remains that you
have a thousand dollars less than you might have. Even though
you may have millions to back that up, there is the deep-down
feeling that wealth too is vulnerable. (Many of the wealthy are
penurious only because they are fearful, deep down in their
unconscious, that they won't have enough. Money is an emotional
symbol of security to them). You begin to grow suspicious of all
people, and ask yourself, "If I couldn't trust Jack, then whom *can*
I trust?"

And Jack hates you for hating him. He hates you because he
has lost security in losing you as a friend. Then why did he take
the money? Because he had to gamble immediate need against the
ultimate value of your friendship. He is not blameless. Thievery is
not to be condoned. Yet Jack may have been conditioned for his
reprehensible action by fear, whose roots go back to infancy, and
beyond.

The fight for power will also divide friends. Two men are in
line for promotion. Only one gets it. The other says, "Good luck,
Sam old boy. The better man won."

From then on they drift apart, separated by the deep jealousy and hatred of the loser. What has happened? Sam's friend, although perhaps financially well off, needed still more to quiet his fears. He needed, he thought, to be top dog; he needed power to convince himself he was not as little and as scared as his unconscious knew him to be.

If you remind yourself that some of the most hateful characters you know are not hateful in themselves but the victims of their insecurity, perhaps you will not find them so despicable. You can't hate a snake because it bites or a bee because it stings. Each does it in self-defense. Each does it out of fear. Each does it in order to survive.

Few things, for example, upset me so much as the unrelenting divebomber tactics of a mosquito on a humid August night, after I've gone to bed. I need my rest, and I dread the weariness that besets me after a night of broken sleep. So I get up with murder in my heart and a rolled-up paper in my hand ready to annihilate him if I can only find the sly little fellow.

Being a doctor, I think of the millions of people whom similar sliver-like demons have infected with malaria, and I hate this one all the more.

But it isn't long before I ask myself why I am so viciously angry. I try not to allow myself to be thrown off balance because my sleep was interrupted. Is the mosquito purposely vengeful? Does he know me from Adam? Is he being sadistic, nasty and inordinately troublesome just because I am I? Does he hate *me?*

Of course not. The mosquito is hungry. And, being hungry, he forages for food. Since it is natural to him to find his nourishment under my skin, he bores in!

Mind you, if I see him on the wall or ceiling, he is doomed. I weigh the importance of my night's rest against the life of that mosquito and the paper makes an arc direct to the target. At least, justice from my point of view—surely not from the mosquito's, who had his rights, too—has been done without rancor or hatred.

I do not want to leave the impression that any of us should go through life willingly allowing ourselves to be bitten, or willingly turning the other cheek after the first has been slapped. What I do want to convey is that if you henceforth regard your fellow man as basically wanting to be good but basically being scared, you will have a better picture of him. And you will more likely frame him in the future so that he looks prettier than he has in the past.

Many of your enemies would be friends again but they are afraid to subject their ego to rebruising. Many of your friends may be close to being your enemies, if you do not, by daily evidence of affection and regard, convince them that they have nothing to fear from you. Even to this day, to show their friendliness, men shake hands—a practice said to have been originated ages ago to prove that danger was not concealed in the hand.

The root of fear is always there, in each one of us. Today mine may become the full-flowering plant (I may be scared to death about something). Today yours may only be a root below ground (you may have only a vague uneasiness, and you wonder at my open manifestations of fear).

Admit that you are frightened *always:* that only the degree of fear changes from day to day. If you *will* admit it you will automatically become less frightened about it. The child who climbs onto a pony's back for the first time, more easily rides off if he says: "Gee! I'm scared." If he keeps it to himself, he is more likely to burst into tears and cry: "I want to go home." And his worried parents take him off the animal because he has found no release from his fear.

Having admitted you are consciously or unconsciously fearful, your next question to yourself should be: "Why am I frightened? Just what is making me nervous?" You cannot effectively meet your problems until you understand their true nature.

When you point your finger at the tiger that is ready to spring, you at least know where and what he is. You can aim your gun at him or turn and run for cover. There may be no pleasure in the killing or the running, but the acute fear is soon over, and you can go about your regular business, relaxed and efficient.

Nine times out of ten, however, you will find that the things you are afraid of are not real; they are not immediate. Think back—how many of the things you feared have ever come to pass? Must you go through life running from imaginary tigers? If you can convince yourself that most of your anxieties have no basis in reality—that they are merely an antiquated part of your animal, savage, and childhood heritage—you will find life easier and sweeter.

Fear is built in as a part of us from the beginning, in company with hundreds of other nicer instincts that have been handed down to us. But it need not be a permanent part of our inheri‑ tance.

Chapter 2

Some Can't Relax

S OME PEOPLE DON'T DARE TO RELAX. How many times have you
heard someone say: "I like to work because then I have little
time to worry"? Everybody seems to be running away from himself, from his fears. The man who knows what he is afraid of is
the lucky one—he can help himself.

But the persistently anxious person is not so fortunate. This
type of individual cannot calmly tell his physician about the
potential danger to him. He has vague fears. He knows there are
tigers around but is unable to point them out because he cannot
recognize them in the first place.

So our hapless worrier stands there in the forest, rooted in
anxiety, unable to run away from the danger. Instead of experiencing acute fear and then the welcome reaction of relief, he
wallows in disheartening, chronic anxiety.

He has morbid fears, distorted fears. The very act of living
becomes conscious effort. He does not even trust habit to take
over the ordinary responsibilities. In addition to fears about
financial security and a well-provided-for old age, he may have
an ever-present fear of illness and death.

He distrusts the efficiency of his heartbeat. He tampers with
his breathing, and what should be automatic becomes a sighing

(often irregular) respiration, which produces chemical changes that in themselves intensify his anxiety. Not enough that he is a neurotic—he becomes a hypochondriac, who translates every harmless sputter of his motor into a threat of imminent wreckage and fatality.

Why will a man rarely admit that he whistles as he walks by a graveyard? Why is he always making himself out a hero, when all his life he is nothing more than the scariest boy on the block?

I think the answer is evident. The whistling reassures him, the talking like a lion-heart diminishes his fears. Even the hypochondriac refuses to confess he is subject to fear. How often have I heard nervous patients say, after detailing dozens of symptoms: "I know I sound like a hypochondriac, Doctor, but—" Or: "I realize I may seem like a neurotic, but—"

I have wondered why Tom, Henry or Mary can't be scared and admit it! Even heroes, on receiving the Congressional Medal of Honor for bravery in the field, admit: "I was scared."

Fear being universal, it should carry no stigma of shame. We should not laugh at fright, acute or chronic—we should sympathize with it, whether it be a child's or an adult's. When a child wakes from a nightmare with a cry of terror, the normal parent runs to his bedside and calms him with soft, reassuring words and a kindly arm around the shoulder.

A hypochondriac is very much like a frightened child. Only his fright is even more intense—and more lasting. The hypochondriac cannot control his feelings or his "symptoms" by an effort of the will. He is a really sick person, emotionally if not physically. But too many people are unaware of this. They use the word "hypochondriac" as a term of censure or reproof.

Don't ever reproach a hypochondriac. Remember that, except for the grace of God, there go you! Today you are well integrated, calm, imperturbable, the master of yourself in relation to your environment, and owner of a working philosophy that gives you inward peace—whatever may happen. Tomorrow?

Tomorrow, many things may happen to throw *you* off balance

and make *you* a hypochondriac. The sudden death of your closest friend may make of you a cardiophobe, fearful of heart disease. A member of your family stricken with cancer may transform you into one who constantly questions the state of his bowels. (That bleeding after the last bowel movement—even though proved to be due to hemorrhoids—must surely be due to cancer of the rectum, you think. That cough—is it TB?) And so, the brave one of today may, however he may doubt the possibility, become the fearful one of tomorrow.

Do not show disrespect for the hypochondriac. Unquestionably he can become a bore, but be as patient with his apprehension as you might be with a child's.

Hypochondriacs vary from A to Z. They come in all grades of variety and severity. There is the one who surreptitiously feels his pulse, examines his tongue in a mirror, and takes his temperature daily; yet, he keeps his fears to himself. He does not belabor you with his symptoms. Another will have heart skips, yet die a thousand deaths without even visiting his doctor to learn what he believes will be the fatal pronouncement. Another. with migraine headaches, "knows" he is slowly dying of a brain tumor. Another with stomach discomfort is "sure" his hyperacidity is really a bad ulcer.

These are the silent type of hypochondriacs. These are the ones who limp through life when they might skip through if they had the courage to consult a doctor to learn the truth.

So many thousands, the roots of whose fears do not necessarily extend back to the neurosis of youth, might be cured by one visit, with complete reassurance by a sympathetic, understanding physician. It is too bad, to put it mildly, that so many remain so silent.

Then, of course, there is the voluble variety who has contributed to the baneful, uncomplimentary definition of "hypochondriac"—as we now use the term.

He is the fellow who "lets out on you" (and little do you realize how much good you are doing him even though you are a bored and unwilling listener). Somewhere back in his infant

years, during childhood adjustment, or in his teen-age years of
growth, this man who has you by the lapels had the seeds of his
present neurosis implanted in him, probably through no fault of
his own.

Perhaps a cold, unsympathetic stepmother or mother produced
the first personality injury. Perhaps a father too involved with
business enterprises; one who gave his son life, but had reserved
no part of his own life to contribute to the boy's growing up.
Perhaps a baby-sitter set off a personality explosion in an impressionable youngster by telling a horrible story that watered the
plant of fear—a plant all too ready and ever ready to grow.

Perhaps an unbeauteous child had to grow up in the shadow
of his or her sister's charm and popularity. Being a wallflower at
a dance is bad enough; being one through adolescence without
respite is actual suffering. Perhaps the child grew up in the home
of an invalid father, mother or grandparent. Perhaps he lived
among outspoken fears, discussions of illness, and its symptoms.
Perhaps at intervals he had to play nurse to pains and groans and
discomforts.

Perhaps financial insecurity had dug a hole in him in childhood. Poor parents often unconsciously force their own sense of
insecurity on their children. Perhaps he wanted to be a lawyer,
but his family cajoled him into giving up school. Now, as a plumber, he feels he lost his chance in life.

Perhaps he got a wrong steer on sex when a child. Perhaps
masturbation in youth gave him a complex, a fear that he would
never amount to much, or at any rate didn't deserve to—so he
thought. We can find 1001 reasons in the lives of 1001 people,
any one of which may transform them into neurotics and hypochondriacs.

Unnatural fear for one's health may at some time rise in the
breast of any of us—however strong-willed we are. All it takes is
apparently forgotten episodes during youth (such as I have mentioned), plus some episode in later life to set it off.

The powder is there, forever dry, waiting for the charge, the little spark to explode it. And it is surprising how little it takes to produce the explosion.

A soldier will face battle after battle with fortitude and courage. One morning in the presence of his fellow soldiers, he will get a dressing-down from an overbearing sergeant (perhaps one who reminds him unconsciously of his father) and presto, something snaps in his mind, whether he realizes it or not. Forever after, he may be at the mercy of a heart skip which he thinks will kill him; or he may get headaches like the one he got when the sergeant unnecessarily rebuked him in front of the others. (As an unloving or insensitive father had, many years before.)

From then on he is certain that he has a weak heart, or a tumor gnawing at his brain. He may become too tired to walk, carry a knapsack, or manipulate his rifle. His hands shake, he perspires easily and is always exhausted. Here we have one man with what we call soldier's disease, or effort syndrome, the inability of healthy organs to perform their functions. Although proven physically fit, his body becomes as useless as that of the patient who suffers from a physical disease.

We must remember that hypochondriacs do not imagine their discomforts. Often have I heard one say, and he meant it: "Doctor, I'd let you cut my arm off right here if I could be sure just what it is that's making me feel so miserable. I wish I were dead."

The hypochondriac begs over and over again to be informed just what it is that is setting him apart from his happier fellows.

"If you only told me it was ulcer, I'd gladly say, 'Operate tomorrow, Doctor,' " such a patient said to me not long ago. "Or if you told me I had TB I'd take a course of treatment at the sanatorium. If you said it's my heart—that I have a bad murmur —I'd accept it and live accordingly.

"But all that you tell me is that everything will be all right. You say you are sure of it, because all of the examinations are negative. Negative! Negative! Negative! That's all I hear. My X rays are fine, you say; my electrocardiogram shows a good heart muscle; all my blood tests are perfect. But what is it? Why do I feel this way? Will I ever feel better? Doctor, it's an effort for me to smile, an effort to work. Why haven't I even the strength to eat? Even moving my bowels has become a project, too. For heaven's sake, do something, or I'll do something pretty quick."

There you have one tune played in minor key on the instrument known as man. Vary the story, and vary the human, and think of the hundreds of thousands of individual but similar *Pathétique* symphonies in living that are being played daily. Think of the minds of men torn between accepting what they call "a rotten existence" and terminating it by their own hand.

I sometimes marvel at the fact that there is not more actual suicide committed. But hypochondriacs "hold on" with both hands, usually, even though they tremble and sweat. The psychiatrist sometimes says they unconsciously want to suffer.

The good, understanding doctor will continue to cheer these cheerless souls. Often such patience pays dividends. Many times I have seen apparently hopeless derelicts made into useful men and women again.

Sometimes a sympathetic family physician can accomplish it all by himself. Sometimes—and perhaps we don't consult him often enough—the psychiatrist will caulk up the leak in the mental boat. It often takes months or years to straighten out a confirmed neurotic.

The hypochondriac must feel that we haven't given him up. He must find at least one to whom he can come with his story, symptoms, and hurts. Although not due to organic disease, the discomforts bother him as much as—if not more than—actual organic disease.

Neurosis, of which hypochondria is a part, is a tree. Most important are its roots sunk deep in the patient's past. The limbs and branches are its flowering. If the tree is producing bitter fruit, the surest way to destroy the crop forever is to cut down the trunk, or, better, still, to tear out the roots. That is the doctor's job.

Chapter 3

Resentment Is Slow Poison

SOME OF YOUR EMOTIONAL TROUBLES you would never think of carrying to your doctor. You don't even know they are troubles. You take them for granted. You consider them a normal part of living. Yet they blast your days and shatter your nights.

Slow, seething resentment, that simmers like water in a pot and never comes to a boil, is responsible for much of our physical and mental distress. If we are chronic haters, consciously or otherwise, inevitably we suffer for it. Most of us have at times been resentful, jealous, envious; many of us have been hostile. What matters is how long we stay that way.

I remember a New York cabbie recently summing up his philosophy in these words: "I never envy or hate the next guy. I always figure that perhaps he's got more reason to envy or hate me. Why should I eat myself up?"

Just then a large car, top down and chauffeur driven, passed us. "See what I mean?" he said, jerking a thumb at the well-dressed man in its back seat. "He don't look too happy to me. But I wouldn't resent it if he was."

The cab driver's face did not belie his words. Here was an essentially happy man. Somewhere along the line he had learned that envy and resentment don't pay.

Enrico Caruso, a sensitive artist, was an overly sensitive human being. As a young man, singing in his home town of Naples, he was given an icy reception. The audience sat on its hands unresponsively. The papers gave him unfavorable criticism. Years later, returning there at the height of his career, he bitterly refused to sing.

All those years he had carried the serpent of resentment within him. Caruso "ate himself up." Like all resenters, he hurt himself more than the innocent objects of his resentment.

Resentment (another name for hostility and anger) is born of frustration—of jealousy, envy, stubbornness, false pride, childish immaturity and the inability to find a suitable outlet for inner aggression. Whatever its cause, it is potential "poison" for your mind and your "innards."

In ancient Greece, Hippocrates suspected this relationship. It has taken psychosomatic medicine two thousand years to come into its own; now we are certain that state of mind affects state of body. Hippocrates couldn't *prove* it—we *can*.

For example, consider Tom, a fifty-nine-year-old man with a permanent "hole" in his stomach, the result of an emergency operation performed when he was nine. Call it an "open window" that scientists can look through at will. Every morning, as a part of his job, he comes to a laboratory in New York City and offers himself for study.

As he lies on the table, the investigators—Dr. Harold G. Wolff of Cornell, and his associates—peer through the stomach opening of this amazing human guinea pig. They carefully observe the reactions of his stomach's mucous membrane to fear, disgust, anxiety and resentment.

Once, as Tom was lying there relaxed—the inner wall of his stomach a normal red—an associate of Dr. Wolff purposely intimated that Tom had misplaced an important laboratory report. Immediately he became anxious and frightened; he got paler in the face *and stomach*. When the papers were at last discovered, his face became pinker and his stomach normal.

Tom, as any one of us would do, showed definite physical reactions when feeling resentment and rage.

Another morning, while Tom was on the table, the associate said he was going to fire him for inefficiency. In the words of Dr. Wolff: "Tom got red in the face, saying, 'Yes, sir,' 'No, sir,' not expressing his anger in words, but exhibiting it by color changes. Yet when my associate left, Tom was boiling with anger and said, 'I could choke that man,' as a final comment on the subject."

As Tom spoke, they looked through the opening and saw that the stomach wall had become fiery red (and covered with many small hemorrhages) ; the hydrochloric acid secretion had increased, and the stomach contractions were more rapid.

Here was the direct response to resentment and anger. These changes in the stomach might last for minutes or months, depending on the weakness or strength of the emotion. What happened invariably to Tom, can happen to you or me.

We now understand the mechanism that underlies such expressions of resentment as: "He is a pain in the neck"—"his nostrils dilated with rage"—"hot under the collar"—"nauseating experience"—"it turned my stomach." All these are specific body responses to a state of mind.

Likewise, we know that resentment will make the previously controlled diabetic "spill sugar." He may require more insulin for a while—and wonders why. Resentment will aggravate a toxic thyroid; may bring on an attack of asthma. It may translate itself into chronic anxiety and diarrhea; into acute anxiety and "nervous breakdown."

See how else it works in actual practice. Here is a highly regarded business executive complaining about his ulcer: "Doctor, I can tell when it's going to kick up. When things get rushed at the office, when I'm under pressure—that's when I get the pains."

In his case it wasn't actually the hurry and scurry that upset him. A psychiatrist to whom I referred him later, disclosed that the cause of his discomfort was an unconscious resentment against his wife.

"What am I knocking my brains out for?" the patient had asked himself whenever he got too busy. It seemed he couldn't (consciously) forgive himself for being "fool enough" to work so hard for one he resented. When the psychiatrist brought it all out in the open, his resentment disappeared—and (in this case) so did his ulcer.

There is a saying that there are two kinds of people; those who *give* ulcers and those who *get* them. Unfortunately, too many of us have the knack of giving them to *ourselves*. The resenter suffers more than the "resentee."

The same holds true for high blood pressure. "Take it easy. Watch your blood pressure," says one man to another who is "blowing his top." Yet doctors realize that it isn't the sudden outbursts that are so bad; rather it is the patient's low-burning, sullen resentments against himself and those around him that aggravate the hypertensive condition.

Dr. M. Ralph Kaufman of New York's Mt. Sinai Hospital substantiates what doctors observe daily in their experience with high-blood-pressure patients: "You will find that there are many patients—such as those with hypertension—who will not take the opportunity to talk about their resentment. If you ask them why they won't talk about it, they will tell you that they've never been able to talk about being angry. If you ask them, 'What do you do about your anger?' some of them will say, 'You know, Doctor, I swallow it.' That is a very frequent way of putting it, they swallow it; they just allow it to tear them up inside."

We are all human; we all get angry. What makes hostility abnormal, however, is its depth and intensity. For example, it is all right for a child occasionally to be resentful against his father or mother—how long this feeling lasts is what matters. Fleeting anger is not harmful. If the child in a tantrum tries to kick down a door, that's acting normal if it does not become habitual.

Doctors have a saying: "Beware the patient who praises you

too highly; he may learn to hate you more." An excellent diagnostician related an unusual incident about a patient that bears out this truth: that love and hate are on opposite sides of the same coin, and enter into all human relationships.

For twenty years the patient had been one of this doctor's greatest boosters. Now, she was sixty-five, and complaining of sudden and persisting indigestion. Caution was the watchword. He ordered X rays. A few days later she returned to his office for the report. Fortunately the news was good: no growths or abnormalities. "What!" she said. "I spend thirty-five dollars for pictures —*and no cancer!*" She stomped out and he never saw her again. Hostility had broken up another fine human relationship.

Blind resentment is a worn but truly descriptive phrase. Unseeing, it rushes in and crowds out the finer qualities of understanding, sincerity, sympathy, forgiveness, and humility. People lose perspective when they become resentful. And resentment knows no age. It must be nipped in the bud early or it will poison us one way or another.

I remember a married couple, each in the eighties. Although the wife had never suffered from physical ills, her mental distress made up for it. One shudders at her sixty years of painfully twisted married existence.

Many years before, she had confessed to me her hatred for her husband. Her resentment stemmed from an innocent, mildly cutting remark he had made about her in front of company. You or I would have forgotten about it long ago. But she remembered.

Although her husband was a good father and provider, and as attentive as any wife might wish, her concealed resentment simmered as a slow form of hatred. It poisoned not only *their* relationship, but her own with the world. As they grew older, and he became the feebler of the two, she apparently "took good care of him." Friends admired her constancy, patience, and seeming concern for him. But to me she confessed: "Doctor, I like to button his shirt, put on his shoes and help him in all ways. The more I have to do it, the more it brings home to me how weak he is—

and how he made me suffer all those years. He's getting his deserts for what he said to me over sixty years ago."

A sense of prolonged grievance can live only in the individual who is out of balance. Only in the one whose thoughts are always turned inward more than outward. It thrives in the selfish person and stews him in his own juice.

Many of us are like a little boy who has a roomful of toys but is unhappy unless he has as many as—or more than—any other kid on the block. Marcus Aurelius once wrote: "How much trouble he avoids who does not look to see what his neighbor says, or does, or thinks, but only to what he does himself." Envy and jealousy are common ingredients of resentment.

The higher our pile of corn, the happier we think we shall be. The duller our scissors from cutting coupons, the sharper our satisfaction—we suppose. The big car, the pretentious home, the valuable paintings, the sables, the pendants, the bracelets and many-carat rings—these, we think, are the final measure of happiness and content. If our neighbor has more than we, dissatisfaction spills over and mars our days.

But you never can tell by appearances. If you were able to change places with your neighbor you might easily come out the loser. Trader beware!

For example, you might trade a normal blood pressure for two million dollars—and a two hundred blood pressure.

You might envy your neighbor his wife, and, if a trade were possible, end up with a shrew.

You might resent your neighbor's handsome boy friend and—on marrying him yourself—find you had all the worst of the bargain.

Patients say: "All right, Doctor. There's no question that resentment is bad. But it's one thing to realize it and another to be able to do something about."

True. It isn't easy to change one's emotional makeup that easily. As adults, we are the end-products not only of hereditary forces, but of parental and environmental influences. Nevertheless, it is worth the try. I would never say it is hopeless. I have seen too many persons change their spots.

To be satisfied with the little we have is only one of the preventives of resentment, that two-vialed poison which creates such disturbance in the psyche (mind) and soma (body).

Another is to realize that if you hate or resent, you can often solve the problem yourself. Every case of resentment is not invariably potential material for the psychiatrist. Often you can do a good job of self-evaluation—if you try hard enough. Necessarily, it requires force of will.

Virginia Woolf touched the heart of the matter when she said, "Consider how difficult it is to tell the truth about oneself—the unpleasant truth; to admit that one is petty, vain, mean, frustrated, tortured, unfaithful, and unsuccessful. . . . If you do not tell the truth about yourself, you cannot tell it about other people."

If you are having any emotional difficulties with others, it is essential that you get yourself to admit that your aggressive feelings are perhaps the basis for them. If we all took this step, thousands of parent-child, husband-wife and business maladjustments might be straightened out overnight!

Admit that aggression rises from a sense of frustration and insecurity. Your job is to find out what's bothering you—to bring it out in the open. Whom do you dislike, and why? Don't bottle it up. Talk it out, gripe, explode occasionally, rather than contain the slow poison.

It's worth it when you consider the poisonous effects of resentment on your health, your job, your marital relations and your general welfare. Remember that *you* suffer for it much more than the object of your resentment.

You should develop the ability to step out of your skin, turn around and calmly appraise yourself. "Know thyself" is as good advice today as when first written thousands of years ago.

One of the friendliest men I know says: "I'm a good hater. I get over it quickly. You don't catch me hating by the hour. A minute's long enough."

That advice should be good a few thousand years from now, too. In any language, and at any time, it is a sure antidote for the slow poison of resentment.

Chapter 4

Man Against Man

THERE IS ONE KIND OF RESENTMENT that poisons the minds not just of individuals but of men en masse. It infects whole groups, social classes, or nations. Not a living soul is immune to it. Because it smites so many simultaneously, it is more destructive than the bubonic plague.

Prejudice is a device of man: It grows and festers out of his peculiarly human weaknesses. I have never seen it in the eyes of a cow as it contemplates its companion in the pasture. I have never observed a white horse rear at a black one because he was black. I have seen horses, black and white, as gratefully accept a lump of sugar from a Jew as from a Christian, from a Chinese as from an Indian.

Unfortunately, man, we have seen, is an anxious animal—a fearful thing that sometimes can protect his frail ego only by becoming fearsome to other men that struggle side by side with him for existence.

Yes, I think we can charge it all up to fear—and not to downright viciousness. The human being is a fearful beast, and life in the twentieth century has not been conducive to allaying his fears. He is afraid of himself, frightened by his weakness. This fear, this insecurity, is projected upon his neighbor.

Man's inhumanity to man is more in the nature of defense than of offense. He must continually reassure himself (so he believes) by lowering the fellow next to him. Often he finds the reasons for his acts in differences. "You are black or yellow; *I* am white." That, he thinks, is reason enough for intolerance. "You believe in a God, but he is unlike mine." That, he thinks, is another good reason for fierce discrimination. "Your customs, your way of life, are foreign to ours." There, he thinks, is reason again. By asserting that what belongs to him and his group is better, he compensates for his feelings of inferiority.

You find this not only in our country, where, in the South, for instance, the white man lives on a pedestal in relation to the Negro. You find it wherever you find man, because we are all brothers under the skin in our interpersonal reactions. The caste system in India is but a luxuriant branch of the same tree on which grows social discrimination in England.

A good test of the inherent decency of your own beliefs is your willingness to accept scientific proof that man *differs* little from his fellows. Science tells us there are no master races or inferior races.

The Caucasian, Mongoloid and Negroid are the three primary races. All belong to the same species, Homo sapiens. True, they may differ in nose shape, skin color, and hair texture. But how about basic similarities? Study their anatomy, height, weight, character, and intelligence. The differences here are minute. Stick a thermometer into a million of each group and you will come up with the identical, average, normal temperature of 98.6° Fahrenheit. Test them under similar mental and physical trials: A genius is as likely to turn up among the Negroid group as in the other two.

It is interesting to note, as Stuart Chase has pointed out, that "the thin lips of the white man are nearer those of the ape, while the thick lips of the Negro are further away from the ape."

In other words, there is no physical slide rule for measuring superiority. Our origin is a common one. Natural science classifies us in the order Primates, along with lemurs, monkeys, and apes. Organ for organ, we are similar, and we have likewise a common denominator of animal behavior.

The blood of all races is of one color and has one basic characteristic: It is life-giving. Mankind has one common blood lineage.

The person contaminated with prejudice closes his eyes to this fundamental likeness. Oddly enough, he also refuses to recognize what are the really basic differences. He does not want to see, for example, that one Negro is different from another or, indeed, every other, in many significant respects; that no two Southerners or Northerners are the same. Yet this, too, is a fundamental teaching of the science of our age: *All things are different.* We must learn to react less to symbols or abstractions, and more to realities. We cannot honestly condemn, let us say, the Germans as a group, or the Russians. There are good, bad, and indifferent in almost any group. Politically intolerant, we often fail to recognize the difference between the people that make up a nation and the men who govern them.

Though one group of men belittles another, human society has use for all. You may mock the Japanese, but your child will play with the toys the Japanese have made. You may cast aspersions on the Negroes, but your life will be better for the inventions and other contributions individual Negroes have made. You may ridicule the college professors, but their discoveries are helping to make your nation secure.

Two thousand years ago Marcus Aurelius Antoninus indicated how dependent on his neighbor each of us is when he wrote: "A man must not be angry with, or hate, his fellow man—for we are made for cooperation like feet, like hands, like eyelids, like the rows of the upper and lower teeth. To act against one another is contrary to nature."

Our duty as reasonable, truly compassionate human beings is

to be forever cognizant of our humble beginnings, our common heritage, our mutual dependency. And to recognize that man, unafraid and rational, is inherently a fine animal. He has come a long way since he dropped from the trees. His potentially good heart will catch up in development to his mind as soon as he finds the way to lessen or banish his conscious and unconscious fears and learns to think scientifically. These, I believe, are the prime ingredients for the workable formula against intolerance.

Until that day, that millennium when all men become brothers, we must try to understand each other. Rabbi Joshua Loth Liebman put it well when he wrote: "A love of neighbor manifests itself in the tolerance not only of the opinions of others but, what is more important, of the *essence* and *uniqueness* of others . . . Tolerance is the positive and cordial effort to understand another's beliefs, practices and habits without necessarily sharing or accepting them."

Chapter 5

Self-Confidence: How to Acquire It

I F YOU ARE TO UNDERSTAND and get along with others, you must not fear them or torment yourself with the thought that they are better than you. You must have confidence in yourself. Courage is a red-blooded word; confidence is of a less intense hue. Yet quiet, day-to-day self-confidence is the more deserving of respect. Courage is a sprint; self-confidence is a long, grueling race.

Courage takes many forms: if you are a woman, it may simply mean wearing Oxfords to a party when you know that every other woman will appear in high heels. For some, it takes more courage to investigate a mouse at midnight than to go hunting wild elephants at high noon. And, very often, the only difference between bravery and cowardice is the opportunity for running away gracefully.

It is at this point that courage and self-confidence diverge. In living, often you cannot run around every obstacle gracefully. You either surmount it or stumble gracelessly. The self-confident do not stumble.

Like many other virtues, self-confidence can be acquired. It takes more or less self-hypnosis.

For example, the difference between the man who is self-assured when called upon to make a speech and the man whom fear covers with a film of cold perspiration is merely one of confidence. You may say, "Oh, well, you can't compare the man who is used to making speeches with the one who hasn't made many—or any." True. But you must remember that the speechmaker was once a neophyte himself.

There was that first speech he steeled himself to make. He had the courage to test his self-confidence. And as on rungs of a ladder, he methodically climbed to his present eminence as a speaker. Somewhere along the line he gained confidence. Somewhere he had to fight it out with fear.

When I was in high school, I used to play the violin in the school orchestra. My seat was on the outer apron of the stage, facing the auditorium. I remember how I used to dread the ordeal of playing in full view of my schoolmates. I knew I was silly in thinking that I was being observed closely, yet I couldn't even get up the courage to look sideways and glance at the audience for a few moments.

There was a morning many years later when this lack of self-confidence welled up and almost engulfed me as I stood alone in the center of a stage ready to make a speech.

As a young doctor, I had been asked by the principal of a high school if I would address the combined classes on "health preservation." I said yes and almost bit my tongue in saying it. For a week I was restless and anxious, and my nights were disturbed. Why had I been fool enough to accept, I asked myself.

If the talk were to be given in a ballroom, or clubroom, or anywhere else, I thought, it might not be so bad; but to think of giving it in a high school auditorium—alone on the podium—when I had been afraid years ago, merely looking out at the audience from my inconspicuous place among the second violins!

At last the day came. The principal and the dean met me and escorted me to the platform. We made small talk as the hall began to fill. I could not look sideways now; or tune a fiddle to distract myself as the group of faces became more numerous. I had to *look out at them*. This in itself was painful to do.

I heard the introduction, I felt the hushed expectancy of twelve hundred teen-agers, and then I was on my feet. I had determined I would not fail. Previously, I had tried to impress myself with these thoughts: Speaking to a thousand persons is no different from speaking to two or three. Don't be afraid to look a few listeners squarely in the face as you talk. Think of an opening remark to get you going; rely on your knowledge of the subject to take you through your speech; remember a closing remark to end it.

My voice first came to my ears as a stranger's. It seemed far away. But I continued in spite of an urge deep within me to run When I had finished, the sense of relief directed my eyes to the clock behind me. I had spoken for forty minutes without referring to my notes.

It seemed to me that few times in my life had I known a greater thrill of accomplishment than I experienced that morning. It wasn't alone the fact that I had made a speech; *I had made it solo.* I had had to overcome the lack of confidence I felt years ago each time I stepped to the platform.

Since that episode, I do not lack confidence on my feet. To this day, even when I am generous in my own estimation, I do not consider myself up to the standard of a mediocre speaker. I know my limitations. But I have lost the fear of standing before an audience, large or small. If called upon to speak, I at least know enough to rise and acknowledge the invitation. Then comes the choice of just saying "Thank you" and sitting down, or saying a few words if there are ideas I want to express.

Why this sudden confession of my personal problems as a speaker? Just to impress you with the need for acquiring self-confidence. Read Dorothea Brande's *Wake Up and Live.* I have recommended it to many patients who have been indecisive and hesitant about their capabilities. It has worked wonders with some.

Miss Brande's open-sesame to the locked door of self-confidence is these words: *"Act as if it were impossible to fail."* Repeat and repeat them, she says, until you believe in yourself. Her formula has worked. Some psychologists suggest that the road to self-confidence will be an easier one to negotiate if you are careful to attack only small obstacles at first. Do not endanger your journey by first attempting to overcome a large threat to your abilities. The reasoning behind this is that early defeats will discourage you prematurely.

I think there is a more certain way to achieve success. Tackle the big ones and the little ones are as nothing. Speak to a thousand and your talk to a small group is that much easier. Sell a hundred-thousand-dollar apartment house, and you will be a super-salesman when you put a shack up for sale. Write a book and the article becomes less formidable. Clear away the most difficult and pressing problems on your desk and the smaller ones become routine.

Self-confidence comes also if you can convince yourself that the next fellow also has his inferiority feelings. Many a beauty queen is outdistanced in life by her plain, self-confident sister. Self-confidence comes of knowledge and proven ability. But often these are not enough. You must use self-hypnosis to convince yourself of your assets. It is a fact that a determined, self-confident football or baseball team can often defeat its more favored opponents. Like the coach encouraging his team, you must tell yourself over and over again that you can and will succeed.

It is self-confidence I have been writing about. Overconfidence is often as bad as underconfidence. Midway between the two is best. Whatever your problem, whatever your goal, first prepare well to achieve it. After preparation comes self-hypnosis. Remember Dorothea Brande's phrase: *"Act as if it were impossible to fail."*

Chapter 6

Respecting the Clock

F EAR WEARS MANY FACES. One man is tense and sleepless, dreading the task that lies before him tomorrow. Another is worried about a wayward child. Another, about the inexplicable turning away from him of a friend. Another, about his own symptoms, which he translates into fatal illness. These, and others like them, make up a rather large segment of the population. No man born of woman is free from some worry, I have said.

But suppose you are the fortunate one who—for the time being, at least—is worry-free. How thankful are you about your good fortune? Are you fully alive now? How do you avail yourself of what life has to offer? After all, life—like good wine—can be really enjoyed only when you sit back utterly relaxed and unhurried.

Let me say here that if you haven't become the master of time, you will never enjoy life to the full. You may appear busy, absorbed, and exhilarated—but so does a mouse on a treadmill. If you allow the clock to wiggle its fingers at you; if you let it constrict you and your activities; if your time is not your own, but time's; if your day—every day—is set in an inelastic mold; then it is evident that you are really another one caught up and knotted in tension. The hands of the clock have you by the neck and alternately choke you and let you go. Sometimes they press

41

too hard and too long and you actually succumb to the pressure of time.

Just consider the telephone. How necessary it is to modern life, yet how much of a nuisance it is at times. The doctor knows this too well. On the days when time is unkind, the jingle of the bell plays a depressing tune on his jangled nerves. Often there is the raucous bell that wakens him at 3 A.M. (How often have I turned off the alarm and, in my sleepy state, wondered why it continued to ring. Not until I lifted the telephone receiver did I know the answer.)

And the awakened doctor, if he is like me, spends hours fighting to fall asleep again. At first there is one thought—extraneous—that comes to his consciousness. Then others—like water through a small opening in a dike—seep through and inundate his mind. He thinks of the patient, other patients, and of other things. How everything is magnified at night. Sleep is a jealous mistress.

Overcoming the persistent, all-encompassing enmeshment of time is possible, nevertheless. Most of us end our day in tension because we begin it in tension. We are behind time even before we swing out of bed onto the bedroom floor. We get up too late.

Just consider this. If you are always in a hurry—fast shave, gulping your breakfast, just making your train into the city—maybe your alarm clock is to blame. What do you usually set it at? Seven A.M.? Then get up at 6:15 or 6:30 (and go to sleep earlier). The leisurely start will provide the properly relaxed mood for the rest of the day. You will be surprised and happy at the difference in the expression on the face of the clock. It becomes much more respectful. There is no more thumbing of its nose at you. Tension is dissolved and dispersed with despatch.

Remember, also, not to try to force twenty-eight hours of activity into twenty-four. It can be done—but at the price of deadly tension. Better to plan to do less work at a slow pace, than too much at the cost of efficiency and ease. When you come home, relax with a drink and newspaper for a half-hour before dinner.

You see, freedom from real trouble is no guarantee of freedom from tensions. The wide difference between tension and relaxation is greatly out of proportion to the small amount of planning that is essential to avoid the one and enjoy the other. Unless you are a beachcomber, or otherwise in complete retirement, you cannot expect to have a clear, unobstructed track for the entire day unless you have planned it that way.

You must respect time, or the hands of the clock will twist you dizzy. If you respect time, it will respect you. And you can't help but respect it if you continually remind yourself that it is one of life's most valuable commodities.

Some people want to slow down, but they can't. They are like a runaway horse—out of control. If they are fortunate, sometimes a doctor is able to catch them by the bridle, pull them up to the side of the road, and save them. All this before they do themselves, and those close to them, irreparable harm.

Some people's tension has a physical cause. Take the man whose thyroid is overactive, who is driven—even when he sits—by an insatiable force that will not rest until it makes a mad maelstrom of his mind. His thoughts race, his heart races, he sweats, his eyes pop, there's a fine tremor in his hands, he perspires; he is as unable to control these symptoms as a man is to breathe easily after running a mile.

But the doctor can help. One of the thiouracil drugs or an operation on the thyroid will wash out the tenseness in the hyperthyroid case.

There are neurotics with a normal thyroid who are also driven. Usually by obsessions of the compulsive type. They are always in a hurry. There is so much to be done. They peck away at innumerable daily tasks; they are overwhelmed by life's problems. Even mailing a letter or driving a tack in the wall assumes such importance that the main goals in their lives are never reached.

They become sidetracked—shunted off into regions that give them little satisfaction. As they cannot concentrate for long, they cannot accomplish. And not being able to look at the results of their labors, they go through life dissatisfied and unhappy.

You see, tension and relaxation depend not alone on your environment; they depend even much more on your physical health and state of mind. Simply stated, tension is a bad habit; relaxation, a good one. If tension keeps your nerves drawn taut for many of your waking hours, you can do something about it. Re-examine your day, re-examine your life. Your doctor can help you on the physical side. You can help yourself on the mental and emotional sides. Planning your day is the first step. The second is to slow down. Easy does it, and undoes tension.

Part Two

———

THE DOCTOR
DISSECTS YOUR HABITS

Chapter 7

Your Habits May Make You or Break You

M<small>ARK</small> T<small>WAIN</small> <small>ONCE SAID</small>: "I've always been careful about smoking; I never smoke but one cigar at a time."

He, of course, was being facetious. Most of us go through life at the mercy of our habits. Every day we are caught not just on the double horns of a dilemma—on the dull horn of good habits and on the sharp horn of bad habits—but on a third horn as well: *bad* good habits.

Somebody has said: "Bad habits are like a comfortable bed, easy to get into but hard to get out of." That holds true for all kinds of habits.

We live by habit: eat by it, sleep by it, learn by it, work by it, play by it, love by it, hate by it, and sin by it. And just what is this powerful force in our lives? Habit is nothing more than the repetition of a reflex act until it becomes so perfected that the act at last is an unconscious one.

What is a good habit? Essentially, it is a mechanism which allows man to live his life more fully—and without detriment to himself. It gives him time to think, to work, and to enjoy; to encounter and overcome the day-to-day minor obstacles and problems unconsciously, while he goes about tackling (unencumbered by trivialities) the major problems of existence.

To see clearly how you develop your habits, observe a child as he learns to walk. See how he concentrates, moment by moment, on equilibrium—on placing one foot before the other. See with what determination he picks himself up and has a go at the floor again.

Little by little, as the child grows, what was effortful becomes effortless. Habit has taken over. The process of walking has become "as easy as walking." The child's brain is left free now to concentrate on other activities.

If you ride a bicycle, recall how, when you were first learning to pedal, a magnet-like force seemed to pull you toward each pole you passed. Only after repeated attempts had jelled into habit were you able to disregard the pole or tree at the side of the road.

And do you remember the old days—really not so many years ago—when learning to drive a car was the supreme test of one's coordination and concentration? There were no simple pushbutton and lever techniques as there are today. Nowadays, steering, shifting and braking are not strange, formidable operations —at least with late models. Driving a car today is more quickly relegated to the unconscious mind than was possible a few years back.

What is a bad habit? As contrasted with a good habit, it is the repetition of a reflex act that is potentially harmful to *you*—not to the next fellow. Often you are unaware of a bad habit's potentialities for actually harming you.

And how about BAD good habits? These three little words speak for themselves: Good habits can be bad as well—and often are.

Your good habits are not all white simply because you put the black label on your bad ones. In the very act of living there is a blending of these color tones. When you misuse a good habit— a white one—it takes on a shade of gray.

For example, you may consider it one of your great virtues that you read a lot. Yet, overreading may cause eyestrain or loss of sleep. The good habit, in the use you put it to, turns bad. Another example: You may proudly say: "I'm not miserly"— but the opposite pole of free spending may be worse in your case.

Or you may pride yourself on being an abstainer, whereas in your way of life alcohol may be beneficial. Or you may congratulate yourself that you do not overeat; yet are unaware that you have the bad good habit of *under*eating to the point of incipient malnutrition.

Do you strive to make your home the neatest one in the block? Does your husband fuss with his clothes? Your efforts may beget you nothing more than the whispered criticism that you are a "slave to your house." As for your husband, people may stick the label of "fop" or "clotheshorse" on his back. Or, suppose you become so engrossed in a hobby that your business suffers slow disintegration. Is that hobby a good habit or a *bad* good habit? And so on, ad infinitum.

Habits can be made or broken—or modified. They need not remain fixed and unalterable. Lucky for you and me that the stuff we are made of is still malleable. We are not hard, brittle clay that resists all attempts to reshape it.

"A journey of a thousand miles," says Lao-tze, "begins with but a single step." The first step in changing our habits does not consist merely of good resolutions and the will of the moment. These will not make us change our ways. We make resolutions under pressure, break them as soon as that pressure lets up. A quip of Red Skelton's aptly illustrates this tendency in our nature. The humorist was flying over the Alps in a passenger plane when its engines broke down. Somehow, the pilot managed to make a successful landing after the odds had seemed against it. Leaving the plane, Red turned to his fellow passengers and said: "Now, folks, you can go back to all your bad habits."

Practice and more practice is the "first step" in habit making or breaking. Suppose you want very much to get rid of a bad habit. There are numerous methods, but you must *want* to give it up rather than *wish* to give it up if you expect to succeed. Enthusiasm backed by daily strength of will is needed to break a bad habit. *Never* break your resolve by reverting to the old habit. Just one more cigarette or just one more drink may negate the entire program of rehabilitation.

Depending on the habit, you may try different ways of breaking it. Some should be broken off completely at the very start. With some, you should taper off bit by bit. Replacement is an excellent method—if, for example, you smoke cigarettes and are worried about inhaling, try chewing gum instead. If you wish to conquer the reflex of fear, face up to the object of your dread; the person who is afraid of animals should try raising one. But in all these methods repetition and resolve are essential.

As a doctor, I have had the opportunity to see the wheels of habit as they actually revolve in many persons young and old. I have come to the conclusion that we allow too many of our habits, physical and emotional, to work against us. We persecute our bodies and badger our minds. With fear and tension, indecision and overconfidence, stinginess and overgenerosity, and a host of other habits and attitudes we undo ourselves. To date, as I've said, our hearts, rather than our heads, have ruled our lives. To catch up intellectually is essential for well-balanced living.

So now let's look again into our full-length mirror where before you saw the image of fear and tension. This time you will see your habits—habits that help you, habits that harm you. You may find that you have been guided, more than you have realized, by *bad* good habits rather than by unqualifiedly good ones. If you are open-minded and courageous—if you sincerely want and strive to do something about what you see in the mirror—the short, hard jolts of painful realization will be outweighed by a happier, more fulfilled way of life.

Chapter 8

Too Sociable—or
Not Sociable Enough?

MAN NEEDS MAN. He needs social intercourse with his fellows. If he is alone long enough, the odds are that he will be talking to himself just to hear the sound of a human voice—even though it is his own. We band together into families and communities because we are—all of us—insecure, and require the reassurance which the very presence of other human beings affords.

Observe young kittens, how they range themselves on one another—like clusters of grapes. And see how puppies cuddle up in a close group for warmth, comfort, and reassurance. Human beings are much the same.

We require others to be social with. When we return to our homes and our beds, there is that warm satisfaction that comes with knowing there are others that care about us. It is not sufficient that the family regards us well. Like little children who react to the pat on the head after a deed well done, we grownups warm to outside praise and friendliness.

For example, it is not enough for a man to paint a fine picture. Although his greatest reward perhaps comes in the actual painting of it, his satisfaction will be incomplete unless onlookers

express their admiration. And so with the man who writes a
book. He, too, is repaid in the actual writing—but not fully. That
comes only when he knows his words have been read—and liked.

No one is averse to honest praise and appreciation of work
accomplished. But only a small minority paint, sculpt, compose,
write, or engage in other creative work that can win wide acclaim.

The excellent mechanic who runs his machine is unsung. The
bookkeeper, the candlestickmaker, the truck driver, the carpenter
—these may find satisfaction in doing a good job, but miss the
kudos of their fellows. Yet their egos, too, must be nurtured and
fulfilled.

So, after working hours, they make plans to mingle with their
fellows. Whether they realize it or not, the mere presence of others
performs a certain rejuvenation of the spirit. It connotes the
acceptance of the lone one by the pack. This, in itself, is satisfying
and reassuring.

In social life, reassurance can become more specific. You may
be regarded as a "regular fellow" at a poker game or the finest
player in your bridge club. You may be invited to parties because
you are the one they count on to sing, play the piano, or tell
stories. You may be in demand as a speaker at conventions or as
a toastmaster at dinners. Or you may be popular for no other
reason than that you are a pleasant, good fellow, one easy to
have around. Whichever you are, your functions as a social being
and the approval of your friends lend roundness and fulness to
your existence.

Happy is that man or woman who seasons his life with just
about the right amount of fellowship. This is a good and necessary habit. But it can be a bad one—over- or under-seasoned.

No matter how strong-willed you are, you cannot live without
contact with others. If you come home from work night after
night and rarely "go out," you soon begin to feel lonely and
unhappy. Passing your time by yourself can get to be habitual.
It is like a deep rut, and you may be stuck in it so long you will
find you have no friends to pull you out. At first of course, you

feel self-reliant. Books, music, television, radio are, you think, all you need for contentment. But you will find yourself profoundly dissatisfied when cut off from friends.

At the other extreme is the person who "just can't stay home." He is the typical joiner. He belongs to one or two of the national lunch clubs. He is a member of two or three lodges. Perhaps he is also on the board of a charity organization. He *never* opens a book or listens to music. He is restless; he cannot sit still and relax. He must be on the move to the homes of others, or always entertaining friends at his home. Like a mouse on a treadmill, he must be going or doing. One night alone with his family and he is lost. He becomes insecure and depressed.

Any of this person's activities may be needful and good in themselves; but *in toto* they indicate a restless, basically unhappy fellow who is running away from himself. He needs constant reassurance: the slap on the back, praise, the kind word, and other ego fodder.

Spending your time sociably is all right in moderation. Too little and too much are bad habits. Take stock of yourself: Where do you fit in? If you are too much alone or too much with others, ask yourself why. Perhaps an honest self-appraisal will indicate that you have been running away from life rather than really living it. Such a self-examination, made from time to time, will help you to keep your daily activities in better balance and point the way to making more of your life.

Chapter 9

Tear Down That False Front!

THE MORE I SEE OF HUMAN BEINGS the more I find the man who looks and acts like a genius probably isn't one; and the man who looks and acts unimportant—like Einstein, for instance—may well possess impressive talents.

When I observe immodesty in a human being, I wonder how he can be so blind. What mental block prevents him from seeing himself as he is? The mirror of his mind, if he could and would look into it, would throw back at him a caricature he might never forget. No human being, however great his accomplishments (artist, inventor, writer, builder, scientist), should expect an accolade from his fellow humans, or presume to impress them with what he has done. He should have only an inner thankfulness for the fortunate combination of genes, environment, and circumstances that have enabled him to be what he is.

In my last chapter, I talked of our need for approbation. The artist, standing in a gallery where his paintings are on display, is never indifferent to the "ah's" and "oh's" of the people looking at his pictures. And the writer, being human, is warmed by favorable reviews of his book. But none of these welcome evidences of public appreciation ever approaches in intensity the inner glow of accomplishment that the dedicated writer or painter experiences in the heat of creation. Giving birth to a book or a painting is at once painful and intensely pleasurable. It is an act the creator must perform, driven by forces within himself. If he loves his art, he accepts criticism as well as praise. The first helps him more than the second, and he knows it if humility and the desire to do better are part of his nature.

Swellheadedness helps no one. The egotist is only deceiving himself, or is trying to. Even the animals behave better. Is a horse unduly proud of his speed and stamina? The elephant of his strength? The dog of his acute sense of hearing and smell? The bird of its gift of flight? You can depend upon it that they accept their talents as a matter of course. Man, whatever his accomplishments, may well learn a lesson in living from the beasts he considers his inferiors.

There are striking examples in the medical profession, as in every other walk of life, of men who have distorted opinions of their own importance. I am always suspicious of the doctor who is elegant in dress or demeanor—smooth in his approach and oracular in his opinions. I suspect his art and his scientific ability. Sir William Osler claimed equanimity as a necessary quality for the good physician. Some men, misunderstanding the definition, have substituted aloofness and a bearing of self-importance instead.

The great men in medicine are the plain men, the simple men, the unostentatious men. They state their findings, their discoveries, their observations with natural, not assumed, humility. They do not say: "This is so." Rather they say: "I think this is so." Distrust the doctor who is positive about everything. The words, "I don't know," never come from his lips. Yet no one can know everything.

The second-year medical student, impatient for the day when he will have his M.D., has already bought a stethoscope; and his razor is sparing his upper lip in preparation for the mustache that will give him reassurance and impress his patients. The young and the inexperienced and the uncertain are all devising ways of improving their outer façade. Either by impeccable clothes, or out-of-this-world offices, or by the attitude of being one of the medical "greats," they go about convincing others of their greatness—but they do not convince themselves.

There have been great men who were insufferable egotists but that in itself takes away from their greatness.

Perhaps the urge to impress others is but a manifestation of infantilism. The child and adult crave, and are used to, approbation. "That's a very good picture, Johnny," or, "That poem you wrote is excellent, Helen," is music to a child's ears. But as the child grows, he finds less and less of the direct form of praise. Many persons are niggardly about giving praise that is well deserved, because they feel to lift up another is to lower themselves. We do not realize how much each of us needs approval.

"Home Town Boy Makes Good." This is true only when the *outside* world has discovered and accepted him as great. The home town is last to sense or appreciate his contribution. To guard against feeling any unnecessary heartache and disappointment if your good work is unpraised and unsung, try to develop the habit of humility. The habit of being able to find fulfillment without the daily approval of your fellows.

One never really learns to get by without approbation. But if you make the effort time and again, you can convince yourself that the reward is in the doing itself. You can learn to accept any huzzas of the populace only as brandy after a delightful dinner.

Albert Einstein, who impresses me as a man of deep humility, has said: "Possessions, outward success, publicity, luxury—to me these have always been contemptible. I believe that a simple and unassuming manner of life is best for everyone, best both for the body and the mind."

Chapter 10

The Art of Being Natural

Most of us are always minding our manners with people. How often are we as natural with another person, or a roomful of persons, as we are when alone?

Think of how stiff and proud you are at a dinner party; then, how you conduct yourself when you get a midnight snack. Compare how you dig into a piece of apple pie and gulp a cold glass of milk, with your stilted, unnatural, good manners when you refuse a second portion of roast beef, although you are still dying of hunger; how you talk to an old friend, with the way you turn stiffly to a relative stranger on your left and make forced small talk that you are secretly ashamed of.

All of us are victims of convention—and fear. Both breed artificiality and self-consciousness. They set up a roadblock between people who might otherwise become close friends.

The actor you like is the natural one. You say, "Isn't he wonderful? Isn't he natural?" My definition of a good actor is one who is *unnaturally natural*. He is so much a part of the character he portrays, you forget (until the final curtain) that you have been seeing your favorite actor.

John Barrymore was not unnaturally natural. He was always his natural self—but not quite natural enough to make you forget him. *He* was Hamlet; therefore he stole something from the effect the character might otherwise have brought to you. How often have you seen a good performance by an unknown actor and wondered: "Who was that?" You were seeing a man so unnaturally natural that his part, small or large, could not help but affect you. It wasn't necessary that he be a "name" player.

Most of us are greatly impressed by naturalness, and wish we could go and be likewise. I always associate naturalness with great appeal. All little children are appealing—they act as the spirit moves them. Kittens and puppies are charming, too, not just because of their size or their antics, but because they are unaffected —naturally natural.

Forgetting yourself, look around you tomorrow. Make secret note of everybody you meet directly or see casually. In your home, the office, in the street, at a concert—wherever you happen to be. Grade them for naturalness. How many—if any—will you give 100 per cent?

For example, on the morning of N day I set out to observe. My wife, without realizing it, was my first object of study. It didn't take long before I had my impression. She rubbed her eyes, yawned, and said, "Please don't forget to send that check today. I promised it to Mr. Black yesterday. You'll find the prunes on the top shelf. 'Bye." Then she was asleep.

I graded her 100 per cent. *She* was not trying to make an impression. The check and my breakfast were on her mind—so she got them off. Without flourish, undue emphasis, or theatricals. Having been up most of the night with the baby, she was tired, so she went off to sleep. No excuses for not being up for breakfast. Quite refreshing as experiment number one.

My car being in the garage for repairs, I took the bus. Since I was a stranger to the driver, he just looked at me as if he were looking at a blank wall and without a perfunctory smile or word, he turned his face to the road. I mentally jotted down another 100 per cent. I took my seat and looked around.

Those people who were reading were perfectly natural.

I observed two men in conversation. One, the younger, had jumped up from his seat when the other had preceded me into the bus. I suspected that the younger man worked for the older one, who now said, "Hello, Grimes," and took a seat next to him.

I could not help but see, here, the too common example of over-solicitousness, fawning, loud laughter, and unnaturalness we observe in one person trying desperately to make a good impression on another.

This young man failed my test with a zero. Unfortunately, unless he changes, he will probably fall short in the estimation of his boss and all others with whom he comes in contact. Until he learns to be himself, he will throw himself, and his personality out of joint trying to please everybody. He will be like a sailboat making needless tacks into every new breeze and getting nowhere.

Youth is more apt to be unnatural than maturity. A young person is in the full fire of ambition. He wants to succeed. He wants marriage, children, a home, a summer place—perhaps a yacht. So he may say to himself: "I'm going to make myself liked. It isn't enough to be conscientious and able. The boss and the fellows in the office have to *like* me, too, if I want to go ahead."

So, instead of just being himself, he tries to be all things to all men. He becomes obsequious. He has a smile for the smiler, and a serious mien for the frowner. He laughs boisterously at the boss who prides himself on being a raconteur; and keeps himself unnaturally stiff and well in hand for the boss who is a stickler for more gentlemanly behavior.

Such a young man—he might very well be the one who greeted his boss on the bus—is apt to be disliked, or, at least, thought a fool. When he grows old in the same office, without advancement, he will curse his bad luck, the bad judgment of his superiors in overlooking him, and the good luck of the "nincompoops" who were promoted over his head.

It is true, of course, that many office "politicians" and "back-slappers" succeed; nevertheless, the honest, natural hard worker usually has the greater opportunity for advancement.

Others may play a great part in your success, but look to yourself first. Others will or will not have the urge to help you along, depending on what kind of person you are. If you are that rare person—the unnaturally natural person—your success is usually assured. People go out of their way to help along the natural person. They meet so many of the other kind that make their days bristle with unnecessary annoyances, that they welcome the easy-to-be-with person who does not make them feel unnatural.

Recognizing unnaturalness in others is easier than diagnosing it in yourself. Anybody can say, "That one is unnatural, this one isn't." But how can you tell which type you are?

First, you must ask yourself, "Am I unnatural?" The answer is there before your eyes if you are willing to see it. Here are some of the telltale clues:

Are your hands in the way when you have to make a speech or walk into a crowded room? Do you consider yourself shy? Do you have an inferiority feeling? Are you ashamed of skinny legs, a homely face, a limp, a lisp, a stutter, or the cut of your clothes? Are you ashamed to be caught talking to anybody you consider below your social standing? Are you always wondering whether John Smith likes you, and, if not, why not? Are you always agreeing with people lest they dislike you? Or, are you unnaturally combative? Do you eat like a bird in the open and take a big bite of a sandwich when you are alone?

Alone, that is the criterion. How differently do you conduct yourself when you are alone—and when two other eyes, or a million other eyes, observe you? Fie upon the man with a camera! He won't let you be natural when you try to be. If you look at the camera with a natural tendency to be serious, he asks you to smile. And what will you see on the developed film?—the unnatural grin of a moron. You were doing what "didn't come naturally."

Resolve to be yourself. Don't put up a false front, a shaky façade. At first your friends will wonder what has come over you. After a while they will like the new edition of you. People like real people—not affected people. Laugh at jokes you like; say "not so good" if you don't like them. Tell a man who is in trouble, that you wish you could help him, but only if you mean it. Otherwise, it is more natural to keep quiet.

I think a natural snob is more tolerable than an unnatural one, a natural liar more tolerable than an unnatural one. Natural badness is more bearable than unnatural goodness.

There is a fable about a little dog who used to jump on his master's lap to be patted. A goat standing in the yard, being of affectionate nature, withstood as long as he could the temptation to imitate the dog. At last he, too, jumped on the master's lap, but knocked him over, chair and all. Whereupon the man rose and beat him to within an inch of his life. The poor goat couldn't understand.

I hope, after reading what I have been saying, you know the reason. No matter how hard he tries, a goat can't act like a dog.

Don't ever be the goat in the fable, if you can help it. The more natural you are, the more people will like you. The you— the inner you—somehow gets over to the other fellow, no matter how thick the camouflage. Putting on an act doesn't help in your relations with your fellow man.

Strive to cultivate yourself as a natural, spontaneous person inside, and the rest will take care of itself. You have heard the saying: "My friends will believe me; what others think doesn't matter." Well, let that be your motto for conduct in life. Don't wait until you are fifty, sixty, or seventy to become natural. Of course, these qualities count at any time, but they count most when you are a young person, coming along in life. Go through life being as natural as you can, hoping that people like you, but not really caring too deeply whether they do or not. If you act natural, you will live a fuller, more relaxed life, and that is true success.

Chapter 11

Control Your Temper!

Your mind is a fireplace, and its temper is the wood. If you are that unusual creature who—by training or by gland—has no temper, then your fire will not flare up, out of control. The kindling is not there. If so, you are a rarity. Temper is no stranger to infancy or old age. And in between, of course, all degrees of men and women are at the mercy of the flame.

The kindling and the wood lie there in the fireplace forgotten in the warmth of the day. Men, women, and children go about their regular chores. All is sweetness and light. The night comes to gather in the family: the father, mother, children, and perhaps a mother-in-law or her husband.

Night after night nothing untoward happens. Then comes the holocaust, apparently from nowhere. As if kerosene were sprinkled on the paper and the chips of wood; as if a half-dozen matches were simultaneously touched to the paper; comes the sudden blowup: the blast of the full blaze.

Perhaps it happened at the dinner table. You asked for the salt. Nobody made a move. You turned to your mother-in-law and asked again. You forgot about her bad left ear. All you knew was that you were beginning to sizzle inside. You looked at your wife. She was spoon-feeding Junior, who had been yapping in his high chair.

It wasn't the salt. Why didn't *somebody* in the house know you were around? You were feeling sorry for yourself; you knew it. Yet you couldn't turn it off. Down deep you knew it was the conference at business that was the kerosene in this instance. You had lost a good account. Sitting around the table, the boss and the rest had tried to show you where you had made your mistake. But like a fool you defended yourself—knowing all the time they were right.

That was what was eating out your insides. Usually you welcomed the first hour at home when in the peace of your home you "unwound" from business. Today it was different; you resented it. It was the little boy in you insisting on taking it out on a table leg by a kick; or on your family by an outpouring of bad temper.

So you raise your voice: "Can't a man have a pinch of salt in his own home? I'm not asking for uranium." (The kindling was lit.)

"But, Harry . . ."

"Never mind the butbuts," you say. "And, besides, the meat is overdone; anyhow, it'll take more than salt to help." And you shove back from the table, excuse yourself (although you hate to), grab the paper, stumble into the studio room and bang the door.

Before you sprawl in the leather chair, you reopen the door—knowing full well you have heard nothing—and shout, "What did you say!" as if anxious for somebody to answer and make a real fight of it. But all is silence except for Junior's chattering to himself. Again the banged door and you sit there looking at the headlines, unable to concentrate on the finer print.

Your fire has passed through two stages of kindling blaze and log fire. It is beginning to die down now into the slow, glowing heat: a mixture of resentment against the world—and against yourself for having acted without restraint.

From here on, this night, one of two things happens—depending upon yourself.

Either you come out of that room in five or ten minutes, the

Control Your Temper!

blaze out and the ashes white and clean. You come and say: "I'm sorry I acted like a boor. It was all my fault. I had a bad day at the office, but that gave me no right to take it out on the rest of you." A kiss all around and making up all around.

Or you continue to crackle. Your draft is half shut, your logs are wet and your smoke pervades the house. A black pall has fallen on the family. Even year-old Junior knows all is not well. An evening is spoiled—perhaps a week of evenings. You continue to whip yourself and your family needlessly. Your combined streak of sadism and masochism is fanning your temper.

Many of us can't count ten under stress. We say we will—next time. But when the waves of heat rise up, each hotter than the preceding one, we blow up into a tantrum much before we get to five (if we have started counting at all).

Have you ever seen a ball player explode after an umpire's decision? Have you seen him throw his bat or take his hat and flick it into the dirt? Perhaps you have seen him push his nose against the umpire's and, red-faced and in high voice, try to get him to change his decision.

Have you ever seen the umpire reverse himself? It *has* happened. But when? How often? Well, the player knows that, too. If he is smart he will blow up fast and let the blaze burn down quickly to clean, sweet ashes. If he chooses to simmer he may find himself waved out of the game.

Life, too, is a game. More important than a baseball contest. If you continue to blow off steam, you are liable to blow out a cerebral artery or throw your heart out of kilter. If you allow the dirty gray-red fires of temper to smolder, you may even be inviting an ulcer, diabetes or hypertension. Not to mention what it does to your happiness and that of your family.

Bad temper is a habit. It sinks its roots deeper with each succeeding tantrum. You will not have to tear it out by the roots if you prevent the roots from taking hold.

Ask yourself what bad temper ever did for you. It gives you a false sense of power and accomplishment. At the time, it elevates you—in your own mind—over the one you are shouting down. But whom do you think you are fooling? The onlookers view you disdainfully as a weakling who would be strong. And in your private heart, you are ashamed of yourself for behaving like a spoiled child.

A temper siege unfailingly lowers you in your own estimation. Afterwards, it takes a lot of pulling to lift yourself by the bootstraps to your former level of self-sufficiency and respect.

The seeds for bad temper are planted in childhood. Although we all have an ego, the self-centered person who expects his world—and those in it—to conform to his every whim, spells his ego with an abnormally large E.

When established early, habit pathways become as well worn and smooth as a new four-lane highway. It takes raw courage to recognize your temper is building up to high speed—it requires strength of will to swerve from the smooth, easy road, to slow down and take the rough detour away from the tantrum.

Only in this way, however, can the habit be broken. It is painful but worth it. It gives you a feeling of maturity and control. You, and not your passions, are in the driver's seat.

When bad temper arises later in life, there are many causes. Illness is one. The stricken person feels he has a right to berate God and man for the infirmity he has suffered, while others have been spared. There are too few Helen Kellers among us.

Old age is sometimes an inciter of ill-temper. Its chief use here is in making a few last attempts to show the rest of the family who holds the ruling rod.

Another cause is sudden riches or elevated position in business or in the local or national community. Within the swelled head there is plenty of room for bad temper.

There are persons with strong inferiority feelings who will try to bolster their ego by abusing a person not in a position to strike back—a waiter, for instance. And there are those, like an occasional man with a ticket, uniformed, riding a motorcycle or in a police car, who "let out" on the supposedly strong ones in the sleek limousine.

Wherever you have man, you will have temper. Leo Durocher

once said: "Temper? Everybody's got a temper. It just shows different ways."

Recognize the truth of it. Forbearance is your best weapon against the dragon, temper. When you feel his hot breath upon you, begin to count—slowly. When you get to ten, stop—and think.

If you can smile, even when you feel you are cracking the skin of your cheeks, the dragon will turn and run.

Chapter **12**

Why Some Persons Are Difficult

IF YOU WANT VERY MUCH to get along with your fellow man, it is essential that you develop one important attribute: the ability to put yourself in his place. You may think that this is easy; that you already are that broadminded person who lives and lets live; who forgives his neighbor his human shortcomings. But nine times of of ten, this is true only when you do not have to bear the brunt of his displeasure and the many irritations he can visit upon you.

For example, if your friend Harry comes to you with a long story of the many uncalled-for indecencies and unfair practices your mutual friend George has committed, you do not find it difficult to review the situation dispassionately. Harry, you think, is upset out of all proportion to the importance of the matter in hand. So you try to calm him. You tell him to forget it; that life is too short to waste on needless worry.

But all the time you are talking to Harry, you are disappointed at his inattention. You are surprised at his inability to control his emotions. You congratulate yourself that you are so serene and objective by nature, as compared to him.

Just as it is not a great task to philosophize on a full stomach and a few glasses of sparkling burgundy, so it is a simple matter to advise another when you yourself are not affected by what is disturbing him. "Fair play," says Shaw, "is a spectator's virtue."

Suppose, however, that *you* are the one involved. Suppose that your best friend has let *you* down. Suppose *you* are the subject of unmerited obloquy; suppose another has needlessly singled *you* out for an outburst of unprovoked temper; suppose *your* ego is tramped upon and badly battered for what you consider no reason at all. Then comes the real test.

Keeping your feelings in check is all a matter of training. At the outset, let me admit that no amount of intellectual muscle ever will overcome entirely the brute strength of powerful forces in the unconscious mind that have been bred in man for at least a million years. Nevertheless, the habit of emotional control can be achieved more often than you realize. Although the intense emotional reaction against hurt cannot be entirely subdued, the period of discomfort can be shortened by self-training.

What is your reaction when a car tries to beat a red light and crumples the fender of your car? Your *new* car? Sometimes words cannot express it. You merely get out and—as calmly as you can— ask for the other driver's license. So far you are surprised, and also pleased, at your self-control. But this man, palpably in the wrong, at once begins to berate *you* for your careless driving.

"Why don't you watch where you're going?" he yells. "You were driving too fast. I've got witnesses in my car to prove it."

The neutral color in your mind fast changes to red. Your emotions charge his. There is a free-for-all, and one or both of you go down in the raised dust of invective and insults.

If your friend Harry, whom you advised so easily, were here now, he would probably say: "Now take it easy, boy. Life's too short, you know. Remember?" Each of us should have a friend Harry as our conscience to help us overcome such emergencies. We cannot be prevented from experiencing emotional upheavals, but we can learn to build storm cellars against these inner hurricanes. And the refuge is simply the awareness that you are dealing with another human being—not with yourself. Realizing that, you automatically put yourself in his place.

Why does this man, you must ask yourself (even as you gaze

upon your once beautiful car) , act like this? Why is he so unreasonable? What's bothering him? Is he disgruntled at the loss of a job? Is he worried about a sick child so that this added discomfort sets off a temper tantrum? Is he himself sick? Is an ulcer eating at his equanimity? If you can train yourself to believe that where there is effect there is cause, you can find excuse enough for another's bad behavior.

And when you are able to do this under pressure—when your own ulcer or home conditions are also wearing you down—you are a candidate for a diploma of Master of Living. For it is in the little daily victories over needless irritations that the balance of happy living must swing in your favor.

Chapter 13

Are You a Good Listener, Good Talker—or Neither?

ONE OF OUR MOST FUNDAMENTAL and important habits—everyone acquires it—is talking. In talking, we convey as much about ourselves as about the subject of our conversation. Good or bad, sparkling or dull, productive or unproductive, the nature of the stuff we store on the winding shelves of our brains comes out indelibly stamped on our words.

Some talk a lot. If you could look at their shelves you would find that the talking has completely emptied them. Others say little, yet have shelves that are well stocked with good thoughts. The happy medium is best: to be able to speak intelligently and still have much left over. Still, you and I know empty-headed people who keep quiet as a pose. They think this proves them to be deep. And you know others who have the compulsion to talk away all the while. Just where do *you* fit in?

Let's first consider the talker—the fellow with the oversized "conversation bump" on his cranium. You have seen him—and heard him. Who hasn't? He is as likely to take hold of your ear in the roar of a subway car (he will challenge any competitive sounds) as he is to corner you atop Anacapri—where his words tumble forth like the lava and smoke from Vesuvius across the bay.

Talking is a compulsion with this fellow. If you are a stranger he may buttonhole you at a party (his friends are now too wary to be trapped so easily). He will talk, talk, talk. If you are a talker yourself, you will find that a headstart is all that he needs. You become, by necessity, a listener—or an interrupter. (What greater disappointment to a talker than to be forced into being a listener!)

At first the talker seems a friendly sort. You admire the ease with which he "breaks the ice." He skips right by the kind of weather we have been having. He seems interested only in your experience with salmon fishing. (A rare bird, you are beginning to think.) But in less time than it takes you to clear your throat, he has—by clever manipulation—changed the subject from *your salmon* fishing to his experience with catching kingfish in the Gulf Stream last year.

Talking is all right in its place, but too many of us don't know the place. You may talk much too much or much too little. Personally, I think most of us talk too much. We wouldn't if we occasionally stopped to realize the uselessness of it. Words should be employed chiefly to get our ideas over to the next person— either to inform, to convince, or to entertain. But often we speak too much for other reasons—egotistical ones: to demonstrate what wonderful and learned fellows we are.

Some of us talk simply because we have to. There is no ulterior motive behind our barrage of words; we simply have the compulsion to wag our tongues. Others start talking because of insecurity. They cannot be alone with a stranger or an acquaintance without diving headlong into the conversational pool. They reinforce their confidence in themselves with words. They overpower us with words and feel stronger as a result.

Not talking is not living to the man with the need to talk. When he meets someone who says nothing to start a conversation, our talker finds the silence unbearable. Every passing second increases his discomfort. If you don't believe me, the next time you see a talkative friend in the elevator, say "good morning"— and nothing else. Play it as a game. Say not another word. Watch him fidget as you whiz by each floor. Before you come to your destination, he will be sure to say something, foolish or otherwise. Unless, of course, he is playing the same game you are.

I am making no plea that you become the stony, silent man. That, too, can be overdone. What I am asking is that you develop sufficient strength of will to keep quiet when there is nothing to say. It's all right to be friendly enough (say "nice day"), but know how to stop there if need be. You will be surprised, and pleased, at the satisfaction you will find in the new evidence of greater strength and control.

It is as true now as when first uttered, that "most people who have a diarrhea of words suffer from a constipation in ideas." And this is a widespread failing. The earpiece on most people's telephone is the least used part of the instrument. We are talkers —not good listeners. Probably the basic reason is that most persons are more interested in themselves and what they are going to say than in the other fellow's views.

How often have I berated myself for giving a detailed outline of treatment to a patient who seemed intelligent yet proved that he was a poor listener. You would believe that a man suffering from heart disease or diabetes would keep his ear open to every word his doctor said. Whether or not the doctor's delivery were attention-catching, it would seem natural that the patient should be able to repeat—almost word for word—the doctor's directions. I should think ordinary self-preservation would guarantee that.

But it does not follow. I have discovered and observed countless reactions of patients that contradict common sense. Some are too restless to hear. Some interrupt every other phrase with a question of their own. When asked to repeat certain directions, they say they "didn't quite hear" what was said.

Perhaps patients should be forgiven because they are taut, nervous, and upset. But, actually, nobody seems willing to listen. Observe, for example, the way some persons answer the telephone. What you will hear is practically a monologue—a one-way conversation. The only proof you have that someone is on the other end is the fact that the phone rang to begin with.

If the speaker happens to be your wife and you, as a good psychologist, want to suggest indirectly that she was quite talkative, try asking her: "What did Annie have to say, dear?" She probably will reply—and how true—"Oh, nothing much." If you are fortunate, she will now realize what you meant by your question. But if you press the issue further and remark, "Well, I'd say you didn't give her the opportunity," you will surely be in for it.

Most women—and no fewer men—are sensitive about this fault of overtalking. So much so that they will rarely admit they talk too much. Some persons have blind spots for this failing. They do not see themselves or hear themselves as others do. And because they are overly sensitive to hints that their vocal cords never get a rest, "even their best friends won't tell them."

Are you guilty? Do you want to reform? The best way to break the habit and become less of a talker and more of a listener is to develop a real interest in your fellow human beings.

Good listening will open up a new world to you. It will make you a broader, better-informed person. Believe it or not, there is even a humanitarian aspect to this. By hearing people out you are helping them out, particularly if they are telling you their troubles. Talk provides a natural release for tension.

And becoming a better listener, letting the other fellow talk himself out, you will be pleased to find that he will listen to you with greater attention. It is his unconscious way of showing his appreciation to you for having listened to him.

How often have you analyzed the reason why you had a wonderful evening with friends? You will probably recall that nothing unusual was on the evening's agenda. Just your friends, you, and your wife. Yet when you are preparing for bed you will say: "That was certainly a nice time at Bill's tonight." Your wife may nod her head but not too enthusiastically. Perhaps she was on the receiving end of his wife's talk all evening. But you, fortunately, had an exceptionally good listener in your friend Bill this night. You discoursed freely on whatever came to your mind, from apples to zebras. You confided your fears and hopes to him.

And all during this outpouring, Bill, the good listener, rarely spoke, merely uttering a remark now and then to encourage you.

Give Bill a break the next time. Resolve to become interested in the next fellow. Show your interest by being a good listener. The feeling of inner strength and understanding you will gain will repay you a thousand times over for your self-control.

Chapter 14

Gossips Are Unhappy People

Sometimes people not only talk too much — they talk meanly. Malicious gossips deserve compassion rather than censure. It seems they can no more control the wag of their tongue than the beat of their heart. However, unless you have the makings of a saint in you, you will find it hard to view them with complete charity.

All human relationships depend upon a delicate balance. It takes little to upset that balance. Friendships, new and old loves, firm business relationships, marriages, political alliances: all are often at the mercy of another's unkind word.

I remember more than one Damon and Pythias relationship that was wrecked by the "big lie" hurled at it by a malicious or envious third person.

I recall many incidents in my office in which husband and wife were contemplating separation because hateful, unfounded gossip by a neighbor had inoculated one or the other with the germ of baseless suspicion and distrust.

Some persons forsake the tongue for the pen. Then, editorial columns in the newspapers devote space to condemning the lowly, nefarious practice of "poison-pen letters."

But word-of-mouth gossip, which can be equally destructive and unfair, goes unheeded because it is so difficult to pin down.

"He said . . ." or "I heard her say . . .": such expressions often do not reveal the true origin of slander. It is difficult to prevent reinfection when we are unaware of the source of the disease.

Gossip spreads by infiltration. Once it begins, it is difficult to stop. Often the central character of it all is entirely unaware that he is surrounded by it. He may sense it in the changed attitude of those around him; but not being sure, he passes it off.

There are judges who are labeled wife-beaters; politicians who are said to have "girl friends"; bankers "whom I wouldn't trust with my daughter's piggy bank." When we hear such accusations, some of us are willing to accept them with this statement: "Well, where there's smoke there must be fire." But for those of us who are unwilling to become partners to subtle or outright calumny there should always be this reservation: "Is the smoke clean or dirty?"

The desire for revenge is often the motor that starts a tongue wagging: The judge has handed down an adverse decision; the politician has given the choice job to another; the banker has refused a loan. Out of such innocent acts does gossip sometimes manufacture its bitter hatreds.

It is an accepted fact that bridge-table gossip has made many a doctor or broken him. I have heard people say: "Dr. Blank is a fine doctor, but I hear he drinks. He . . ." But such conversation usually trails off into nothingness, because I never stay to hear it out.

Perhaps you, too, have heard malicious persons accuse a doctor of being hard hearted, avaricious, deaf, blind in one eye, old-fashioned, too newfangled or alcoholic. Or, plainly refer to him as the fellow "I wouldn't let treat my dog."

Look behind these vendors of venom and often you will see a former patient of such a doctor who has not yet paid his bill; who thinks he has been overcharged; or is just plain malicious.

On the other hand, have you ever thought how easy it is to instill confidence—and how rapidly it spreads? Book publishers who spend thousands of dollars on advertising in newspapers and magazines will tell you that such methods of spreading favorable reports about a book are as a pebble to the beach, when compared to the powerful influence of "word-of-mouth" advertising.

If one hundred persons, for example, like this book enough to "rave" about it; if each speaks enthusiastically of it to ten more; and each of the thousand new readers influences ten more, and so on, printing presses would be running full speed to catch up with the hundreds of thousands of orders. *Gone with the Wind* was such a book. Word of mouth—the human tongue—sold it, not alone publisher's advertising.

In the same way, in daily life, are reputations made and broken. Your life and mine, your success or failure, are more dependent on your neighbor's (or community's) tongue than you realize.

It takes two to make gossip. There must be the one with the tongue and the one with the willing ear. Gossip that falls on a deaf ear dies a quick death. Whatever generates gossip, it will wither away without the ear to receive it.

You would gossip less if you knew the basis for it. If you are a gossip, you are most likely a quite insecure person. You, unconsciously, do not esteem yourself very highly, so you attempt to raise yourself to the next fellow's level by pulling him down to yours. That's easier than getting there by personal achievement.

A gossip is essentially a very unhappy person who spreads misery so he will have company. The unhappiness of others coats his own itch with healing cream.

I have heard it said that gossips are delightful companions. One is never bored in their company. There is always something new, something titillating and fresh to talk about when they are around. Nothing like a nosey, gossipy person, they say.

As for myself, I would rather consort with the Sphinx than with one of these. I prefer getting my news from periodicals and newspapers. I have always felt discomfort in the presence of gossip; I have an allergy to wagging tongues when the subject of conversation is another human being and his weaknesses.

I'm not alone in this. People, generally, suspect gossips. But they enjoy listening to them because their egos become recharged as their own unconscious inferiority feelings are further submerged.

We do not—often enough—sing the praises of others. The expression "Pass out the bouquets while people are still alive and able to smell them" is old but it still makes sense. Too many men who might have enjoyed a modicum of praise for work well done are dead when their merits are recognized.

In the main, I feel that most gossips are not malicious. People do not mean to be unfriendly. It is all a self-protective process that ultimately gets out of hand. As in the story of the fish you caught, the inch becomes the foot. The apparently innocuous remark of the first tongue becomes the malicious exaggeration of the twentieth.

If you are a gossip, you may or may not be aware of it. The only way to find out whether you are one is to listen to yourself. You must develop, as the musician does, the "hearing ear." You must become aware of any dissonance in your speech, must learn to be on the alert when you are talking about a third person. When you hear yourself speaking all evil and no good, on an intensely personal level, then you may almost be certain that your feelings of inferiority, and not your rational mind, are wagging your tongue.

You can help to make yourself and others happier if you fight this tendency (it's infantile) within yourself. However much you dislike a person, resent him, mistrust him, you should determine not to say anything about him unless it is good or at least harmless. This takes practice—and great resolve.

There is no specific formula for becoming a non-gossip, unless it be awareness and questioning one's own motives. Whenever you are tempted to listen to (or to make) unpleasant remarks, consider whether you would do so if the person under consideration were present. Say nothing you wouldn't say if he were listening. If your remarks add up to a balanced and unemotional appraisal, you may practically be certain he would not object.

We have at our disposal many wonderful instruments and faculties that can make our world a better place to live in. Not the least of these is the power of speech. Man was able to take a great stride forward from the cluster of his gibbering, apelike ancestors when he learned to talk. But only when he learns to talk—and think—more rationally and with an acute awareness of what he is saying, will he be able to make the most of this wonderful acquisition. Tongues, like atoms, should be used to build, not to destroy.

Chapter 15

Heads or Tails?

W E HAVE JUST LOOKED at one bad habit, gossiping. Now we must face up to another. Gambling is one of the stronger urges in the human makeup. As with gossiping, even children are subject to its sway. It starts with the matching of picture cards and the development of skill to win at "mibs" and fill up one's pockets with shiny, colored marbles. From there to matching pennies and betting on the results of high school football games is a natural step.

In adulthood, gambling takes many forms. There is a wide choice to suit the individual's temperament. You may try a lottery in Mexico or France, the Irish sweepstakes, the numbers racket, cards or roulette, chess or checkers, dog-racing, cockfighting, or betting on any form of sports. Lloyd's of London, although a staid and respectable insurance company, probably knows more about the human's gambling propensities than the rest of us. Even the most staid of us—like Lloyd's—is a gambler at heart.

Such a deep-seated drive cannot be passed off as "just one of those things." The human is driven to do things for a reason. In the case of gambling, it is probably a desire for forgetfulness in addition to a desire for money. The thrill is not so much in winning as it is in taking yourself away from the ordinary, mun-

80

dane things in life. A little of this is good. But when you do it
to excess, it becomes a running away, a partial killing of yourself.

For example, the chronic bridge-players or daily mahjong
addicts are to all intents and purposes simply anesthetizing themselves against intolerable situations or are fleeing from ennui.
They will be the last to admit it, but in most cases it is true.

And their husbands who play poker three or four times a week
are not spending all those late hours for the purpose of winning
a lot of money. They will tell you themselves that it generally
all evens out at the end of the year. What they are doing, really,
is running away from reality. They will say they play simply to be
in the company of "good fellows." Yet, if you ask them, they will
admit the only time they see these good fellows is at the poker
parties.

Have you ever kibitzed a pinochle or bridge game? What impressed you most? Was it the skill of some players and the inade-
quacy of others? Probably not these things alone. What you have
felt was the total concentration and absorption of the players. If
you, as the kibitzer, so much as moved or coughed, you could
feel the unconscious resentment of those at play—you felt like
an intruder. They had temporarily withdrawn from life and their
usual surroundings and problems. Whether they won or lost,
they were satisfying their unconscious urge to forget.

I have known a number of persons who actually committed
slow suicide by becoming followers of the horses. One man had
built up a large business after hard years of application and self-
sacrifice. In his early fifties he suddenly lost interest in his work.
When customers wanted him personally, they couldn't find him.
They took their business elsewhere, even before it became common knowledge that he was spending his time at the track.

He lost steadily and heavily. One- and two-thousand-dollar bets
soon dwindled to the ten-dollar size. He mortgaged and lost his
business; and then he mortgaged his home. The last I heard was
that his son had had to leave college in his junior year to go to
work to support his mother and a younger sister. His father had
left home to follow the sun and the horses. He was now a tout

and had cut himself off from his family and his community.

What was behind it all? Why should an apparently successful family man give up everything to chase a will-o'-the-wisp around the race tracks? In his case I knew the answer. Although supposedly happily married, he and his wife had been on bare speaking terms for the past few years. He told me that business and life in general had lost all zest. When I reminded him of what he owed his children, he shrugged his shoulders as if completely indifferent to their welfare. He was in a severe depression but refused to see a psychiatrist.

This man was a potential suicide of the acute variety. His downfall began when he went to the races one afternoon at the invitation of some friends who wanted to cheer him up. They succeeded too well. He was elated, he thought, because of his winnings. Actually, he felt like himself again because for a period of four hours he had been able to lapse into complete forgetfulness.

Thereafter, he would come home, arms and pockets full of papers, charts, forms, and prognostications about the next day's races. He would spread these out on his bed after a hurried bite and study them with greater concentration than he had ever given to his business. Sometimes he would drive down to the railroad station at night to get the latest results of the day's racing. Each added hour that he devoted to the racing itself, or to reading and talking and studying about it, was sixty more minutes of painlessness and anesthesia.

Unquestionably, gambling is a form of chronic suicide. If you have ever taken a special train to a race track you will know what I mean. You will remember the tense faces studying the papers and forms, the total abstraction as each man retreated into himself, oblivious of the person sitting next to him.

There are, of course, some islands of gaiety on the train when a group of three or four people are together on a day's jaunt to their first racing afternoon. But the regulars are the "lost ones." They have an air of curious detachment and resignation. They look like people who have given up—and they have. They return day after day because they have found it is the only way they can continue to live painlessly.

Some people turn to painting, collecting stamps, reading mystery stories, or watching baseball for the normal forms of human forgetfulness; others find that they need stronger anesthetics; they drink or they gamble. Few of us are entirely immune. All of these things, in moderation, serve a good purpose. But, overdone, they are as surely a sign of emotional illness as a fever is a symptom of physical disorder.

Chapter 16

Why Women—and Some Men—
Are Tired

A GREAT NUMBER OF PEOPLE WILL CONCEDE that gambling is a bad habit. Yet these same people would raise their eyebrows in astonishment if I placed much of shopping in the same category. It can help cause chronic physical illness. Many a diagnosis is made more difficult than it should be, simply because the doctor sometimes forgets to ask a leading question. "Do you like to go shopping?"

Most women take pride in their expertness in the art of buying. The two cents off the dollar and the mark-down on the price tag act as powerful magnets that pull the female of the species to the great wonderland "downtown." And "downtown" is the reservoir which collects much of woman's energy and often leaves her depleted.

I recall case after case of women who have been exhausted. Physical examinations, blood counts and other investigative procedures were negative. Medical history did not reveal family tension or other worries as causes of the fatigue. Further questioning into habits usually elicited the provoking factor. In some cases it was loss of sleep; in others, too much work around the house. Snooping in corners for dust is not conducive to rest.

Then, the inevitable question about shopping. And the usual answer: the guilty smile.

If you are the man of the house, have you ever accompanied your wife on a shopping tour? Not for an hour, but for a day? Then perhaps you understand how and why so much valuable energy can be expended. Your experience was probably a replica of John's and Mary's, which I am going to relate.

It begins the night before, as Mary reads the evening paper. "John," Mary says to her husband, "Knox's is having a simply marvelous shoe sale tomorrow. Besides, I've needed a new hat for a long time." It continues the next morning. There is an unusual air of expectancy and excitement at breakfast. At least, John senses it in his wife. The children are off to school. John is having a day off from work and is anticipating a lazy day of puttering around the house.

"John, why don't you come down with me to help me pick out the hat? I'd love it so much. And besides, it's a special occasion—the last time we shopped together was when you chose that beautiful hat before we were married."

What can a man say to that on his tenth wedding anniversary? So John and Mary start out, on what appears to be a simple jaunt to buy a hat and pair of shoes. They wait outside Knox's until the doors open.

A long line of women has already formed. John stands out like a sore male. Women behind him look at him in open distaste and dislike because he is taking up room in *their* line. When the doors open, there is a surge which culminates in a sweeping charge for the escalators. Mary leaves John, shouting, "I'll meet you in 'shoes,'" and is gone with the pack.

He can at last distinguish her riding the escalator, with her competitors standing on the moving steps above and below—all giving off that aura of tenseness which you expect in soldiers going over the top or charging an enemy hill. John decides to browse around the displays on the first floor. Then, a half-hour having passed, leisurely he takes the escalator to the shoe department.

Mary is not to be seen. John had not counted on brigade after brigade of reinforcements. While he was browsing, the escalators were disgorging bargain-hungry women into the shoe department. They are now deployed four and five deep. Where is Mary?

He shoulders his way through a thinning sector. There she sits slowly shaking her head as a salesman removes a shoe and replaces it in one of a half-dozen open boxes which surround them. She catches sight of John and, as he comes closer, she mumbles something to the salesman, who turns to the following customer as if dreading the next of a long line of ordeals he is sure to face this day.

"John, dear, the shoes were nice but not just what I wanted. There's one pair that interests me, but . . . let's go to the hat department. I'm sure that won't be too crowded." John is amazed at Mary's apparent coolness and remarkable equanimity, when he considers the battle she has recently been a part of.

The hat department is not crowded. After trying on a dozen hats, Mary tells the saleslady she wants to think it over, and signals to John. "It's only eleven o'clock, John. Let's go up the street to Sage's. They have a new line in. We can have lunch there and perhaps take in a good movie before the dinner party."

That perks John up a bit, so he says, "Why not?" Well, to shorten the story of John's day of disillusion, the tour lasts until five. Mary comes out of it with a pair of shoes that she doesn't like. John is beginning to feel mean. (Man is jealous of his days off.)

The anniversary dinner is late, the food is undercooked, and the celebration a failure. Mary stands up well until after dinner; then she begins to fade. In fact, what has irritated John is seeing the darkening circles under Mary's eyes. "Why did you have to go downtown today, of all days? I couldn't say no to you because you were so set on it. Common sense should have convinced you to put off your shopping until tomorrow. Why do you women knock yourselves out so unreasonably?"

And that is the plaint of many husbands. And that is the wonder of doctors. Do women have a streak of masochism? Do they relish the aftermath of shopping: the rushing home, the late dinners, the aching feet, the disgruntled dispositions, the utter exhaustion?

Shopping, to some women, is like poker and horse racing to the confirmed gambler; like tobacco and alcohol to addicts. Some women simply dare not look at an advertisement; dare not go window shopping; dare not talk styles with their friends. If they do, they are soon on their way.

An incident like Mary's shopping day would remain a trivial incident if it happened only occasionally. But many women have the compelling urge to go downtown almost daily. As if cleaning their home and provisioning it were not burdens enough, they submit to this soul-wearying regime often.

The shopping habit can only be broken with difficulty, but it is worth the try. The wife, as the core of the home, needs to conserve every bit of energy she has. Unplanned shopping dissipates it. Chronic fatigue in the housewife spreads its effect to her innocent husband and children.

Nothing tires a woman so much as shopping—except, perhaps, trying to convince her husband to sign the checks.

Chapter 17

Turn That Knob!

ALTHOUGH I MAY SEEM TO RAIL against man's unwisdom, I can never entirely overcome my wonder at his resourcefulness, ingenuity and inventiveness.

In Baltimore, years ago, as a student at the University of Maryland Medical School, I remember being wakened excitedly by my host at whose home I was spending a week-end. "Come down—*quick!*" he shouted after his vigorous shoulder-shaking had torn me from a deep sleep.

Being on obstetrical call at the time, I was sure that I was being summoned to a delivery. When I ran downstairs, I found my friend seated in front of a large contraption, his fingers manipulating some dials, earphones clapped to his head and a look of disbelief and ecstasy on his face.

"What is it?" I asked. "Who called?"

He paid no attention except to put a forefinger to his lips and say "Sh-h."

I looked at the clock. It was after midnight.

Suddenly he jumped up, handing me the earpieces. He shrieked: "Pittsburgh. I've got Pittsburgh. *Imagine.* Pittsburgh. Listen—it's KDKA!"

As I listened, the wonder of it came over me. And I thought: "It's here. I'm in attendance at the birth of a new infant." To me every outburst of static was like the screech of a new baby. It was wonderful—and it still is.

The baby has long since become a child, an adolescent and a grownup. Unfortunately, however, it has not grown to full stature in maturity. In some ways it is a giant, in others a dwarf. And, in this respect, radio resembles its makers.

I am not one to condemn radio unreasonably, because radio's faults will never neutralize the good it has done to mankind. To my mind, what outweighs its every shortcoming is the entertainment radio has brought to the tens of thousands of invalids who will never again walk out through their front doors; who will never again go to a movie or the theatre; who will never go to a lecture hall; who will never again ride in a car; who will never know the simple pleasures of the outdoors.

One need only think of a symphony program to forgive a soap opera; of an educational forum to bear a bloodcurdling children's program; of calm, unsensational advertising to forget the nausea-provoking commercials that tempt one to seize the set and throw it out the window.

People have the habit of condemning the whole, and not its bad parts. Every new invention, from the wheel to wireless sound and vision, contributes to the forward progress of the human race. Although we are at once the master and the servant of our inventions, the benefits of being the one outweigh the disadvantages of being the other. Our inventions are no worse, or better, than the uses we put them to, as I said a while back.

Radio is still as remarkable to me as when I first heard the call letters KDKA. As I listen to one program, I think of the many others I might enjoy at the turn of a knob. And when I turn off the set, I muse—at what is going on in the atmosphere about me. Although there is no sound, I know voices are talking, whispering, singing, shouting; that all manner of instruments are giving forth music; that there is tragedy and comedy waiting for the listener who wills to hear.

It is a bad good habit to keep the set turned on for hours irrespective of what comes out of the loudspeaker. Radio confers its favors only on those who deserve them. You can separate the good from the bad if you are sensitive to the bad. And if radio upsets you so much you cannot bear it, all you have to do is snap it off.

Some of radio's greatest detractors see it only as a machine of evil. They curse it for being a child-spoiler and for inducing adult amnesia (yet they keep it playing). Be discriminating. Do not condemn the whole for its parts.

And so with television, the new addition to family life. How often, even at this early stage of its infancy, have I heard people actually go into hysterics at the very mention of television. "I *know* I should never have let Tom have a set installed," a patient told me. "It has disrupted our whole life. The children never eat in the kitchen any more. They sleep less. The horrible programs give them nightmares. We never gather around the piano or play games any more. I don't know where or how it will end."

Training, madam. A turn of the knob, Tom. Don't blame it on the set. Pick your programs, choose your time. Radio and television are still young. Their possibilities for good are growing; are tremendous. Man looms larger in my estimation for their presence.

Part Three

———

THE DOCTOR LOOKS AT SEX, LOVE, AND MARRIAGE

Chapter **18**

The Happy Marriage

Many a woman—who chose her husband as carefully as if she were picking out a new spring hat—still wonders if she made the fortunate choice. And many a man—who chose his wife with the infinite care with which he lines up an important putt—often deplores his score in the game of matrimony. Hats and games, however, can be altered at will. There is something less changeable about a mate.

You hear speeches by couples celebrating their twenty-fifth or fiftieth wedding anniversaries, to the effect that "We've never had an argument." All has been sweetness and light!

Yet casually ask any happily married man and woman—who are not on a dais, trying to prove themselves the exceptions—and they will admit to frequent differences of opinion.

The great in our time—and others—are quite frank about expressing opinions that we little people tend to conceal. For example, here are the words of Mahatma Gandhi on marriage: "I have led a fairly happy married life the past forty years in spite of occasional jars. . . . We have had occasional bickerings, but the end has always been peace between us. The wife, with her matchless powers of endurance, has always been the victor."

From between these lines of Gandhi's there emerges this ogre:

93

the constant battle of the sexes. "The end has always been peace between us."

Marriage need not be a recurring series of battles and peace conferences. But by the nature of man and woman, it must necessarily be the source of many differences of opinion. Let's go a step further and put it this way: Unless they are saints, when two human beings live close together, there is bound to be friction.

There's the rub. Each one of us is a bundle of deeply grooved habits. Every man and woman is jealous of certain of his traits; sensitive about others. You cannot live a few years with a person without learning what these habits are—and also that you cannot budge them with a crowbar. There is only one course open—you had better learn to live with them. Either you adjust or you are lost.

Listen to Sir Arthur Keith, noted British anthropologist: "In no two is the balance alike, and each different brain has to deal with a different tide of experience. I marvel, then, not that one man should disagree with another concerning the ultimate realities of life, but that so many, in spite of the diversity of their inborn natures, should reach so large a measure of agreement."

That goes for marriage, too. I sometimes wonder how some marriages last as long as they do when I consider how many and diverse are the cross-currents in which husband and wife are tossed about. I don't mean just the great, sweeping ones—chronic alcoholism, infidelity, economic hardship, impotence, frigidity. Even more I mean the smaller currents—the conflicts born out of jealousy, loss of respect for each other, irritability, disagreement over unimportant details, lack of interest in each other's interests. I mean the conflicts that arise when a man puts business ahead of marriage, or a woman places a career ahead of husband and children. There are many of these problems in even the best of marriages, and, added together, they make a current that is often strong enough to upset the ship.

But if we try, we can prevent this disaster. Marriage can be a success if each partner is willing to make adjustments—to "give and take." The statement is very simple, but the doing is not.

It means forming new habits and abolishing many old ones. It means accepting your mate for what he is and not trying to make him over—as if you were a little god and he a devil. It means accepting the realization that all love, "true" or not, does not forever run smooth.

I have been married sixteen years and have practiced medicine about twenty-five; I don't believe I shall know much more about marriage a quarter of a century from now. As a doctor, a father, and a husband, I feel myself fully initiated and qualified (at least as much as anyone else) to write a formula for happiness in marriage.

I think that mutual respect is of first importance (leaving sex aside for the moment) in the successful marriage.

Oliver Wendell Holmes has said: "The nearer you come into relation with a person, the more necessary do tact and courtesy become." We married folk tend to forget the importance of this.

Too soon do we take one another for granted. We do not realize that both man and woman resist the loss of their identities. They are willing to merge, but not completely. Any normal ego resents that.

The young lover's gallantries, attentions, enthusiasms, showers of gifts, and overwhelming passions cannot go on forever. No woman expects her husband to continue through marriage at the pace of courtship. If he did—and no man can—she might be the first to say: "Oh, don't be a boy!"

But every last remnant of courtship should not be cast out by a husband. I believe we should think of love as a fire. It must constantly be fed if we expect to obtain the warmth and comfort it can give every one of us.

All the love offerings—the kindling and wood of affection—are not the same. Each has its place and its time; each is equally important. And as a fire is not made on hot days, so there are certain times when love's gifts are held in abeyance.

The wife who thinks her husband is not affectionate enough should remember that sometimes the deeper the feeling, the less the demonstrativeness. She should realize, too, that for many a loving man, before he is married, lipstick is a nuisance; after he's married it's his only reason for not kissing his wife good-bye in the morning.

Wives should take to heart the revealing truth in a statement made by Dr. Frank S. Caprio: "Remember that the average husband is no Romeo. In fact, given a number of years of marriage, Romeo would have become the average husband."

Each husband and wife should make allowances for the other's likes and dislikes. The man who is grouchy at breakfast—who takes a long time to wake up—is thankful for the wife who understands sufficiently to leave him to his morning paper. (I think it was Churchill who said he attributed his long, happy marriage to the fact that he and his wife had had breakfast together fewer than half a dozen times.)

On the other hand, in the evening a husband should have ears and sympathy for his wife's account of a trying day, even though it seems inconsequential as compared to the importance of his.

And the wife needs to listen, on occasion, as she did when she was being courted, to his thrice-told jokes; and to have a willing and sympathetic ear for his business problems and worries. She needs to realize, too, that although it is a man's misfortune that he must live with the face that he was born with, *she* has the ability to make herself pretty (but all too often forgets to, after the children come).

A husband should remember there are times during each month, perhaps for a week, when, due to her monthly sickness, his wife becomes irritable and hard to live with. He should be especially patient with her then.

If there are arguments, it is, as Browning said, "good to forgive, best to forget." But some of us refuse to do either. Men and women often too prematurely abandon the ship of matrimony when it has sprung only a slight leak.

Of the approximately 800,000 divorces in this country every year, I wonder how many men and women who are splashing about in the cold, uncomfortable waters of loneliness look up at the side of the ship and say: "I wish I hadn't jumped." Most show their inner need for marriage by "trying it" again with another partner.

In my practice I have seen innumerable break-ups and near break-ups. In some marriages, failure seemed inevitable. (Though a noted psychoanalyst has said that never in his extensive practice had he seen a case where divorce was the only way out.) Chronic alcoholism or insanity may have thrust in their ugly heads. Perhaps there was no genuine love—on one side or both—even before marriage. Childlessness may have been the cause. Infidelity, promiscuity, and cruelty are often too difficult to bear. Such are among the major reasons for divorce.

But think of how much unnecessary unhappiness and how many divorces are caused by petty differences. One man I knew was getting a divorce because his wife was a poor cook. He was tired of eating out of a can. As a cause for divorce this may sound laughable, but it isn't to the parties concerned, when it comes at the end of a long history of friction.

Here is a wife who is considering divorce simply because John looks at other women openly and admiringly. He finds the normal man's pleasure in looking at a pretty leg. His wife is the victim of a rigid romantic delusion—that one loses all interest in members of the opposite sex when one marries. Probably at bottom she is unsure of herself.

Sometimes a couple quarrel seriously over a third person. Fiction has made much of the "triangle" in marriage—the husband and wife and the outsider who claims the affection of one or the other. But often there is an outsider who is an insider as well. Everyone has seen the effects of this triangle on marriage: the husband, the wife, the mother-in-law!

When I watch a mother-in-law consciously or unconsciously laying a marriage waste (she is, in the old phrase, "more to be pitied than blamed"), I have to wonder whether we are really the higher animals we pretend to be.

Do we have less sense than the dog who has her litter of puppies, brings them through infancy, and then cuts the family ties

—or willingly allows them to be cut when the pups are given away? Are we not as smart as the birds who accept the final flight of their fledglings without remorse? The fact is, the animals seem to want their young to go off as soon as they can take care of themselves. The parents have lives of their own to lead, and do not wish to be bothered by their grown offspring.

But the human holds on to his child. Even though, as an adolescent, he himself developed a normal hostility to his parents in the growing-up process, when he becomes an adult he in turn does not willingly let his child lead his own life.

Mind you, there are some mothers-in-law who are perfection. But they are few. If a mother-in-law (especially the husband's mother) comes to live permanently in a couple's home, the marriage must be exceptionally strong if it is to survive.

If in some way, like losing a card in the shuffling of the deck, we might willingly lose our parents in the crowd of humanity, perhaps parents and children might be better off. This thought is not an original one. Over two thousand years ago Plato, in his *Republic,* made arrangements for all children to be segregated from parents at birth. Although many have voiced approval of his plan since that time, no one has yet put it in operation.

I hope—if you are a mother-in-law—you will take this in good part. I do not write out of personal vexation. I happen to be blessed in having a good mother-in-law and my wife can say the same. I am merely recording a judgment on what I have observed, and it is written partly tongue in cheek. One cannot really lose mothers-in-law in the deck. Most of us must reconcile ourselves to having them, and the more cheerfully the better. In a way, a mother-in-law is part of the person we marry. We must accept her as such a part—a part rarely seen, if she causes disagreement— and not allow her to blight our lives, any more than we would other minor sources of difficulty.

So much for mothers-in-law. I shall probably not hear the end of them, after what I have written above.

Frederick Loomis, an authority on marriage, has declared: "I am quite sure that four-fifths of successful marriages are made so by the wife, though the converse—that four-fifths of the failures are due to the wife—is not at all a necessary or likely conclusion."

Many men and women will argue with that conclusion. But I am certain that few will disagree that it is at least a fifty-fifty proposition.

I think that Cyril Connolly in *The Unquiet Grave* puts it in a way the majority of us will accept: "In a perfect union the man and the woman are like a strung bow. Who is to say whether the string bends the bow, or the bow tightens the string? Yet male bow and female string are in harmony with each other, and their arrow can be aimed. Unstrung, the bow hangs aimless; the cord flops idly."

I think of woman and her home in the same light that I consider the captain and his ship. She is responsible for the necessary provisions; she sees that the decks are scrubbed and the brass polished. She has complete charge—although most husbands are unaware of it—of the course that the ship-of-home shall follow. And she, like the captain, makes momentous decisions in good weather or foul, in health or in illness—and would be the last to leave the foundering ship if she decided it had to be abandoned.

If all this is true, it becomes evident that the house is a good one—or bad—depending in greater part on the wife.

We must admit, however, that the most experienced and able captain could not sail any battered old hulk of potential driftwood or scrap iron in perilous seas. Nor could he repair every leak. The husband may be shiftless, lazy, and a poor provider. He may be a chronic alcoholic. He may be unfaithful. He may be jealous of his children. He may not care for his children.

These are the traits that we often find in the psychoneurotic. A wife cannot do much with him. The psychoneurotic—anxious, out of balance, fearful, irritable, chronically fatigued, depressed, and generally unhappy—has problem enough in living with himself. He cannot adjust normally to a wife. Nor can the normal wife possibly find happiness in a home with him.

A good captain cannot be a neurotic, either. He must possess the gift of objective judgment. He must be able to stand off and

examine himself impartially. What kind of questions will be raised
for such an appraisal?

Is the wife a good captain of the home? Does she provide good
food? Is she a nag? Is she short-tempered? Does she show lack of
interest in her man's interests? Is she forever comparing him with
Sam Jones next door who is always getting raises—and therefore
better clothes for Mrs. Jones than her own husband is getting
for her?

A captain can easily raise or lower the morale of his associates.
And so with wife and husband: Her actions can drive him to do
things which are far from his nature.

I have seen more than one man in alcoholic stupor who later
said that what invariably forced him off the wagon was his wife's
constant nagging.

"When I get through work," a patient of mine told me, "I have
nowhere to go. I know that after a full day, when I'm tired, there's
nothing I'd rather do than go straight home; perhaps have one
beer and read how the Giants have made out. On very rare occasions when I have been able to do this—usually my wife wasn't
home yet—it was like a little bit of heaven. And I never took
more than *one* beer.

"But after a few nights of nagging, fighting over nothing, Doctor, I can't bring myself to go straight home. I need fortification
to bear up under the strain. I suppose another man would beat
up his wife, or take it lying down but I go out and get drunk and
beat *myself* up."

I talked to this man's wife. I could see there was no simple
solution. Each had lost respect for the other. Love was cold—and
beyond warming. They had two married children. I wondered
why they didn't separate. They were still in the middle forties.

Yet they remained shackled by hate and intense resentment for
one another. Each had reached for a suitcase many times with
actual intent to leave the other. Always, however, something
would swerve them from their decision: a telephone or doorbell,
or a superheated blowup that would relieve the immediate pressure
to depart. I did not know the man and woman very well. I can

only guess why the marriage ship was foundering after years of being buffeted about on the stormy sea of incessant quarrels.

It takes two to run a ship: the captain and the crew. I have found that many differences of opinion arise because a decision has never been made about "who is captain." Here you have perfect conditions for the initiation of a tug-of-war.

Our male-dominated society early instills in man the belief that woman is his chattel. That he is the strong one, the smart one. His wife may grant all of this. At least she will, if she is a good practical psychologist. But she knows deep down inside her that all men are incorrigible romanticists.

To man, business is romance, love is romance, living is romance. He thinks his feet are on the ground, but they are not usually. Women know instinctively that man is forever the boy; that even a little girl is more motherly and more of a house manager than he will ever be if he reaches ninety.

Man is strong outside his home; he is the weakling—only the crew, not the captain—when he opens the door and closes it behind him. Most men should let their wives have complete charge of the house, yet be willing to offer constructive suggestions on the running of it. And most women should not interfere with their husbands' business—unless the husbands, too, ask for constructive criticism.

The happy home would result from such fusion of two good spirits and two good wills. Love would flourish, respect for each other would remain on a high plane. And mutual respect is, as I have been more than hinting, quite fundamental. Love withers without it.

I said to a man who was having trouble at home: "You say you are not an angel, but that most of the rift at home is being caused by your wife. You say your home is messy and dirty. Your meals are mostly eaten out of a can. That she's not doing a good job in bringing up the children. That she is short-tempered with them.

"Tell me, how long has this been going on? Not long. I remember you both quite well. As short a time ago as last year both of you were clear-eyed and happy. One year has made this difference. Why? At least, guess at what might be a valid reason for the way she has been acting."

He uncupped his chin from his hand, stood up, and began to pace the floor. You could almost hear him think. He shrugged his shoulders a few times as if talking to himself and finding no answer for himself. He sat down, lit a cigarette, and blew smoke toward the ceiling.

"Perhaps—" he said. Then he stopped. After a moment's hesitation he began to speak again. "I've been trying to figure it out. I'm not perfect." (All of us say something like that when we want to talk about ourselves in an uninhibited way.)

"I know I have faults. But good God! I'm a good father, a good provider. I'm home nights. I don't get drunk with the boys. I don't gamble. I don't go out with other women. Until lately we were perfectly mated sexually. What, in heaven's name, have I done that's really wrong?"

I asked: "Has you wife ever told you about any discontent she may have? You say you're not perfect. What has she complained about? What has she wanted that you haven't given her?"

"I'll tell you," he said, "although it seems too silly to mention. I'm certain a little thing like that can't be the cause of our trouble.

"About a year ago she told me that her fur coat was eight years old. I was surprised. I said it looked just the way it did the first day she put it on. It did, too. I told her she could get along without a new coat for another year or two. That the house needed a coat of paint and, besides, we needed to turn in the car for a new one. She only asked me once more, about a month after that, and we dropped the discussion. I'm sure if she were still thinking about the coat she would have said more about it. It can't be that!"

But it was. His wife told me later that it wasn't the coat so much as what it stood for that disrupted her usually even way of life.

"I knew Jim could afford the coat, the house-painting job, *and* the new car. Ask him. I'm sure he won't accuse me of being a spendthrift—of making him work his fingers raw. I figured that Jim had been taking me too much for granted. If he didn't love me enough to write a check for what he could easily afford— simply because I *wanted* it, and wasn't being unreasonable—then nothing mattered. Marriage and everything with it fell flat. I would go on, but he would give in or I swore our life would never be the same." (You see here stubbornness, with perhaps good reason, pitted against a man's blindness and thoughtlessness.)

In another chapter, I have written about temper and how it can disrupt one's life. If you care at all for your own happiness—and your family's—you will understand how the devilish swish of the tail of the tantrum can sweep through your home like a tornado. Temper, unmindful of how severe the damage it causes to things and people, can destroy a home if uncontrolled.

If your husband says you have a terrible temper, consider it and discuss it with him calmly in the happy interval between storms. If you say he has the temper, have him do likewise. Such discussions can prevent a more formal discussion of complaints in a divorce court.

Admit you have a temper even if it hurts. And this will not be as painful as you imagine—after you have said it.

Once I was called to see a woman in hysteria. When she quieted down long enough for me to be able to hear, her husband said: "All I did was to ask her not to say 'ain't.' I didn't really criticize her."

When she heard this she foamed at the mouth again. "We've been married twenty years. A day hasn't gone by—counting leap years—when he hasn't corrected me. I can't stand it any more."

I gave her a sedative and walked into the living room with him. "Is this true?'

"Sure, Doctor. But, my God, you'd think I'd beaten her. I didn't realize it had bothered her so much. I swear she'll never hear about it from me again."

It is such little aggravations that add up over the years. An honest talk—with white handkerchiefs waving to prevent a new sudden outbreak and disruption of the truce—will often be all that is necessary to prevent outbreaks of temper and tantrums in the future.

Stay away from your husband's—or wife's—sensitive spots. You can't help but know what and where they are.

Chapter 19

The Truth About Sex

NATURE HAS US AT HER MERCY. She is a past master at making us want intensely the things that she wants us to want. She gets her way through our appetites, not our minds. Her chief desire, it seems, is to have life go on. To accomplish this, she must create in each living thing the desire to live. Self-preservation is, admittedly, our strongest urge. But it is made up of layers of lesser urges which add up to this strong pull—as great for the individual as is the force of gravity for the universe.

Man would not care whether he lived or died if not for his insatiable appetites. Nature gives us functions for self-preservation and wisely makes their fulfillment range from simple pleasure to ecstasy. Even the physiological functions of eating, drinking, sleeping, and eliminating are pleasurable.

When you sit down to a full-course dinner, not having eaten since breakfast, every mouthful becomes a gustatory revel. When you have sweated out quarts of fluid and depleted your system of salt, is there anything more refreshing than a glass of cold milk or beer? Not having had a bowel movement in a few days, how pleasurable is the very act of evacuation and the sense of relief and lightness thereafter. None of us, having so many times by necessity suffered the discomfort of an overfull bladder, can forget the pleasure of the first few moments of pressure-release.

These urges and appetites are familiar to all. Each one of them has been made pleasurable so that the individual will *want* to work the necessary gears that keep the machine to its efficiency. How we look forward to sleep when exhausted. Nature makes this enjoyable, too. If sleep weren't the pleasure it is, more of us would continue to overwork ourselves into earlier graves.

But nature was faced, at the outset, with a grave problem. It was almost as though she said, "Granted that I can keep most living things happy in their essential day-to-day functions; but how can I be sure that these living things will care enough to want to procreate? After all, there's much sadness in the world. Suppose, for instance, that people got together and said collectively, 'It is enough that we have lived and worked and suffered; we will not visit this hard life on our unborn children. We strike. We refuse to carry life on. We will not cohabit. We hereby, one and all, snip the life-line.' It would not be long before man returned whence he came—to nothingness.

"I shall have to overcome that urge to race extinction," said nature. "I must inculcate in man—and in other living things— the ultimate in ultimates of desire and subsequent supreme pleasure." And nature got to thinking and came up with the answer: sex.

"I shall make the male and the female. I shall give each a bit of the characteristics of the other. But neither shall ever be complete in himself or herself. There shall ever be in one the intense need for the other. That need shall be satisfied only in the periodic ecstatic embrace of the two—the sexual embrace. It shall be the culmination of earlier satisfactions between the two: meaningful words, the meeting of eyes, the touch of the hand and the kiss. Early desires of the two shall be fanned into love. And of love shall come a child, and of children the renewal of life. In that way, I can be sure that man—and beast—will continue to populate this planet."

No one who has ever experienced sexual pleasure will deny that nature has fashioned her over-all plan for race survival with all the cards in her favor. Where's the normal man or woman who can completely suppress the recurring urge for intercourse? It is a hunger that cannot be denied. It is a hunger like the hunger for food. (Only greater.) It is a thirst like the thirst for water. (Only a greater thirst.)

Sex is here to stay. And sex can't be as naughty as our medieval and Puritan forebears led us to believe. Nature devised it, not man.

Sex is here to be discussed intelligently, dispassionately. Think of it as an appetite. Although its pleasures are more exquisite than eating, consider it for a moment on the level of eating. For example, study your companions at a dinner party. Observe their appetites.

Here is a thin, pallid type of woman who picks at her food. The appetizing dish set before her awakens no intense desire in her. Due to illness or a natural incapacity, she feels that eating is nothing more than a necessary evil she must accept in order to keep her body together.

Next to her sits a full-blooded, massive man of forty who cleans his plate and eagerly accepts a second portion and a third. His conversation is meager until he finishes the pleasurable business at hand. Not until he has lit his cigar over coffee does he expand into the brilliant conversationalist he is known to be.

These are the normal extremes in appetite. As you look around at the rest of the diners, you will see others who are hungry and not so hungry. Nature has given each his measure of appetite for food.

Some have abnormal appetites. Take the person with an intestinal worm, an overactive thyroid or diabetes: he will eat and eat and eat and still be unsatisfied. The craving cannot be stilled. Temporary surcease, only, comes to such a one with eating.

On the other hand, consider the woman with a "nervous stomach," who shrinks to a weight of eighty pounds. "I can't eat," she says. The desire isn't there. We must also spoonfeed her to start her back on the road to normal nourishment again. We call her condition anorexia nervosa.

Nature has failed these overeaters and undereaters. They are the sick ones.

We find the same variations with sexual appetites. They can be normal and abnormal, as with the need for food.

The nymphomaniac and her oversexed male counterpart, the satyr, are abnormal. They are carried away by excessive appetite for the sexual act and never really reach fulfillment of desire. They are at the mercy of their sexual anatomy and of their glands or their psyche. Unlike the man at the table who is at last satisfied by a third portion, they go on trying to satisfy their sexual appetite and end up with sexual indigestion—a symptom of psychiatric imbalance. Such appetites cause untold tragedies for their possessors and others.

Not much happier is the lot of the frigid. Those who sit at the table and nibble. Those who accept sex because they have to. Those who love, not only without pleasure, but with actual dislike and distaste. They suffer and their mates must suffer with them. There are at least hundreds of thousands of husbands—a smaller number of wives—who consider themselves trapped for life, unable to assuage normal desire unless they find satisfaction outside marriage.

What is normal sex life? The band of normality is broad.

Some time ago a man sat before me and said sheepishly "I think I have been having intercourse too often, Doctor. Do you suppose it might be affecting my health?'

How often? He had relations with his wife once every two or three weeks. Even then he had to force himself, to whet the desire. Had he ever had it more often? No. Except on his honeymoon, and then it had required effort.

I would call him on the low normal side. There are thousands of "undersexed" men like him. Perfectly normal in every way— their sexual appetite is merely below the average.

I told him he wasn't overdoing. Was his wife content? Oh, yes— no complaints. Lucky man, I thought. It doesn't always work out as smoothly as that. I told him he had nothing to worry about.

When he left I thought of another patient, a man of sixty-five who was a high normal. He had told me that he had had intercourse with his wife (barring menses) every night of their married life, for forty-five years. And that each still thoroughly enjoyed it.

Once a week, once a month, once nightly—the rhythms vary. Each falls into his own naturally. Illness, depression, and emotional upsets often reduce the sexual appetite. Change of life often increases it. In the dangerous forties and fifties some men often have their "last fling." The appetite increases abnormally. It is as if the man knows he is soon to go hungry; he had better stuff himself in anticipation.

Every day of his practice, the doctor sees the results of sexual aberration. It is the cause of much unhappiness which often can be eliminated. If you are troubled about such matters, confide in your doctor. Talk to him frankly and he may help. For mature consideration between doctor and patient is most often the key that will open the door to a better understanding of sexual problems that are undermining one's happiness.

For example, consider the "problem" of masturbation. It is widely misunderstood. Parents come to the doctor, almost hysterical about a young son. They have caught him "playing with himself." The doctor can give them facts that will help to straighten out their thinking. (And, incidentally, allow their son a greater chance for growing up as a normal boy rather than one saddled with a guilt complex for the rest of his life.)

The doctor can tell them that masturbation *does not* cause pimples, insanity, weakness, impotence, weak eyes, nervousness, and dozens of other afflictions. If it did, at least 90 per cent of the male population would be involved—because at least 90 per cent of the male population have masturbated at some time in their lives. (So has a large percentage of the female.)

It is because of the parents' undue alarm (the father, at least, should know better), because of the unnatural anxiety they transmit to their youngsters, that masturbation is harmful; not so much the act itself. The parents are often the greatest contributors to the growing boy's mental conflicts and maladjustments. They inflict on the youngster personality damage that may last into adulthood.

The Chinese have a different approach. They allow male chil-

dren to masturbate at will, and neither encourage nor discourage
the habit. They seem to realize that when you bump head-on
into nature you always come out second best. Children will
masturbate—often simply because it provides a pleasurable sen-
sation. If chastised or punished—or merely reproved—by parents,
they may masturbate all the more. The less fuss made by parents,
the better.

Parents might be reassured (and surprised) if they read Professor Kinsey on the problem of masturbation. They would learn
that highest frequencies are between the beginning of adolescence
and age fifteen. That about half of the single male population
is still masturbating at fifty years of age; that among married
males the highest incidence (over 40 per cent) occurs between
twenty-one and twenty-five years of age; and that in the middle
fifties over 10 per cent of married males continue to masturbate.

Kinsey goes on to say: "There are boys who never masturbate.
There are boys who masturbate twice or thrice a lifetime; and
there are boys and older youths who masturbate two and three
times a day, averaging twenty or more per week throughout
periods of some years."

These are the facts, Mr. and Mrs. Parent. Don't worry about
your boy. Like all the other youngsters, he will grow normally,
and mature into a normal adult—if only you give him the chance.
Don't forcefully stifle all his "urges" or you may do more harm
than good.

Some parents are worried because their adolescent sons have
frequent nocturnal emissions ("wet dreams"). They think these
will weaken and sap the strength of their offspring. One father
told me he believed that semen is formed in the brain and spinal
cord, and that every needless emission drains the dreamer of his
very intellectual marrow. That was why he was worried about
his son. He felt better when he learned that there is no connection between the two; that nocturnal emissions are normal and
not weakening; that even up to the age of fifty about one-third of
the male population still occasionally have these experiences.

However great the concern of parents about what they consider their children's sexual aberrations, if they are honest and frank they will admit that their own sexual problems cause them the most concern. This has been my experience in practice. The problems of teen-agers take second place to those of their parents' sexual maladjustments. And not surprising, when you consider that in about 75 per cent of marriages that end in divorce, sexual difficulties between the partners are the greatest contributing cause.

This was not always so. In earlier days, women expected little enjoyment out of sex—they thought of themselves primarily as child-bearers. They tended to take sexual frustration for granted. But, as Dr. Milton R. Sapirstein points out in his brilliant book *Emotional Security,* "Women have now emerged from their beaten and submissive role, to play a more meaningful part in society. They vote, they work, they think for themselves, and they expect sexual gratification."

And there is the nub of the potential discord: sexual gratification. Each normal partner desires it intensely, and is thrown off balance when deprived of it. He (or she) becomes unhappy, resentful, and confused, and blames the other. Frigidity in a wife has driven men to drink, suicide, or extra-marital sexual satisfaction. Impotence in the male has produced similar reactions in some females.

In rare cases, frigidity is permanent. It may never be possible to arouse profoundly frigid women. Somewhere in their emotional life, as a rule, forces beyond their control practically "unsexed" them early. They cannot even imagine what it is to experience the climax of the sexual act. Beauty of face and form is no guarantee of sexual vigor, but many a man never discovers this until after marriage. Sometimes a psychiatrist can help the wife. Sometimes he can't. Psychiatry does not pretend to have all the answers. Often the husband needs treatment as much as the wife.

Cases vary. I remember a friend and patient, married for ten years and the father of four children, who finally found the cure in divorce. "My wife is as irresponsive as a board—always has been," he told me. "I don't blame her, but it is senseless to go on like this." Months later he was radiant and fulfilled. He had found a wife who complemented his sexual desires. And his former wife? She married a widower who, she said, was able "to give me for the first time in my life—imagine, me, a mother of four children—the kind of happiness I never even knew existed in the world." Frigidity, you see, sometimes requires the right husband (but more often a psychiatrist) for cure.

Impotence is another cause of marital discord. The wife who is passionate is left suspended in a vacuum of distraction by the husband who is unable to bring her to sexual fulfillment. Sometimes the husband's failure begins during the honeymoon; sometimes, later on in life.

Just as with frigidity, the cause of impotence is usually psychological, although there may be contributing factors like the physical and physiological. One man may be "able" with his wife and "unable" with another woman. And vice versa. Whatever the cause of impotence, it is not due to sexual excess. In fact, it has been found that those men who develop early sexually and who have considerable sexual drive are prone to be virile longer than men who have always had a weaker drive.

It is interesting to note that only about one-quarter of the male population is impotent by the age of seventy. According to Kinsey: "Impotence in a male under fifty-five years of age is almost always the product of psychologic conflict." This underlines the fact that it should be the doctor's job or the psychiatrist's —more often than the lawyer's—to straighten out marital tangles.

Another problem the doctor can offer solid advice on is homosexuality. As about 4 per cent of the entire population has been estimated to be exclusively homosexual, it is not difficult to believe that every doctor is confronted by this problem. The cause of one's love for one's own sex is not wholly known. Loosely, we attribute it to deep-rooted emotional maladjustments. Sometimes there is a cure, more often there is not, depending on the degree of homosexuality.

All male homosexuals cannot be recognized by the familiar

tags: mincing steps, broad hips, effeminate voice, and other female characteristics. Some men and women in every business, profession and phase of human activity may have homosexual tendencies. They do not *look the part*.

The real male homosexual is completely uninterested in women as a source of sexual satisfaction. He finds pleasure only with men. His female counterpart finds hers with women. But there are degrees! Some persons may be heterosexual and homosexual; they may be happily married, they may keep their partner emotionally satisfied, yet feel the need for homosexual practices as well.

Men who are fathers, and respected in their community, have come to me and confessed their homosexual tendencies; not so often women, who are frequently more difficult to evaluate unless they are the "mannish type." The doctor possesses no miracle drugs to prescribe for these patients. Treatment consists of willingness to listen and of patience to reassure them that they are not alone, and to guide them in all the details of life that perplex them. Often the psychiatrist can do little more.

As a physician I have little sympathy for the public's reaction to the individual homosexual. Considering his frequent helplessness in the grip of his drives, to heap scorn upon him is like blaming a man for getting cancer or being born an idiot. Sex customs vary from country to country, from time to time. Our civilization—unlike the culture of ancient Greece—considers homosexuality a "sexual perversion." However, we should learn to regard it as a sign of emotional and social maladjustment, to be treated with sympathy and understanding. Not only the physician, but the public, should calmly recognize the problem for what it is and cooperate in attempting to solve it.

Far more serious for society and its members are the sexual maladjustments of normal people. Too many of these problems are due to nothing but ignorance—ignorance on the part of one or both partners.

Here is one example out of hundreds I have encountered. It concerns a young couple, each twenty-one years of age. The wife complained to me of nervousness and sleeplessness. At last, the confession: "I feel worse after intercourse. I don't seem to get any satisfaction from it. No feeling at all, in fact."

I learned the cause soon enough from her husband, whom I sent for.

Never having had sexual relations before marriage, for six months of their married life he had *thought* he was having intercourse but *wasn't*. Not until his wife had a simple operation on a hymen that had resisted his previous efforts, did each experience true intercourse.

Here is another common case—a woman who resented having intercourse while nude. She refused to realize that for many normal men visual contemplation increases enjoyment of the sex act. Her husband's insistence and her profound modesty (it originated in a stern upbringing) were fast speeding them toward a breakup until careful guidance set them straight.

I have encountered more than once the traditional-minded male who became disgusted with his wife because she preferred at times the position above him during the sex act. It was the only way, she told me, she could come to climax. "If he thinks so little of my pleasure," she declared, "I guess there's no use going on together." This man had to be shown the physiological facts* that made it advisable to comply with his wife's wishes.

These cases are legion—the woman who dislikes her husband's unrestrained sex play, the husband who cannot reconcile his wife's sexual abandon with her "innocence and purity."

The cause of these various misunderstandings is ignorance of the basic nature of the sex urge and of its many *normal* variations. Our own society is at fault. Blame it on our grandparents and parents, and on theirs in turn. What is cloaked in secrecy and shame and ignorance always produces distorted viewpoints.

Too many people are unwilling to examine the sexual side of their lives. It should be a simple and blameless thing. What is sexual satisfaction, after all? It is rooted in what is commonly

---

*An excellent explanation of the physical and emotional aspects of sex and the nature of the orgasm will be found in *Sexual Feeling in Married Men and Women*, by G. Lombard Kelly, M.D., published by the Greystone Press, New York, N. Y.

termed the "climax" in each partner. Dissatisfaction comes when only one, or neither, obtains it.

The husband who "withdraws" just before the climax because his wife fears pregnancy becomes unsatisfied and nervous.

The wife who rarely or never reaches climax because her husband has not taken the time to arouse her is also overcome by a feeling of dissatisfaction.

It is because man is generally first to reach his pleasure—his orgasm is elicited often in two minutes—that woman frequently is deprived of hers. Her dissatisfaction, acute or vague, reacts upon her husband. This is the basis of many divorces. In countless cases, however, the man is not really to blame.

Says Dr. Kinsey: "Considering the many females who are so adversely conditioned to sexual situations that they may require ten to fifteen minutes of the most careful stimulation to bring them to a climax, and considering the fair number of females who never come to a climax in their whole lives, it is, of course, demanding that the male be quite abnormal in his ability to prolong sexual activity without ejaculation if he is required to match the female partner."

Sexual fulfillment, in view of these common difficulties, cannot be achieved overnight. It often takes years. The husband should try to delay his ultimate excitement; the wife should try to hasten hers. But both partners should realize their limitations, accept them and make concessions. Only when each is willing, with patience and understanding, to learn to complement the other's physical needs, can sexual harmony and the fullness of marital happiness be realized.

Chapter 20

You and Your Child

F ROM THE FIRST TIME of her child's suckling, till that future day when he is a full-grown person with rights of his own, the mother does much more than she realizes to fashion him into a successful or unsuccessful adult.

"Successful," of course, is one of the vaguest words in the dictionary. Here I'm not using it in the sense of financial success —it implies that to too many people—but success as measured by the individual's ability to fit well and happily into the world around him. True, I have seen neurotics develop in the best of home atmospheres. Nevertheless, in more cases than not, the child who is potentially a normal, well-adjusted creature grows into neuroticism largely because of the faulty upbringing a parent gives him. And that parent is usually the mother.

Philip Wylie's diatribes against moms and momism are often well based. Although a father may not be without blame for his child's failings, consider the time element: see how much more opportunity there is for the mother, consciously or unconsciously, to cast her spell over the child from the very day of birth. Of course, the father may be an alcoholic, neurotic or psychotic. Under these conditions he will leave his mark on his offspring even though he sees him only seldom. But the mother!

A poll conducted by George Gallup, not long ago, showed

that by a vote of more than 2-to-1, American adults of both sexes said (looking back on their childhood) that their mother had greater influence on their lives than their father.

According to modern psychologists, even the week-old infant can sense a mother's rejection, or her acceptance and protection. The mother either wants her child or she doesn't; she either loves him or hates him from the first; or else she both loves and hates him. (If you accused a mother of hating her own child, she would most likely claw your face. She might be unaware that the hate is buried deep in her.)

Why should a human mother dislike her own child? Even a cat will nurse a baby skunk and show her own no undue partiality. The mother cat, the mother hen, and the mother dog are protective by nature. They would fight against great odds to save their young. So would the majority of human mothers. Most children feel that they are loved. This gives them the sense of security and the strength they need in order to grow into normal adults.

But there are a goodly portion of neurotic mothers. Their early environment, like a fire, burned fear or anxiety into their personality. And once burned, forever cautious and fearful. The scar never completely heals. The mother who is herself a neurotic because nurtured by a neurotic mother, now completes the cycle by visiting her own childhood displeasures upon her own child. Knowingly or unknowingly, she forces her own unhappiness upon the helpless infant and child.

The seeds of fear and hatred, long dormant, may begin to grow because a child comes inopportunely. Either too soon in marriage (before the young couple have had the opportunity to adjust to one another) ; or too late, when all the other children have grown to maturity. The family may not be psychologically or economically prepared for the child, and the mother resents the burdens imposed by the newcomer.

The mother may be jealous. The child consumes a great part of the father's affection and the hapless wife actually becomes envious of the infant. This is a common marital triangle which fiction has yet to discover.

Sometimes the mother is irritated at her child because it has come between her and a career. Then, again some women aren't mothers by nature. They lack the capacity to stretch their natures enough to leave room to enfold the baby comfortably.

All the world loves a lover, but nature above all loves the child. It is the end nature seeks: the child at the breast, and then the child grown and her child at her breast. Nature is more interested in the chain than in the links. Unfortunately, life weakens some of them.

A common complaint of women who come for treatment of their nervousness is this one, in the very words of the patient who uttered it to me: "I don't mind it so much for myself. But my husband and especially my children catch it from me."

The mother who talked this way realized she was disrupting her home, perhaps indelibly stamping discomfort and anxiety on the minds of her children. But other than occasionally admitting she was wrong, she rarely did anything to control her misbehavior.

"I am short tempered. I shout in the little one's ear and then my heart breaks when I see how cowed and fearful she gets. I suddenly strike out at my Johnny when he least expects it. When I am upset I don't care whether my hand slaps his ear or his backside. The kids mind me now, but they hate me, and I don't blame them. And as for my husband, I know he detests me because I'm so hard-hearted toward the children. He has given up making scenes, but I can see the hatred for me in his face. And I know the kids are on his side, too."

"How long has this been going on," I asked her.

"Oh, about four years, now." (The children were four and five.)

"Have you had any help in the house since the babies came? Have you been away alone with your husband for at least a few days?"

The answer to both questions was no.

All the symptoms were familiar, the diagnosis was on the tip of my tongue: chronic fatigue. Too often this is the major factor in causing daily home eruptions. Even if a woman is normal and well-adjusted, constant overwork will wear her down, make her tense and unhappy. Every day becomes a battle between her fatigue and the household duties that intensify her exhaustion. Sleepless nights with a colicky child, diaper changing, formulas—playing the never-ending role of amusement-provider, cook, dishwasher, clotheswasher, drier and presser—you have to be built of iron to take these in your stride.

Then there is the daily onslaught on dust, because its battalions continually re-form and accept no defeat. And, of course, the major job among all the rest—of keeping the husband happy. Of satisfying his romanticism and his stomach. Of being the wonderful combination of maid, cook, nurse, baby-sitter and lover. Is there any wonder that neurosis is implanted in each succeeding generation?

Taut nerves can stand just so much stretching. I remember many early morning calls, when a distracted husband said: "Come quick. Mamie seems out of her mind." And in Mamie I would see the end result of these daily processes of nerve depletion: hysteria, mild or severe, and likely to become chronic. Often, a boat trip or two weeks in New York to see some shows, plus some help in the home would be prescription enough to straighten out such a family.

Sometimes the case is not so simple. The children (or worse still, the only child) may suffer a mother's rejection because all is not right between her and her husband. Perhaps he does not satisfy her sexually. Perhaps he is a disappointment as a provider. Perhaps a relative has turned her against him. Perhaps she begins to hate him for other reasons.

A child is seldom unaware that he is rejected. He does not have to be struck, or treated cruelly. He senses that he is not loved. He has a feeling of loss or deprivation. And with each succeeding abrasion of his little mind, there is rubbed off the courage that each of us needs to face the exigencies of "just living." In its place chronic anxiety is implanted.

Do you remember, as a youngster, wondering what would

become of you if anything happened to your father and mother? That is a natural thought, and arises in every child's mind, even without the influence of day-to-day doubts and fears. Think, then, how the minds of infants and small children must turn and turn, trying to make sense out of the chaos of a badly broken home. Here is the soil for insecurity.

This, in the final analysis, is the mother's greatest challenge: to bring up her children with sweetness, love, and understanding—even though she be misunderstood and her own life soured. To have always ready the protective caress, and give concrete evidence of love for her children; to allow them elasticity of movement within their growth requirements; to let them hear a soft but firm voice when they have done wrong, and not become abusive or impose too many restrictions—instead, to show fairness and even temper. And by her own example to prove to them that courage, not fear, is their heritage.

Always, she should feel her job as a mother is neither a minor nor a mean one. In reality it is one of the most exacting and noble careers a human being can undertake. In Dr. Milton R. Sapirstein's words: "It probably takes more endurance, more patience, more intelligence, more healthy emotion, to raise a decent happy human being than to be an atomic physicist, a politician or a psychiatrist." Mothers build the future, and, as they succeed or fail, so will tomorrow be bright or dark for the next generation.

Part Four

———

THE DOCTOR CONSIDERS
WORK AND PLAY

Chapter 21

Do It Now!

"**D**o it now!" I have seen a neatly framed copy of this reminder on the desk or wall of many a successful person. Now that they have achieved their goal, one may wonder why they don't throw this slogan into the wastebasket. The reason is obvious. They realize that it is easy to fall back into the bad habit of procrastination.

Every human being has a streak of laziness in him somewhere. It is a yard wide in some; in others—the human-dynamo type—it is barely perceptible. Many of either type will tell you they are procrastinators before they start work every day.

Writers are like that. They know they will write this morning, but seize upon any excuse to "put it off" for at least a few minutes more. This is true no matter how much they love their work.

Take myself, for example. This morning I came to my room prepared to begin my stint at exactly eight-thirty. I had planned to put in five hours of work. Just as I was set to begin, my unconscious (which, like everybody else's, dislikes work) began to play its tricks. "Your pencils need sharpening," it said.

I fussed around for a few minutes getting the points down to the necessary ten-thousandths of an inch. In trying to be meticulous I broke many points and had to resharpen them. Having finished with the pencils, I thought it might be wise to fill my pen (which, incidentally, had plenty of ink). Just as I was ready to begin, I decided I had better reread what I had written yesterday and the day before as a warming-up process for today's job.

Then I felt the desire to look up something in a book. It had no connection with my work today. I was obliged to exert force of will to put the book back on the shelf. I began to write a few minutes after nine.

My unconscious had gotten in its dirty work by offering reasonable excuses for making me put off the job in hand. Fortunately, this is a rare occasion with me. Most writers accept it, daily, as simply a warming-up period. To them it is as necessary as is a windup to a pitcher or a boxer's prancing around in his corner before the opening bell.

But all of this is not the procrastination I have in mind. What I refer to is the forever putting off until tomorrow what you can do today. It is dismaying to think of how much the world loses by the procrastination of members of the human race—of the untapped resources that go to waste. Many a Shakespeare or Shaw dies without ever having put pen to paper. ("If I only had the time.") Many a potential Beethoven, Silbelius, or Gershwin goes on living in discontent for which he can find no reason. Perhaps for years he has felt the stirrings of composition within, but "never had the time" to study harmony or practice on a musical instrument. (On the other hand, lack of procrastination is no guarantee of genius.)

The difference between success and failure is often simply this: *the ability and will to find time.*

The hare and the tortoise have their human counterparts. The writer who finds only one day a week for twelve hours of work and coasts for six days is the hare. He may never finish his book. The one who "delivers" daily in spite of all hindrances is the tortoise. His steady, daily writing adds up to an unbelievable number of workdays at the end of a year.

The steady grind is more difficult than the occasional sudden spurts and good resolutions. In steady writing one forgoes many daily pleasures—frequent social workouts, entertainment, and relaxing do-nothing periods. A person likes to sit and twiddle his thumbs and look off blankly into space. But a writer cannot produce if he is a procrastinator.

Any author will smile when asked by a casual friend: "Are you doing anything lately—or just writing?" Most will tell you that the highest hurdle the writer has to overcome is inertia. Every day of his writing he must, in his very fibre, have inscribed the words: "DO IT NOW."

He must meet the unconscious and its wily excuses barehanded, and overcome it in a daily tussle. As the years go on, the unconscious begins to give in. At last, all that is left of its strength is the ability to make us sharpen a pencil or two before getting right down to the job.

But writers are no special class. Businessmen, professional men, stenographers, and housewives are similarly plagued by the desire to put it off. "*Mañana*," they say with a smile.

The clean, neat desk top is not invariably the badge of the efficient businessman. Perhaps he has swept the mountains of memorandums and unanswered mail into already overflowing desk drawers. Many a lawyer puts off the preparation of his brief until the last minute and cuts down its value to himself and his client.

Many a doctor puts off making a few visits until tomorrow because they are not urgent. But comes tomorrow, and these few visits seem like a dozen because he has suddenly been loaded up with emergency work.

As he scurries from one part of town to the other, tired and late for dinner, he says, "If I had only seen Mrs. Jones and Mrs. Smith yesterday, when I had all the time in the world."

Of course, sometimes we procrastinate more than at others: when the jobs are distasteful. For example, we spend hours, days, or weeks simply girding ourselves for the complicated task of filling out our income tax form or preparing a speech, or even doing a necessary household chore.

Whatever the reasons, procrastination is one of the bad habits. It cuts its grooves deep and wide: one bad procrastination leads

to another. The man who puts off personal correspondence
for months (and usually prides himself about it) will often fall
into the habit of putting off an important reply in a business
transaction.

"If my husband hadn't been so careless in answering," a
patient of mine told me, "we'd be on Easy Street. His letter
got in one week too late. They informed him later they would
have been glad to give him the contract for the job but they
thought he wasn't interested in it."

Whatever is put off to the next minute, to this afternoon, to
the next day, is potentially lost. If you were forever aware that
the future (which means tomorrow) is ephemeral, a dream—
until you wake up tomorrow—you would be jealous of every hour
of your day. You would ask yourself if, and how, you are wasting
your present precious moments. Even in not working—in relaxing
—it is often a good habit not to procrastinate.

If it will help, put up that sign: "DO IT NOW!" Follow your
impulses to action as they rise up from below. Piano lessons?
Not ridiculous at fifty—begin them. Painting? Think of Grandma
Moses. You have the urge to kiss your wife? Why not now?

Chapter 22

What Your Work Should Mean to You

IN THIS WORLD, we should be up and doing. But not all the time, and never unwisely. Too many of us seem to do things merely for the sake of doing. We work ceaselessly but hardly know why.

What is work? For you and me it is that activity which we hope will gratify certain basic human urges that most of us have. If you are a bricklayer, you work with anticipation of payday. You may have pride in the job you do, but you are particularly concerned with the money in the envelope at week's end. For that currency guarantees shelter, food and at least simple pleasures for you and family. It promises a few dollars to put in the bank or in a savings bond.

What else does your work provide? If nothing else, then you are not living fully. To round out your daily existence you must return home at night with a feeling of accomplishment; of having contributed to the age in which you live. However small your contribution, you should feel an inner pride. As you walk by the completed structure you should be able to say to yourself: *"I* helped put up that building. *My* muscles, *my* hands have worked and now there is this building which will serve other human beings for at least a half-century."

Suppose you are a painter of canvasses. Your main thoughts are for the beauty and workmanship in the painting. Only later come the down-to-earth thoughts of your need for a roof, bread and warmth. Often, therefore, your roof leaks and the bread is stale, chiefly because the artist in you has willingly reversed the order of the need for self-preservation. You obtain your deepest pleasure and satisfaction in the actual creative process itself; you relegate the need for a livelihood to a secondary position.

I cite the examples of the bricklayer and the artist as extremes. One has the comforts of life merely because he has dedicated his energies to procuring safety and security; the other may be ill-housed, ill-nourished, and a poor provider for his family because the love for his work comes first. The artist has no choice. He is driven to create. Sometimes he is consumed in his own flame; or, to be realistic, starves amid plenty which is not his.

Somewhere in the wide expanse between these two extremes is the soil in which you work. Plumber, businessman, lawyer, doctor, architect, editor, farmer, musician, salesman, clerk, laborer —whichever you are, you work in one of three ways: for self-preservation, for self-expression, or both. The ideal mixture is 90 per cent self-expression and 10 per cent self-preservation. As only relatively few are sufficiently wealthy to live by such a heady mixture, happiness comes to him who, in ordinary circumstances, can come close to using this formula.

If you work *only* for self-preservation you are slowly, but surely, stunting the keen zest for life. There will come the time, even though you amass wealth, when your life will be spiceless. Your wheel will roll along like a flat tire on a cobblestone road. This will be the inevitable reaction when you come to assess your life.

The trouble lies in ourselves as individuals and in the society in which we live. The twentieth century prides itself on its inventions, but the human brain's accomplishments have been lopsided. We are experimenting with bombs made of uranium and hydrogen; we fly at over six hundred miles per hour; we have brought pneumonia and other infections toward the bottom of the mortality tables. We Americans have more cars, more modern plumbing, more gadgets for easy living than the rest of the world put together. Yet, what is more important for our happiness—a job we can do because we are fit for it—we leave to haphazard guesswork.

Have you ever wondered how many square pegs there must be, trying to grind their ways into the round holes? How many maladjusted people who have a tug-of-war with their alarm clocks every morning; who actually have to tear themselves from the warmth and shelter of the bed and push themselves out the front door to a job they detest? My guess is that their numbers run into the millions.

Perhaps you are different. Perhaps you are the one to beat the alarm clock because you are anxious to be at work. You wake with anticipation; you are zealous, ambitious and happy because you have found—probably by luck—the kind of work for which you are best suited. You are already one of the many J. B. S. Haldane pictured in the millennium when he wrote: "The ideal society would enable every man and woman to make the best of their inborn possibilities."

Whether shoemaker or statesman (if absorbed in your work), consider yourself the most fortunate of creatures. To rise every morning, jealous of the sleep which keeps you from your work, is to be born with a happy genius for enjoying life. You cannot imagine how fortunate you are unless you think of the others who live lives of frustration and bewilderment. They know not what to do. They know the cause of their discomfort; but they have no cure.

Here, for example, is a well-known trial lawyer. He comes to me for the treatment of a stomach ulcer. He is not the thin, scrawny type you might expect to find with ulcer; he is well nourished, apparently relaxed and at ease. Apparently. But I know that this man, successful though his community may think him, lives an unhappy life. His wife is a good companion, his children have grown and borne him grandchildren, he has financial security, he has recognition by his colleagues, he is brilliant; yet he is unhappy.

In hasty judgment, you might say: "Any man who has all this and doesn't appreciate his good fortune, deserves to be unhappy. I'd swap with him any time."

Hold on there. You might be making a big mistake.

This unfortunate man is peculiarly constructed. He has the gift of speech and the mind for detail, both qualities essential in a trial lawyer. But he is miscast in the daily play. To me he has confessed—crying, and all six feet of him trembling—that he hates the night for signifying what a day he has lived through; and detests the morning for what it portends in acute discomfort during the day.

Hear him: "I'm the square peg if there ever was one. I've been timid and unduly sensitive as far back as I can remember. When I was in high school, a friend actually forced me into joining a debating club. From somewhere deep down, after that day, words came out of me as effortlessly as water spouting from a fountain.

"I was elected president of the club. My year book predicted that I would become a brilliant trial lawyer. The prediction came true, except for the 'brilliant.' Perhaps this adjective applies to my work in the courtroom—at least my colleagues seem to think so—but as a person, a human being, I am far from brilliant. I am really dumb, stupid and insensible.

"What man would go through what I have and expect to be called otherwise? Every day of my life, since I joined that debating society, has meant a struggle with myself. I have been not only the daily battlefield, but also the fighter. I have taken a mauling and given it. The fact that I continue to go on as I do must mean that I have a mixture of strong masochistic-sadistic tendencies. You may wonder, Doctor, why I am suffering.

"Outwardly, you see every evidence of success. You have seen my home, my cars, my wife and children and you know of the 'big cases' the newspapers play up. I'm supposed to be the local wonder boy in the profession. This is all superficial.

"I'm unhappy because I'm miscast. I'm so constituted that I should be the extra in the background, holding a flag, or something, without a line to say. By nature I gravitate toward the easy way of life. The constant brush with people has been tearing me apart. I'm an introvert, although I'm sure you'll swear I'm an extrovert. I live in a goldfish bowl, but by nature I'd be more comfortable behind drawn blinds.

"Let me confess. Since I was a freshman in high school I've always wanted to be one of these modern farmers with all the new gadgets; answering to nobody for my actions. Natural and contented. Look at me now. You see a successful failure."

Of course, it would have been simple to label this man a neurotic and stick him away in that large compartment of the seriously maladjusted. But that wouldn't have been fair to him. It was possible that his own finger was pointing directly and surely at the cause of his unhappiness.

I believed it was worth investigation because there was little in his history to suggest neurosis. He had been a normal boy; his parents had not dominated him, thus not causing feelings of resentment and frustration. The trouble was that he was in work unsuited to his nature.

His ulcer was surely affected, if not caused, by his daily inner turmoil. He was fifty. Drastic measures were necessary for the cure. He consented to try them. He would take a sabbatical year in California.

In six months he returned, cleaned up his business affairs, sold his home and became a permanent resident in the "gold country." He bought a farm and began to take courses in husbandry and agriculture.

"I guess it's not the talking that was unnatural for me in the law," he told me. "Probably I was born with the facility for speech. What bothered me—now I am sure of it—was the necessity for making people uncomfortable on the witness stand. I'm too damn sensitive for that, although you would never have guessed it if you'd ever seen me go to work on a witness in a courtroom.

I'm a happy man now because I can talk—about cows and chickens and not about people."

He had only one regret—that he hadn't given law up earlier. Incidentally, X rays, after six months in California, showed no evidence of his ulcer. He was cured. (Remove the gasoline and out goes the fire.)

All of us cannot make the drastic change this patient made. But all of us can do something about allowing children—immature and uninformed—to make their own choices about their future without skilled and sympathetic guidance.

I believe that every grade school, high school and college should have trained personnel whose job it is to evaluate each pupil's tendencies, propensities and aptitudes. This branch should be considered more important then the teaching part of the institution. Think of how much not only the individual, but the nation, might gain. Educators forget sometimes that the school is a training and proving ground for life—not a report-card factory.

We humans should at least approximate the efficiency of the hive. We try to be busy as bees, but we are disorganized. We, as individuals, are a nation (and world) of misfits. And we take out our frustration on ourselves and others.

Hitler failed as an artist, Mussolini as a writer, and each turned his inner resentment outward on the world. Had they been steered early into success and contentment, they would not have produced the mess they did.

I have seen a truckdriver with the face and head of a poet, a policeman with the visage of a saint, a plumber with the suavity of a matinee idol. I wondered if they were happy. On the other hand, I have seen physicians, lawyers, and successful businessmen who might better be plumbers, policemen or truckdrivers.

Your job is to assess your job. What is it doing for you? Not only in money, but in satisfaction. If all your life you wanted something else, then have the courage to do something about it— give your present position up at a sacrifice.

If you are middle-aged, it is still possible for you to make changes. Of course, each of us is not as free as the wind. We have responsibilities, families and community life to consider when we make a readjustment. These should be weighed carefully. Problems that seem unsurmountable are not always so.

As a doctor, I have been trained to make decisions unhesitatingly for the good of the patient, unpleasant though they may be. "Be operated. Stop smoking. Lose forty pounds." These represent drastic changes for the patient concerned. But I must request them if they are needed.

Likewise, I do not hesitate to recommend that a man change jobs, or give up working entirely, if his health and happiness depend on such a decision. It is a man's happiness that deserves first consideration in living.

Fitting yourself to your job, and your job to you, is the prime essential for that happiness. John Dewey put it well when he said: "The aggressive pursuit of power and profit to the exclusion of other values exacts a high price in terms of lost opportunities for expansion and enrichment of life."

The *Who's Who* people have also published a book called *Who Was Who.* When they publish a *Who Will Be Who,* then they'll really have something. Where we have failed as a society and as individuals is in not having a plan. Each child should have the benefit of early trained guidance and direction. There would be fewer unhappy people in this world of ours. Every growing child should be screened psychologically. "This is your goal; this direction, not that, if you want fulfillment."

Work is the greatest of joys only when the worker is joyful.

Chapter 23

Don't Be a Successful Failure!

W ITH SOME PEOPLE, work is an obsession. It is natural to want to succeed, but unnatural to think success is so important that nothing else matters. You will see, if you look around, many examples of successful failures in your neighborhood or community. Observe how, in passing, they have littered the road with unhappy wives and children: with enemies who hate the ground they walk on; with yes-men who respect them less than they realize.

Ambition, in normal amounts, is essential fodder for the human ego. But a man's ambition should be neither too great nor too small. Somewhere between the beachcomber (whose ego is close to zero on the scale) and the human dynamo (who sits atop the heap) is the man with the normal desire to make good. He has a more wholesome viewpoint on life than the other two.

I would be the last to suggest that you give up your ambitions; but I would be the first to remind you to realize your limitations. See yourself in whole, not in part.

It is necessary that a man know where he wants to go, then assess his probabilities for arriving. Having these answers, he must also ask himself how he expects to achieve his ambition, and when.

We can make mistakes all along the line. Some men work hard

without knowing their destination. Others, knowing what they want, overassess their capabilities. Again, others who know their destination and fairly estimate their innate capabilities for their work, yet become successful failures because they underestimate the time it takes to succeed. They are the impatient ones, who often, within reach of their goal, turn off in another direction. Thus they throw away the accumulated accomplishments of years of hard work.

For example, I think of a fine medical man who had been assistant in a hospital service in New York for many years. One year, when appointments were under consideration, he was sidetracked for promotion—a younger man received the nod. Although the appointment had not yet been confirmed by the board of directors, the doctor lost all self-control. He belabored the medical board, the board of directors, and everyone connected with the hospital. He sent in his resignation.

Had he "sat tight" for a few more weeks, I happen to know that the promotion would have been his. But the damage was done. His resignation was accepted.

For the last ten years this brilliant physician has practiced medicine without any staff appointment. An unhappy man, he has often told how ambition and false pride can ruin a person's life.

Another example: Here is a young girl, intensely ambitious to be a dancer; she will someday taste the bitterness of disappointment. Three days a week she flies to New York to take lessons in modern dancing. Her teachers probably accept her money with their faces turned to one side. She has the ambition but not the physical equipment. Whatever efficiency and grace she may acquire will be counterbalanced by an unbeautiful figure. Why did she want to become a dancer in the first place? Probably she herself does not know. Perhaps like many excessively ambitious persons, she is compensating. When she was a child, perhaps she was the clumsy, laughed-at-one in dancing school. When she grew up, she would show them!

You see would-be painters who might make a greater success

of salesmanship; and many an unsuccessful salesman who has a natural ability to draw and paint. To me, the extremely ambitious person who is unsuited for his calling is the saddest of all. To work all your life thinking you are going in one direction and to find that you have only been marking time or, worse still, have been going in an offside direction: that is tragedy.

Intense ambition that is doomed to wreckage on the rocks because it does not know which way to steer, is an awful thing to watch.

How can you make sure you have set your course in life correctly? That you are traveling in a straight line? To find out, check your wishes, abilities, and goals with care.

For some persons, a single reading of the compass is sufficient. Because of genius, talent, hard work or pure luck, they reach their destination. Most of us, however, need to take frequent readings to evaluate our true position. If honest appraisal convinces us that we have been heading NE instead of N—or, what is worse, S instead of N—then there is only one thing to do: Take action. And this action requires courage. You may need to give up a job you have held for years and set an entirely new course.

But suppose you are fit for your work. Your destination is well lit up. You see it clearly. You know your itinerary and how to follow it. Then, you may almost succeed—yet fail because you are not content to cruise along the well-traveled route. You are bedeviled into taking short cuts, untried routes that make you end up in a maze of doubt, indecision, and final defeat.

The reason for this is impatience. Unwilling to wait for any accolade and honors your city or county may wish to bestow when you reach late maturity or even early old age—you dream of having the world for your oyster when you are in your thirties or forties.

It is possible to bypass age occasionally when ambition becomes so strong it carries you quickly to your goal of wealth or power or respected stature in your community. I have seen many such young, early successes in my office. But too often the price they had paid in loss of friends, loss of health, and in family unhappiness had tipped the scales against them.

I have asked them: "Successful as you are, would you pay the price again?" Usually, they admitted that you cannot outrace life. It has a way of beating you if you try to beat it.

Consider ambition as a well in a desert. If you are constantly hauling your bucket up, you will exhaust its water and go thirsty thereafter. If you draw water from it in moderate quantities, you will always have sufficient to satisfy your needs.

Too little ambition is bad; too much is worse. I have seen too many physical derelicts, the products of intemperate striving. The ideal life is that lived by the day. To enjoy the apparently trivial pleasures as we go along is more fulfilling than to sacrifice the present for the uncertain future.

Chapter 24

Planning for the Future

MUCH OF THE JOY OF LIVING is lost today by the bad habit of planning too carefully for tomorrow. Man goes about his tasks, so busily fashioning an umbrella to protect himself from the rainy day of the future that he misses much of the warm sunshine the present has to offer.

Charge it up to insecurity—the fear of a penniless old age. Man sees the cold windows of the poorhouse and he shudders. So he redoubles his efforts. He devises ways of making more money. What satisfaction there is in making a bank deposit regularly and watching the total grow!

We are not misers; we are simply insurance-minded. But it does not stop there. Even when the future is well provided for, the wealthy person persists in adding to his pile of stocks and bonds. Some of the most wealthy are the most penurious. Their insecurity goes beyond reason.

I would be the last to advise against Ben Franklin's admonition that a penny saved is a penny earned. I would not tell a man to give up work which he enjoys, because he becomes wealthy as an incidental part of his devotion to his business or profession. What I am against is the compulsive drive to obtain more and more. Satisfaction and a sense of accomplishment, rather than just money, are the things that make one's work truly meaningful.

It is said of Sinclair Lewis that he never knew how many of his books were sold or how much money he made. He even thought it a hoax when someone called to say he had won the Nobel prize. He was interested only in his work and not in how much he could accumulate for tomorrow. His was a rich, productive life.

In my office I have had the opportunity to see the physical and mental wrecks of the overdriven. They do not have the faculty to slow up and take inventory of themselves. They have a direction in life but are unable to read the compass. If you pin them to it, they cannot give you a satisfactory answer. Any more than the little boy, pockets bulging with pennies, can tell you why he is dissatisfied until he has little Willie's money, too.

Man is so constituted that he wants more. (The drive is rooted partly in the childhood fear he will not have enough.) I see hypertensives go on to serious complications which might have been avoided or at least delayed—who get that way because they can't stop building for tomorrow. I hear bad hearts and hear the loud grinding of unmeshed mental and emotional gears in those who cannot slow up their pace today. They seem bent upon their own destruction.

Sir William Osler said that our duty is not to look too far ahead into the future, but to live fully today. He gave as the reason for his great accomplishments as physician and writer this formula for success in living: If you live only for today and measure up to the present twenty-four-hour requirement, it is inevitable that tomorrow will take care of itself.

It makes sense, doesn't it? If we might only erase our fears of the future as easily as we do chalk marks on a blackboard, this would at once become a world more enjoyable and livable. We would see life more nearly in its true perspective.

It is a false premise that the most important thing in life is to think of tomorrow. You are playing for high stakes when you do that. In thinking of the future you must inevitably surrender some of the present. And that is all you and I really have.

The person who lives for today enjoys pleasures that the man-of-the-future misses: the beauty of the night sky embroidered with stars; the laughter of children; the lazy roll of waves on a wide beach; the smell of autumn leaves burning; the complete absorption in a book; the spell of music; the unhurried, unpurposeful talks with friends; the fun of tinkering with ideas and objects; the satisfaction of *today's* job well done.

The list is endless—yet is alien to the man who is always planning big things for the morrow. There is no room in his helter-skelter schedule for the little things. He does not know that one's life is fulfilled by the trivia of the present—not by the large projects of the future.

For pity's sake, I say to patient X (who needs to learn the true values of human existence now or pay for his delay very soon with his life), get on to yourself. Time doesn't just fly. Your days disappear almost with the speed of sound.

Don't be afraid to take it easy. You must learn to judge the narrow margin between procrastination and rest. Procrastination puts off what should be done today—what should have been done yesterday, or last week or last month; it defers decisions, it avoids commitments. Procrastination is not restful, because it is accompanied by a nagging feeling of guilt. Rest, on the other hand, is enjoyable in itself, and at the same time a preparation for new tasks to be approached with zest and competence. And a relaxed mood is often the best preparation of achievement later on. There is a time for everything—for action and for rest. Combine these judiciously, and you may consider your way of living balanced and harmonious.

Let go. Relax. Make the most of today. Don't go around like an express train racing from one worry to another, too tense to see the beautiful valley down below. Let your clock measure out enjoyment, not servitude. Try to live between the excursions of the minute hand. Be jealous of the hour hand. Don't let them go round without your having been aware of time's passing. Be miserly of today.

If you live life this way, when you add everything up tomorrow, you will find—perhaps to your surprise—that you have been earning compound interest. Unaware of your growing gains in the bank of living, you have made yourself rich in body and mind. And you will suddenly perceive that tomorrow, when it comes, is only today.

Chapter 25

Slow Down!

IF YOU ARE LIKE MOST OF US, sometime or other you have exclaimed: "I wouldn't be caught dead in a hammock!" Such a remark is not generated by any heat against hammocks themselves. It is due, I think, to your deep desire not to be thought soft—or caught soft. The man in you, or the woman in you, rebels at the label "lazy." In fact, throughout our folk talk you will hear epithets like: "You lazy——!" These are intended to take you down a peg—not to compliment you on your ability to relax between cares of the day.

The efficient machine is the periodically rested machine. You can run a high-powered car for hundreds of miles at very high speeds and it will not fall apart suddenly. But keep up the pace, day after day, and the glistening chromium and smooth-acting engine will be ready for the junk heap, many thousands of miles earlier than its sister car that has had a modicum of care.

Human machines are similar. In the first place, remember that all of us do not operate on an equal level of efficiency. Some of us are the latest-model Cadillac and others of us are born with a body-model equivalent to a five-year-old lower-priced car that has already become a member of the 100,000-mile club.

You have met people who say: "I was born tired." I see many

such in my practice. They make out all right if they are content
to cruise along at a speed befitting their engine. However, when
they get delusions of grandeur, when they think they are as strong
as the next fellow, when they attempt to prove it by jamming the
accelerator down to the floor board in an attempt to "hang on"
to the big car's tail light, then they invite disaster.

Know your engine and run it according to its horsepower—you
will go farther, even if not so fast.

The other day an executive of a large organization was in my
office—chief complaint: tiredness. And why not? He is forty-two
years old. When I saw him first two years ago he was close to
exhaustion and collapse. I could find no organic cause for his
symptoms then; and now, examination is still negative.

This man has an expensive make of machine. Nature has
been kind to him. He is six feet one; he weighs two hundred
pounds. Yet I know many a bantamweight who could have easily
pushed him over a few years back. (Though he is still tired,
I'd advise nobody but a heavyweight to tangle with him today.)

What about this man? Why did he have chronic exhaustion?
He isn't the type who was "born tired." He himself told me the
cause: "Doctor, I guess I've just burned out my motor. You see
before you an awful fool."

I asked him to elaborate.

"I'm my own worst enemy. I've been giving myself a terrible
beating for years. I know I'm doing it but I can't stop. I'm not
the kind of fellow who can sit down for half an hour and relax.
I can't read a book, finish a paper, or sit and talk for an hour.
Call me 'fidgety Phil.' "

He looked at me sheepishly and went on: "All my life I've
felt driven to be on the go. I went in for athletics in school.
Guess I was happiest then because I was young enough to 'give
out' and yet recuperate. And I continued after college. I've given
business the same 'college try.' No vacations, twelve hours of
work a day—and taking it home at night with me. At business, if
the elevator is slow in getting to me, I think nothing of climbing
two or three flights, two steps at once, a number of times during

the day. You see before you a human dynamo that's just about run down."

I looked at him and he knew what I was thinking. I agreed that he was a fool. I would not argue that he wasn't. Later, after all the examinations had indicated that he still had a good engine to work with, we sat down to talk it over.

I had never seen such a restless person. He just couldn't sit. If metabolic studies hadn't been negative I would have felt sure that he had hyperthyroidism, or some kind of neurosis on the way. It was my turn to talk and his to listen.

"Calling yourself a fool may give you a sense of release and satisfaction, but it does nothing to neutralize the speed with which you are burning yourself out. I'm not here to lecture to you. You came here for advice, not a sermon. So here are the facts.

"You have your own life to live; the choice is yours; I have no right to say, 'You *must* do this, you *mustn't* do that!' Now, you don't have to be a physician to know what the trouble is. You have the heavy foot. You bear down too hard on your speed control. And because you could put that marvelous physique of yours through a lot of pounding and come up fresh the next day —when you were a boy—you think that you (of all people) have been given the only perpetual motion machine in the world.

"You are human like the rest of us. Speed has caught up with you, fouled your engine, and exhausted you. I have given you the overhauling. All you need now is to drive yourself at thirty miles per hour instead of eighty—until you have regenerated your batteries. It will take time, but you will see results. Here's your program. Follow it and you will be all right. Don't—and you will wind up wrapped around a telephone pole.

"First, take six weeks off. Not next year. Leave day after tomorrow. You need a week to wind up some affairs? Sorry. If pneumonia struck, or a heart attack, you would not be granted a single hour to wind them up. I'm giving you forty-eight hours."

He looked at me, speechless. But he hadn't heard all yet. I went on:

"When you are away, you are to be in bed ten or eleven hours every night. You are to nap for an hour or two every afternoon. You may play nine holes of golf a day—no tennis, or overly long walks. Swim a little, play cards a little, relax a lot. These six weeks will, for the first time in years, give you the opportunity to meditate. To ask yourself: Where am I going? What's the rush? Where does the compulsion arise? Am I running away from my family? Am I insecure? Has the almighty dollar or position in the community blinded me to the important things in life?

"You will return a wiser man. But then comes the test. You must be sure not to get into the old rut again. If you do, there's no hope for you. There will be no need for you to return to this office because I lose interest in intelligent fellows who lose interest in themselves. But, mind you, I won't be angry with you—just sorry for your wife and kids."

He nodded. "But, Doctor, suppose I do all you say. Can you give me specific directions for staying out of the rut?"

My answer was simple. Ordinary, sane common sense, on his part, should have made it unnecessary. But he had to hear it from a doctor.

"Resolve not to work more than eight hours a day. Resolve to take at least one hour for lunch—outside of your office. Warm milk and a stale cheese sandwich are for a mouse—not for a man. Resolve to 'take five.' If you know anything about the entertainment world you will recognize this expression. After intense, protracted rehearsal an orchestra leader or a dance director will use this term. It means take five minutes out for a smoke or any other form of relaxation you prefer.

" 'Take five' may also mean take a half-hour or an hour. In the same way, resolve to break up your working day by frequent periods of relaxation—a fifteen-minute nap on a couch, a sprawl in your chair with your feet on your desk, a refusal to answer all phone calls during these vacuum periods. Resolve to cut down engagements to a minimum. Resolve to get into bed at eight o'clock two or three nights a week. Resolve to practice being lazy. *And it will take a lot of practice.*"

And it did take a lot. He is still practicing at it; but you should see and hear him now. See how he lounges in his chair as he talks. Two years ago he was forever coiled up, ready to spring. See how relaxed his face is—the tense, hard lines above the mouth have become smile grooves.

He talks about fishing, the latest book, the week end he took off, and the golf he shot. Tired? Yes, a little. But normally so. He knows where he is going and why. He has bypassed the urgency, the speed, the restlessness. And he has accomplished it without the help of a psychiatrist—and with little help from me. All he needed was a good steer and he has been a much happier and healthier man since.

Do you have the same problem this man had? Take stock. Where are you on the scale of endeavor? Is your own pace too fast? Do you brag about not having had a vacation in ten years? Then you are high on the scale of endeavor and low on the scale of understanding your own needs. No man can get away with this fast pace without cracking up in the process.

Nature has a way of adding up your ledger. Although she is generous to a fault, there is a side to nature that is heartless. She will add up your column of figures, subtract, divide, compute in calculus if need be—and when it comes time for the final result, nature will use red ink as readily as black. When the results are in, she has no compassion for the individual. Nature can be your ally or your enemy. She is willing to work with you, but just as ready to work for your destruction.

And there must be a streak of laziness in nature somewhere. She seems to resent being driven. She dislikes tension and over-drive. Nature is considerate to the person who works and plays, but not to that one who prides himself on "working hard and playing hard."

I have seen all kinds of go-getters—the smart ones and the dumb ones. They have lost all perspective on what life is about. They are like the restless ant or the bee.

I walked by a place of business one night. Formerly thriving —now up for auction. Its proprietor, a forty-five-year-old patient of mine, had been warned that sixteen hours of work a day was more than an ordinary human could be expected to endure. In spite of warnings, he had kept up the pace for three years: no vacations, no relaxation, no release of tension. He was slowly dying from chronic fatigue. Then a heart attack threw him on his back for eight weeks.

From him: "If I had only listened, Doctor. I guess it's too late."

From his employees: "We knew he couldn't take it for long. The man was crazy."

The man died in six months, leaving a wife and a two-year-child alone in the world.

You may not be a fool—but you may be more foolish than you realize—if you put heart, bone, nerve, and muscle to the same daily strain as you might your own weight in steel. Think it over!

Chapter 26

Exercise: Is It Really Necessary?

Fﾠﾠﾠﾠﾠ OR ME THE WORD EXERCISE SIGNIFIES EXERTION—usually over-exertion. It is essential that you and I agree upon our definition. Otherwise, you will—as have many others—challenge me to stand up and prove my arguments against exercise.

May I say now, that in the event you do challenge me, my answers will drift lazily back to you—not from a standing position, but from easy recline in chair or hammock. I can't get as excited about, and provoked at, the "exercisers" as much as they do at me.

Not long ago I picked up a monthly periodical devoted to the dissemination of data and pictures and exercise formulae that guarantee to make a Tarzan out of a man in six issues. An entire article was devoted to tearing me limb from limb.

I was glad for the writer. Had he not vented so much of his spleen on me, he must surely have ruptured a bulging biceps or triceps. (I was going to say a cerebral artery, but that would not be fair—and besides, as a doctor, and a human being, I would not wish that on my worst enemy.)

In this article, the writer made reference to Dr. Logan Clendening. In effect, the theme of the piece was that I should be hung by my scrawny biceps and thumbs; that what had happened to the worthy doctor was probably—or better had be—in store for me. (The worthy Dr. Clendening died a few years ago.)

And why all this vituperation against a mild, mind-my-own business sort of a person like myself? The answer was in the magazine. In effect, "Now that Clendening and his crazy anti-exercise beliefs have gone, here comes another, Dr. S. [that's me], to step in and carry on the vicious crusade against American manhood and womanhood."

Reading this, I felt like the little fellow, unsuspecting, who walked into a brawl about politics and walked out with two black eyes; "I didn't do anything," he said plaintively. Neither had I done anything—but I don't say it plaintively. (In case you suspect my dander is beginning to rise at this point, let me hasten to deny it. I am not at all upset by the reactions of my big-muscled antagonists. I don't even consider it to be a fight.)

Now, to get closer to the root of the matter, why are we at odds? Rather, why are they at odds with me? The answer is simple.

In a book I wrote some time ago, I had the nerve to say: *You Don't Have to Exercise.* Its theme (as the title) was: *How to Keep Fit Without Exercise.* It was first published before the advent of the atomic bomb—yet, on looking back, I see it created a blast and reverberation among exercise addicts akin to a miniature atomic explosion. And it seems the radioactive elements therein contained are still raising bumps of contentiousness on these modern Greek gods.

Let us have it out, men—like men. Open your minds as you bunch your muscles. Be receptive to facts. Let this be a discussion —not a series of arguments. You know as well as I do that a consideration of religion, politics or exercise, when there are differing viewpoints, seldom ends in agreement all around the table.

Well, those of you who recall the points I stressed will nod assent when I repeat that I did not ask for the abolishment of *all* unnecessary overexertion; I suggested only that *most* exercise be abolished. In the preface I stressed that exercise was often essential for growing children, and in the treatment of deformities which required specific therapy: passive manipulation, massage, underwater therapy and so forth.

The "exercisers" have never even referred to those exceptions of mine. I am sure it's not because they are uninterested in crippled adults and growing children. It just seems so because all their energies are apparently directed toward developing healthy muscles. For them, it is not enough that a man's muscles can move efficiently. They must be made to look formidable; they must ripple when they move—as evenly and gently as water curving on a beach. As a doctor, that is where I disagreed—and still do.

For that reason I have had mail from all corners of this exercise-conscious country, some condemning my dastardly stand, others saying, "I'm with you." And what is my belief? Simply that you can be just as happy, just as healthy, just as fit by getting your exercise in a rocking chair. And that, even so, you can outfight and outlive your exercise-conscious neighbor who goes in for mountain climbing. I am against any unnecessary exertion after the youth has become a man. Shall we say from twenty-five years on? Too young? I think so, too. In fact I stressed the need for no exercise after forty.

Rest Begins at Forty, I said. There you have the broad zone of fifteen years in which to taper down your activities to nothingness. I don't suggest that you live like an amoeba—only that you learn to be lazy. That you accept ease and comfort after forty as one of the natural prizes of growing older; that you accept and invite inactivity with a pridefulness; that you consider "laziness" a badge of distinction and wear it openly.

After forty, you have no earthly reason to become exercise-conscious. Forgo your morning and evening setting-up exercises; turn in your card at the gym; let your correspondence course in body-building lapse; throw away your squash rackets; forget about handball; cut out the ten-mile walk daily.

I have the feeling that I am beginning to lose you, too. You are thinking, "This man has gone haywire on the subject. How about my bowling, tennis, and golf?" This may surprise you, but I recommend them! That is, if you have a strong urge for them.

Of course, if you bowl just because your office is scheduled against a team on the second floor; if you play five sets of singles with an eighteen-year-old just to prove the old man is as good as when he played for Yale; or if you play fifty-four holes of golf on a week end (rain or shine) simply because you "need the exercise" and have no time to play during the week—if you do these things, then I am the obstinate, old ogre again; I say, such exercise be damned.

An enlarged heart is too much to pay for that sort of tennis game. A coronary attack is a price out of line with the "fun" you get out of squeezing in all that golf on a week end.

Now—and I become reasonable again—if you exercise in moderation, that is entirely different. A moderate amount of exercise will do you no harm even though your arteries and heart are not what they were before forty. If still healthy, they will withstand a few games of bowling, eighteen holes of leisurely golf on a week end (with a few hours off in between), and a few sets of tennis doubles with three other fellows who have lived through at least four decades.

A walk of a mile or two is all right. Gardening, too, in moderation is fine, but it can be overdone. After what you read in the newspapers every winter, I suppose it is wasteful to stress the dangers of too much snow-shoveling or pushing your car out of a drift.

Remember that exercise that hardens your muscles will not guarantee you against the onslaught of illness or infection. Germs do not respect Tarzan any more than Mr. Milquetoast.

Do you exercise because you are overweight? Do you want to pull in your belt? Is that the reason you have grown exercise-conscious? Well, lately it has become common knowledge that you would have to walk thirty-six miles to dissolve one pound of fat from your frame. That's too long a walk when you consider all you need to do is forgo pie à la mode and a bit of gravy to accomplish the same purpose.

I often wonder what is so intriguing in muscle-building. In these days when man survives by his brain and not by his muscles, why the need to be muscle-bound? Is it the little boy in us who wants to look virile; so *our* little boy can say to the neighbor's little boy, "My father can lick *your* father"?

Frankly, if the potential contents of my refrigerator depended on my ability to be a good hunter; if I needed legs like small tree trunks and arms like a gorilla's so I might go out and personally grapple with a buffalo barehanded and bring him in as sustenance for my starving family—*then* I would strive to be first on the subscription list; I would sign up at the "Y," run around the track and join with the middle-aged group who run from their offices to go through calisthenic gyrations.

But—and this is why I oppose body building after forty—we don't need muscles in the twentieth century. I suppose I should modify that. Muscles—but not *big* muscles. Just large enough to walk us to our car; just ample enough to permit us to change a flat tire; with resiliency enough to allow us to climb into a hammock or into bed. I'm for development, but not of muscles—except in youth, when games need to be played and life needs to be yielded to more completely and joys tasted with full seasoning.

Am I making myself clear? Or have I seemed to consign our manhood to the category of jellyfish? Am I seeking to make weaklings of us? Will our country be unable to defend itself against aggression? (How many forty-year-olds in the front lines, did you say?) Or are you beginning to see that the exercisers have got themselves excited out of proportion to the provocation?

On the contrary, I believe in exercise for the young—not for the middle-aged. Still, I don't believe in middle-aged spreads, in fat tummies or generalized overweight—nor do I believe that exercise is the antidote for that kind of poison.

All I suggest—I don't ask it, or "say" it, or force it down your throat (as an unpalatable tonic)—I suggest that you exercise moderately *if* you enjoy it, *if* it relaxes you, *if* it releases your tensions. Play golf and tennis because you have the urge and not because your friends goad you into it.

When on vacation, lying in your hammock, wish your friends well as they pass you on their way to the mountains, the streams, the golf and tennis courses. But, mind you, if they *give you that look* as you lie there, wave to them goodnaturedly, smile and turn to your book.

If you can do that without shame or remorse, then I shall know that you are interested in preserving your health and your life, not in extinguishing it. That you are on my side.

By the way, there are a lot of us.

Chapter 27

Vacations vs. Vocations

A VACATION MEANS DIFFERENT THINGS to different people. Some take it as a necessary evil. Others as an evil necessity. And others as the sole recompense for a year of labor. All of us, when we are actually on vacation, try to squeeze out of it as much satisfaction as possible.

There is something about the word vacation itself that provokes a superior smile in many individuals. "Vacation," they will say, "what's that? I haven't had one in so long I've forgotten just what you mean by the word." Or: "I've never had one. I don't need any. I get bored. I want to be back at work." At the other extreme: "I'm so tired I could take off three months and like it. You won't hear *me* saying I'm anxious to get back."

Somewhere, at either of these two poles or between them, you will find your niche. Either you are hot and excited about the subject of vacations, or they are a few weeks of necessary interlude in your labors that custom grants you every year. Either you grasp these relatively few hours of your year with alacrity and anticipation; or you accept them without even stretching forth open palms to receive of their beneficence.

My conception of vacations has been that they are a grossly misused part of our lives. Too many of us think of those few weeks as something entirely apart from the remainder of our working year. With such an attitude we are more likely to subtract from the joy of living than to add to it.

I have seen people who never took vacations suffer for it because an overworked machine had no opportunity to rest its working parts. I have seen others, who, vacation minded, never took the time to plan their vacations. They returned more tired than when they left home.

Yet your vacation is as much a part of your years as are the working days. When you go on a vacation, you do not send your alter ego—you go yourself. No matter how much you are absorbed by your work, no matter how much you love it, you cannot remain efficient if you do not plan to get out of the weekly rut.

Your body needs change of environment. So does your mind. The same people, the same trees, the same hills, are better appreciated if you forgo them for a few weeks and substitute interesting strangers, sand and sea.

I know a number of colleagues who pride themselves upon their devotion to their work. "I can't feel right, taking a vacation. My patients need me."

That has always sounded like balderdash to me. True, the doctor who lives in a country town where there are no other physicians can honestly say: "I can't leave my patients." But the modern city has no actual doctor shortage. The city doctor who will not leave his practice because he "loves it too much" is deceiving either himself or others. Perhaps he is surrounding himself with the aura of the "great healer." Perhaps he is being jealous of a colleague who might confiscate some of his older patients while he is away. Perhaps he does not know how to enjoy himself away from his work but simply cannot admit it, even to himself. In reality, no man in the modern urban practice of medicine endangers the lives of his patients by leaving the city for a number of weeks. His colleagues are eager (he thinks only too eager) to cover for him.

I write of the doctor and his vacation first for a reason. If the doctor can get away for a while, so can you—whoever you are, wherever you are, or whatever you do.

And yet, men and women in other businesses and professions also say that they haven't the time to get away. They "owe it to their clients and customers." Here, too, there is unconscious avariciousness, jealousy, or self-deception. No matter how much a man loves his work, if he is a normal man he looks forward to rest and rejuvenation as well. All of us have a natural streak— and a broad one—of laziness. (I don't use the word in a critical sense. "Laziness" is often a sign of a genuine physical and mental need for relaxation.) We resent, after a while, the deadly routine of living within the confined area bounded on one side by the minute hand, on the other by the hour hand. We welcome the few weeks in which we are the masters of time—not its daily slaves.

Our vacation over—being the perverse creatures that we are— we look forward with renewed zest and interest to being hemmed in again by time for another year.

I tell patients to accept vacations as an essential part of existence. I suggest that they plan for a vacation as methodically and with as great care as they plan their workaday schedule. If you have only a week or two off a year, do not squander it. Vacation should mean change. Make it a real change.

For example, exchange last year's hills and mountains for the ocean and the beach this year. If you are a year-round golfer, leave your sticks at home. Substitute croquet, bowling, or tennis if you *must* engage in competitive sports.

If you are a traveling salesman covering forty thousand miles a year in your car, take a plane or train to your destination. Leave your car in the garage, or bequeath it to a friend while you are away.

If you are a sequestered sort of fellow, force yourself to spend your time at a lively resort. New faces, new viewpoints will stimulate you beyond your realization. And the stimulus will be exerting its effect for many weeks after you return.

If you read a book or two a week at home, take no reading matter with you. If, on the other hand, you look at your shelves lined with books and are filled with remorse for not having taken any down lately, then bring along a half-dozen and resolve to read them.

If you are overactive at home, learn to be lazy on your vacation. The man whom everyone labels a dynamo at home should attempt the difficult feat of going from high to reverse without stripping his gears. From the hum of activity to the lazy humming and buzzing of insects around your hammock is a real change of pace. It is such diametrically opposed states—from activity to inactivity, and vice versa—that are the essential foundations of a good vacation.

The time to plan your vacation is weeks or preferably months before you lock your front door and set out. There are so many questions that need to be put and answers that need to be found. Otherwise your vacation may drain your body and spirit of energy rather than recharge them.

Ask yourself: Where shall I go? For how long? Alone or with the family? Can I afford the best or modest accommodations? Am I going for physical and mental refurbishment, or just for the change?

Suppose your last vacation was spent on a boat cruise. You were queasy or seasick at least fifty per cent of the time. You liked the boat, but oh, that rocking in the swell of the waves!

And now your friend Henry comes to you with vivid, captivating folders describing a trip to South America. You are beginning to weaken. "Perhaps I'm used to the water by now," you say. But consider that most likely you are not. If dramamine did not help you on last year's trip, chances are you would be in for another interminable journey of discomfort. If you are set on seeing South America, fly. At least you will not suffer so long with airsickness.

Can you afford a vacation? The answer is yes. Vacation is a must. But you must choose a spot consistent with the size and contents of your pocketbook. We have all seen the dejected, disappointed expressions on the faces of many people at expensive and fancy resorts. They are all dressed up with nowhere to go.

Bored and doubly downcast because the unsatisfying stay is costing so much.

Yet there are times when a patient's poor health demands an immediate vacation. On such occasions the cost should not be counted. Beg or borrow to get away for the rehabilitation of spirit and body. Never consider such money ill spent.

I remember a number of cases of suicide during the great depression of the early thirties. These people had been wiped out and couldn't take it. I know others, as completely ruined financially as these luckless individuals, but who were able to shake off the effect of the blows. They borrowed money on their insurance to "get away from it all' and make peace with themselves. Somehow they knew how important it was for self-preservation to stand off from the rubble and make plans for the rebuilding.

One went to Europe for three months. Another got into a car with his wife and for six months toured every state in the Union. "I wanted to see," he said on returning, "whether the country was in as bad a fix as the stock market seemed to indicate. When I saw the mountains, the trees, the rivers, the oceans, the buildings still standing, traffic cops still directing thousands of people (none of whom were holding their heads in their hands) I knew that I had suffered only a temporary setback. If the country wasn't licked, neither was I. This vacation has given me the courage to begin all over again." And begin all over again he did. His business and fortune are greater than they were before the "big break."

You see, at times vacations are not a choice, they are a necessity. Never let the length of your vacation—if the choice is yours —depend wholly upon how much time you think you can spare from your work. The length of vacation should depend wholly upon how tired you are and how well you are.

If you need enforced rest because you have had a coronary attack, your future health absolutely requires at least a three-month period of relaxation before you return to work. Perhaps six months. It is wise to lose a few weeks more to gain years of comfortable living. If you are well and really don't need rest, then two weeks should be the minimum allowance. One week is worse than nothing. No sooner unpacked than ready again for packing—and home. If you have four weeks coming to you next year, break them up into a winter and a summer vacation. Two half-month vacations are better for you than a one-month vacation. Make the best of week-ends and the many two- or three-day holidays throughout the year.

Vacations are vacations only when taken away from home. Puttering around at home is no vacation. Entertaining relatives is no vacation. Visiting relatives is no vacation. Visiting friends for long is also a mistake. Don't consider your vacation a failure if you have not scaled mountains, played golf and tennis, and cavorted around all over the countryside.

Ask yourself this on the way home: "Am I pleasantly tired? Have I made new, interesting acquaintances? Am I looking forward to my work?" If the answers are yes, your vacation has been a success. But if you say, "Am I tired! I feel I could go to bed for a week," then your vacation may be considered a failure. And no better luck next time unless you plan it instead of hoping for the best. Vacations require as much planning as vocations.

Chapter 28

Time to Retire

MOST PEOPLE ACCEPT AS TRUE THE STATEMENT: "If you want to die early, retire early." It is no truer than the old sayings: "Lightning never strikes twice in the same place" and "The ostrich buries his head in the sand when frightened." The fact of one of these matters is that a bolt will seek out the spot where another has struck—rather than a different spot. As for the ostrich, he doesn't conceal his head in the sand when scared or at any other time.

Are you afraid that retirement will kill you? Not a chance—unless you have not prepared for it.

If you prepare for retirement, early retirement will save you for living rather than kill you prematurely.

Here is what Irving Salomon, who has studied this whole problem carefully, says about it in his book *Retire and Be Happy:* "Men of advancing years who work under any tension, ought to retire. Men who are beginning to experience excessive fatigue should quit. Men in businesses and professions with frequent frustrations, tribulations and irritations (what business has none?) should retire. Men who cannot delegate authority and so really never experience a true vacation; men who find that their age is lessening their ability to cope with the added difficulties . . . and demands of business today, should also withdraw from the sphere of activity at a suitable time. As pointed out, this is essential if such men want to live out their lives in reasonable health and happiness."

And how to prepare for retirement? Ideally, we should teach children in grammar school, high school and college that they should set their sights for early retirement. Sixty-five? Preposterous. Sixty? Somewhat better, but not good enough. Fifty-five? Now we are getting close. Fifty? Perfect—for some.

Think of it. From the day you are born, to high school graduation, is about seventeen or eighteen years. Eighteen from fifty leaves thirty-two years in which to finish your education, marry, work and prepare for retirement. If you prefer the age of fifty-five, that gives you thirty-seven years. I believe that if you work for the city as a fireman or policeman, you can retire on pension after only twenty-five years or so; likewise if you work for the state; pretty much the same if you have served in the Army or Navy.

If you cannot count on a pension, and if your sights are set on thirty-two or thirty-seven years off, you will put away enough each year so that you come to the fifties prepared. You will figure in the government social security when you grow older (and tell your Congressman now that it should be increased). And figure in your insurance. But that isn't all that is important.

In addition to securing financial reserves, your preparation over the years should be a physical and psychological one. That's where most of us lose out. We haven't, as children and young adults, been taught that old age comes to all who survive middle age. And that it flies on swift wings.

Unpreparedness for retirement can upset the balance of the man or woman who knows only how to do one thing: work. To have a successful life—and a successful retirement—you need to learn many substitutes for work.

Has there been a harder worker than Britain's Winston Churchill? Can anyone say that Churchill doesn't love his work? Not enough that he enjoys work—he likes to lay bricks and he paints. Both activities are creative. When he was not at 10 Downing Street, he could devote his time to writing, speaking, or many other things as well. He was one of the fortunate who didn't need to retire—formally.

He had retired in middle age—really. He just kept on with politics. Perhaps it was a side line to his writing or painting. Which of us knows the work he considered first in importance? His entire life was a preparation for retirement. But as with many others important in history, the call of events was greater than that of retirement. He returned to politics and government twice.

In a spirit of dedication to your fellow man and your country you do not place as much importance on the results of an arithmetical problem that concerns how many years you have left. You give your everything and hope for the best.

Churchill is the kind of man who could have retired from political life at forty-five—if national emergency had not arisen —and have been happy in his retirement. He had prepared.

You can, too. You should. But how?

First, be openminded to the need! Remember that in age you will find yourself to be an extension of your youth; as the uppermost branch of a tree is to its trunk. With a normal brain in the sixties and seventies—one relatively free from arteriosclerotic changes—you will be able to think as well as you did when you were twenty, and your judgment will be better.

But, here is a salient point in preparing for retirement. Your "normal" seventy-year-old muscles—including the heart muscle —will not be able to accomplish one part of what your twenty-year-old muscle could do effortlessly. Doesn't that, at once, give you the hint on how to prepare?

Not your muscles but your mind should receive the preparatory training for the beautiful sunset years.

Not long ago I talked with a successful businessman thirty-five years of age. "I'm going to retire when I'm forty-five. I'll have enough put away by then," he said.

"Good. Fine. I believe in early retirement. Tell me, how are you preparing for it?'

"Preparing?" he asked. "You mean will I have enough money? Sure I will."

"Are you doing anything else about it?"

He thought a moment and added, self-satisfied—as if coming up with the right answer for the school teacher: "I come here once a year for a checkup to keep healthy. That's important."

"It certainly is," I said. "Your health is the concrete foundation for later happiness. But how else are you preparing?"

He looked at me, first bewildered, then blank. He threw up his hands as if to say there was nothing else.

I said to him: "I happen to know you well, as a friend and as your doctor. Right now, you are happy. You leave your house at 7 A.M. and work until 6 P.M. You love your work; you look forward to the daily matching of wits with your competitors. Life is a game for you.

"Your Saturdays and Sundays are filled with golf—or going on picnics or trips with your family. Your summer is broken up by a two-weeks' vacation; your winter by a month in the South. You play handball three times a week and get a lot of satisfaction giving your muscles a workout in the gym. You are so tired that you rarely go out. You are in bed by 10 P.M.

"But, remember, the later years of life need filling, too. The youngsters on the golf course will be impatiently shouting 'fore' so they can go through your slow foursome up front. Golf will not fill your week ends with as much content as it does now. And the gym and handball? Your muscles do not go on forever. Remember what they say of any champion's legs at thirty or thirty-five. Then think of yours at fifty—even at forty-five.

"When you retire—unprepared as you are now—the unfilled weekdays will be actual, long-suffering ennui. You will probably come out of retirement within a year or two and, being unable to adjust to business again, be more unhappy than when you left retirement. Knowing you, I venture to say you are unprepared."

I told this man— as I tell you, my reader—that success in business does not guarantee success in later life. You must start now to prepare for retirement. With the same resolve you go out to get business, you must go out and find yourself two or three outside interests that will appeal to you now and will fill your day in later years; that will answer your morning anticipation with evening realization of a day worthwhile.

Whether it is cattle raising, crop raising or catching butterflies; whether it is becoming a baseball fan or an adviser to a boys' club; whether it is painting or writing; whether it is getting a part-time job for a few hours a day and filling it with your newly found interests: all or any of these will fill the crevices of a day.

"Prepare early to retire early!" That should be a motto in every home. It should be reiterated to pupils as often as "cigarette mildness" is dinned into the ears of a populace unsuspecting that it is being influenced by mass suggestion and hypnotism.

Early retirement will benefit the individual—and the country. Oldsters will not be put on a shelf—they will be in another location of their own choosing. In retiring early, they will be making room for the younger men who are waiting to find their place in the world. The man who gives up voluntarily will retain more respect than the one who is eased out. Older men will still be called in for advice and consultation.

The old, outmoded doctor trudging along with his little black bag—the man who has given fifty years of service to his patients —deserves well of them. Still, I do not envy him. I'd rather give twenty-five to thirty-five years of my life to my profession—years when I can make the fullest use of my faculties—and step aside to make way for a younger man. I would not dream of staying on until a handful of patients grown old with me showed their appreciation of my efforts by presenting me with a wrist watch— or (Heaven forbid, after fifty years) another little black bag.

Part Five

———

THE DOCTOR DISCUSSES
SOME OLD-OLD PROBLEMS

Chapter 29

Sleep Well!

THE MOST TRYING PART OF GETTING UP early in the morning is thinking about it late the night before. So are, in many ways, our present joys diluted by unpleasant, premature thoughts about tomorrow.

I remember how often I have sat in the early hours with a group of friends, all of us waiting for our turn to express views on the international situation or upon our reactions to the latest play. There have been musical evenings, among talented company, when the hours slipped by and morning was already here.

Always, where I was concerned, the enjoyment would be momentarily stilled by thoughts of the early rising tomorrow. That put a dull film on the shining surface of inner satisfaction. It would disappear quickly only to return again, with maximum intensity, when the good company had left—or I had left them.

Digging my head into the pillow after a glance at the clock, I would perform a quick trick of subtraction; and the answer— only a few short hours of sleep left—would send me off to fidgety dreamland and forgetfulness.

Sleep, the universal recharger, is many things to many people. To some it is a nuisance. Such persons require very little. To others it is the necessity of necessities. Without it life is shorn of its full significance. I *know* because I am one of the unfortunate who must have his sleep—or suffer.

People are divided into three classes: the early-to-beds and the early-to-risers; the late-to-beds and the late-to-risers; and a mixture of the two. That man is happiest who can best conform to his inner sleep rhythm. You are unfortunate if your job is such that it throws a wrench into your sleep machinery.

For example, if you are a fireman who is by nature one of the early-to-bed, to-rise class, you will suffer miserably if you work through a week of nightly alarms. If you are a busy physician who "just needs his sleep," yet must work nights as well as days, my sympathy goes out to you!

When I was first in practice I could easily recover during the day following three or four night calls. As time went on, my body rebelled. One can't fight his physical makeup any more than he can change the color of his skin. For the good of my day patients —and for my own comfort as a secondary consideration—I started to send out younger doctors on my night calls. In that way patients received better service the next day and everybody was happy—except those few patients who became annoyed when they discovered their doctor was a human being rather than a perpetual motion machine or a tireless robot.

Arnold Bennett, the British novelist, put forth a theory with which I cannot concur. He believed that all of us put too much stress on the need for sleep. In fact, he said that you can thrive on five or six hours nightly if you put your mind to it.

How can one who experiences it daily, forget about the need for eight or nine hours' sleep? That is like telling a frog to give milk and a cow to hop, skip, and jump. You can't go against nature.

Try Bennett's suggestion if you "need" eight hours a night. I have experimented for one week, limiting sleep to six hours nightly (1 to 7 A.M.). At the end of the week, although not completely exhausted, I experienced an all-encompassing, vague fatigue, a loss of bounce, slower reflexes, a loss of interest, a certain lessened efficiency in my work and my will power to work.

I, like countless others, am a frog who can't be made to give milk.

Over the years I have been astounded at the patients who tell me they are fresh and untired after five or six hours of sleep nightly. They consider that any time spent in bed after five and one-half to six hours' rest is wasteful. They turn and fidget and fret in bed. It becomes a prison to them. They leap out before their lids are opened enough for them to see the day.

These people I consider laden with the richest gift, next to health, that a mortal can have. Consider what its possession means. Consider how many extra hours and years of living are given to such persons. Byron summed it up long ago: "Death, so called, is a thing that makes men weep, and yet a third of life is passed in sleep."

If you can be completely rested and 100 per cent efficient after six hours' rest, you have eighteen hours left in which to live daily. (That was Bennett's reason for suggesting that all of us get along on six hours' rest.) Those of us who require eight to ten hours' sleep for top efficiency—think of what a loss in living we incur.

For example, simple arithmetic will convince you that you gain 750 to 800 hours a year by sleeping only six hours nightly—equivalent to an added month of life. You thereby live thirteen months a year. You automatically change the Biblical seventy-year lifetime of an eight-hours-in-bed man to about a seventy-six-year lifetime. It adds up. It seems that simple.

Bennett's theory is one with which I agree enthusiastically—*provided* you can change your schedule without loss of efficiency. If you cannot change it, you had better settle for seventy years of feeling rested and fit and alive during your waking hours; rather than strive for seventy-six years of days bogged down by chronic fatigue, loss of interest, and an actual prolonged battle to keep your eyelids pried apart.

For the person who requires much sleep and says, "I sleep well any time, anywhere," I think the disruption in his life would be far from a laughing matter were he to essay shorter sleeping hours.

It is advisable that you find your niche. Perhaps you have been wasting a good bit of your lifetime by the habit of sleeping eight to ten hours. Try seven hours for a week; then six for a week or two. That is experiment enough. You do not need a year to convince yourself.

If you are just as fresh and alert after six hours, I strongly advise that you change your sleeping hours immediately. Life is too precious to waste the hours unnecessarily. You have been missing much, but however old you may be, there is still much to gain. Forgo, as of now, those extra two hours in bed.

But suppose you have made the great experiment. You have lopped off two of the precious hours of rest at night. At the end of the week your co-workers remark about the circles under your eyes. At night, when company comes for visiting, you yawn in the faces of your most relished guests. You become forgetful. If you are an accountant, you have lost your certainty with figures; if a surgeon, the knife feels heavy in your hands; if a lawyer, the courtroom nods sleepily at your dull cross-examination of witnesses.

I can only stress the need for the termination of your experiment at once, before you fall into the clutches of chronic fatigue. Then you will surely be in for it. As an antidote for your experiment, sleep around the clock—and you will be yourself again.

I think it was George Kaufman who, when asked why he chose the playwriting profession, said: "It gives me the opportunity to stay in bed until afternoon." I think that's as good a reason as any.

Many a man is in the wrong business or profession. The unhappy, maladjusted and ill-fitted run into the millions.

For example, take the businessman who has a fight on his hands every morning. It requires supreme effort of will to get out of bed—not on occasional mornings—but every morning. By nature, although a successful man, he's more fitted for a profession that reaches its highest requirement late at night (like acting, for instance). He's at 50 per cent efficiency from 7 A.M. to 3 P.M. From then until the early morning hours he is at his best. He's the fellow who is holding forth without pause, the spark plug of the group, while the others cast furtive glances at each other and their watches. Earlier, his gears aren't meshed. Too bad!

There are lawyers who should be accountants, tailors who should be surgeons, and singers who should teach sign language. If you examine yourself and your friends more closely you will be able to make your own diagnosis. By their alertness—or lack of it— at a late party you will easily catalogue each one as a misfit or a fit. It isn't always aptitude or inaptitude for one's job that defines one's degree of happiness in work; look to the glands or sleep rhythm too. If one continually has to row against the current of his nature, his life is full of constant struggle and unhappiness.

You see, I hope, how important it is to learn early what your rhythm is. Are you a night bird, a day bird, or both? Find out your rhythm and that of your children. This is perhaps as important as the various intelligence and aptitude tests that help so much in fitting you to your future job, or your job to you.

That man and wife are fortunate and happy, whose sleep rhythms fit instead of clash. For example, I recall a patient who complained that his wife interfered with his rest. "For years I haven't had a good night's sleep," he said. "I'm dead the next day without at least eight hours; all she needs is five and a half. Our gears are always grinding. When I'm trying to get to sleep, she is in the next bed with the light on, rustling the newspaper. I twist and turn but she just can't understand why I need to —and can't—fall asleep. She gets up early and is wide awake before her feet touch the floor; it takes me an hour to wipe away the cobwebs. I've tried to gear myself her way, but I was exhausted at the end of a week. She doesn't even try to see it my way because she has never suffered physically from lack of sleep."

The need for sufficient sleep must be considered in all good treatment of the sick. Doctors often overlook its importance. Frequently, the patient does not volunteer the information that he has spent miserably sleepless nights. We must ask: Have you been sleeping well lately?

Then and there we often get on the right track of the cure.
The nervous patient who has been regressing does a turnabout a
few days after we have provided for sleep. Chronic fatigue acts
as a ball and chain on any illness. The pneumonia patient—
penicillin or not—will not do well without rest. Neither will the
person who has had his gall bladder or appendix removed—or anyone who has undergone surgery. As for heart cases, if I had
to choose between giving a sleepless patient digitalis, mercurials,
oxygen, or any other specific cardiac therapy, and a sedative
to insure good rest, I would choose the sedative. For a great many
years I have asked the associates on my two medical services never
to pass a patient's bed without saying: "Do you have any pain?
How did you sleep?"

There are many diseases, still, in which the doctor must stand
by helplessly and watch his patient pass the way of all living
things. The least we can do is to provide the last measure of ease
and comfort. The terminal cancer patient, wracked with pain,
should not have that pain—even if we have to do a lobotomy to
spare his last weeks or months; the cardiac patient, wheezing,
coughing, and struggling for breath in his last few hours, should
be given the relaxing, pain-free exodus that only morphine and
other drugs can provide. They all deserve sleep. Doctors should
make the long nights of torture shorter for helpless patients.

So, too, with the less seriously ill. If you are sick, there's no
excuse for your being sleepless night after night. If you are well,
but an insomniac, don't suffer unnecessarily. But don't treat
yourself. Take yourself to your doctor. Don't hesitate to take the
"dope" he prescribes. (Sedatives are not dope.) Take the sleep-
giving tablets or capsules with thankfulness. But never on your
own. They are not to be taken indefinitely. They are only crutches
to help you over the occasional rough spots.

There is no need, here, to discuss fully the theories of what
causes sleep. They range from fatigue poisons in the blood, produced by muscular contractions, to inability of the nerve ganglia
in the brain to keep proper contact with one another.

What causes insomnia is something else again. We know that

overtiredness, anxiety, fear, worry, loss of money, jealousy, and a hundred and one other emotional and physical states are common causes. Sometimes the cause of insomnia lies deep in the unconscious. Whereas some people with neurosis sleep away their lives to forget, others lie awake to torture themselves.

Whatever the causes, there have been thousands of remedies. Counting sheep, according to many, is one of the commonest "sure cures." In my experience, patients say that looking for sheep they cannot find keeps most of them awake.

Whether you are a light sleeper or a heavy one, an actual insomniac or a dead-to-the-world slumberer, your category is not so important as getting the amount of sleep you really need. Ask yourself: "Just how much sleep do I really need?" Test yourself. If you are an insomniac, see if you can get by with less sleep. You may find you are one of the fortunates who require only five hours nightly—that you are not an insomniac at all, that it's only your unconscious egging you to get moving.

Chapter 30

Bowels

T HERE'S NOTHING ODD about showing interest in your own bowels. You have a machine so valuable that money can't buy it, and you are naturally curious about the efficiency of its working parts.

Perhaps we doctors have unnaturally intensified your interest.

Two hundred thousand physicians in the United States ask at least two million patients this question daily: "How are your bowels?" It is almost ritual. If you left your doctor's office without that question and the opportunity to answer, you would feel that your visit was not entirely eventful.

Multiply the two million patients by seven days in the week (it averages that many) and you have fourteen million who have been asked, "And your bowels?" One person out of ten in this country is therefore made bowel conscious at least once a week. Probably this has been going on since Hippocrates started in practice. If the symbol of the nurse is the food tray and the bed pan, the symbol of the examining physician is his direct question as to the state of your bowels.

Have you noticed, though, that he sometimes asks this question as a robot might ask it if you dropped in a coin? Before you have had the opportunity to go deeply into your own bowel problem he is on to the next question about your appetite or sleep. You should come to realize, but perhaps never will, that the bowel problem does not deserve the important consideration which you believe it does.

Most patients, subjected to the bombardment of advertisements that stress the importance of laxatives, have become *too* bowel conscious. If they miss one daily movement, they think they become toxic. They complain of headaches, belching, loss of appetite and upper abdominal distress. They think of the lower colon as a receptacle that must be kept clean. Let them miss one day's movement and they feel they are walking cesspools. The headaches come, they believe, because the foul poisons in the lower bowel are being absorbed into the pure blood stream. Thus contaminated, the blood which absorbs the toxins washes the brain and causes the headaches and loginess. (Actually, the end products of digestion are never reabsorbed into the blood from the lower bowel.)

Think of the tons of water that have surged into the colons of tens of thousands of persons who have subjected and devoted themselves to the ritual of the high colonic irrigation. The manipulators of the rubber hose have made quite a business of cleansing the system, supposedly ridding it of its poisons. (During the past few years the cult has almost died out. Vitamins and antibiotics have become more absorbing—and less discomforting —subjects of interest.)

For pity's sake, once and for all, do not be unduly bowel conscious. Of course, if there is a sudden change in your bowel habit, investigate. If you have lost weight and are having indigestion, investigate. If there is blood in your stool, investigate. But, having found nothing organic after careful study, forget about your bowels. (This will drive some laxative manufacturers into spelling the name of their product sideways!)

The upper intestines are for digestion; the lower, for elimination. You eat. Naturally, you must eliminate. But it is well to remember that your gut is different from the other fellow's.

Yours may be active, his may be lazy. Your peristalsis (which is the kneading movement of the walls of the intestine on its contents that at last forces them down through the rectum) is a personal characteristic.

The shape of your gut is as individual as the shape of your nose. You may be tall and thin and have a long, slinky, inefficient gut. You may have post-operative adhesions that cause kinks and slow up the passage of food. Each one to his own—and each to his own characteristic bowel movements.

I have heard a patient say: "Doctor, I have been constipated for the past month. I have only *one* bowel movement a day." "Only one?" I asked quizzically.

"Well, I've been very uncomfortable. I've been used to having three movements a day all my life."

Another patient will say: "I have been having a movement every day now. I never used to. Never had more than two movements a week for years."

There you have two extremes. These cases indicate that three movements a day may be normal for Smith and one or two movements a week may be natural and sufficient for Jones.

It would be better for you to erect a defense against the daily sniping from the pages of magazines and newspapers. Read the laxative ads if you must, but with tongue in cheek. It is true, of course, that modern man—and woman, especially—tends to be a constipated animal. In general, though, the causes are not essentially physiological. The exigencies, emergencies, and hurry calls of our existence deny the bowels the regularity which they deserve. Most laxative companies would be bankrupt within months if all of us "took the time."

The urge comes. We are ready to answer, perhaps with anticipation of pleasure, because nature has made the bowel movement a pleasurable event. The privacy of the bathroom, the unhurried reading of the paper or book—this is a delightful custom, especially on Sundays.

But what usually happens? The phone rings, it must be answered. After a lengthy conversation, the urge has gone. Or the alarm fails to go off, you are late for the office; no time for an answer to the bowel call this morning.

The bowel resents being unanswered. It sends you stronger signals. But your external pressures are stronger than your internal ones. Finally, in full resentment at being so often and completely disregarded, the lower bowel says, "If that's the way things are, two can play at that game." In the future, signals come at longer intervals—every two days, then every three or four. Now come the common complaints: "Doctor, I'm constipated. I've tried all kinds of laxatives and they don't help."

If you are concerned about your bowels, take your eyes off your navel. Divert your contemplation of life to other fields; do not concentrate on your midriff. These are the things you should know (perhaps I repeat, but the repetition is good for you) :

Each one has his own bowel system. I have seen healthy seventy-year-oldsters who swore they had never had more than one bowel movement a week throughout a long, uneventful lifetime. On the other hand, I have seen oldsters who have had two bowel movements a day as regularly as the sun's rising and setting. I have known patients who considered themselves constipated if their twice-daily movement dwindled to one a day.

Consider your rhythm. If your movements come only twice weekly, and you have been regular daily for years, see your doctor, If he finds everything all right, then the best way to revert to the daily exacuation is to educate your rectal reflexes all over again. Frankly, it's a problem of educating *yourself* rather than your lower bowel. The most important consideration is a prompt reply to the call.

Consider the urge to evacuate as an S.O.S. that must be answered immediately. You would not go off on a cruise in the opposite direction from a distress call from a ship at sea; treat your bowel's summons likewise. Do not procrastinate, do not again give your bowel reason for distrusting your motives or you will become constipated for life (which in itself is not the worst calamity there is) .

When your phone rings and your rectum calls simultaneously, it's the phone that should be disregarded. A long-winded friend can easily start you on the road back to constipation. At business, allow no emergency or exigency to interfere with the "call."

Suppose that you have become a "chronic"; that you are an avid and helpless user of cathartics. Suppose you have tried prune juice (which, incidentally, is usually excellent), hot water before breakfast, bran, and all the "name" laxatives without getting back to the daily rhythm.

Then forget about it. Accept the new rhythm (if your doctor has found no actual disease causing it). Remember that you will not be absorbing poisons because you are not on time. After all, you are not a railroad train that must race to its destination—or else. Even a train can be late. So can you.

If, despite these exhortations, you feel you simply must be more regular, don't resort to daily or weekly whippings by cathartics or laxatives. That is no way to cure constipation. That makes for a more resentful bowel. It becomes lazier and less alert. It refuses to let you know that it is time for elimination, and there you go spinning around in the vicious circle of constipation all over again.

Here are specific recommendations I make to healthy patients: Begin again to answer the urge. Drink six to eight glasses of water a day (most persons are too dry). If your stools are not full and satisfactory, eat roughage like cabbage, celery, and carrots. Too smooth a diet does not give the intestinal walls enough to work on. If your stools are hard and irritating, use a tablespoon or two of mineral oil at night for about a week. After that, only at long intervals. Too frequent use of the oil will prevent proper nutrition because it interferes with vitamin absorption. Never take the advertised laxatives or you will become a slave to them.

If these suggestions fail to cause steady and satisfactory elimination, then better turn to treatment of your state of mind. If what I have told you about constipation has not already lifted, somewhat, your depression about it, then yours is really a fixation on your bowels. If you don't find some way to sweep your mind clean of the sluggish-bowel phobia, then it is your mind that will require spring housecleaning and not your bowel.

Unless you have bowel obstruction with nausea and vomiting; unless you present definite medical clues to a qualified medical man who finds they point to your lower digestive tract as a real threat to your efficiency, comfort, and health, better forget all about your bowels.

But show them common courtesy when they call.

Chapter 31

Smoking: Good or Bad?

TWENTY-FIVE YEARS AGO you could always spot the villain of the play. These days the entire cast smokes cigarettes.

So it is now outside the theater, too. Everybody—from ten-year-old Tommy, lurking in some secluded corner with a butt dangling from his lips, to Grandpa supporting the bowl of his pipe because its stem wiggles between toothless gums—everybody is tobacco-conscious.

If you don't smoke, you are to be congratulated for resisting the daily barrage of tobacco advertising that hammers on your eardrums and blazes before your eyes. It is so powerful and persistent that you don't have to have the curiosity of a kitten to wonder if you are missing some of heaven's blandishment by forgoing the weed. If you don't watch out, someday you will weaken and reach for the weed instead of a sweet.

Some people smoke one cigarette and never touch another. There are others who seem to have begun with two packs a day, and have repeated this twenty-four-hour ritual for the rest of their lives. In between are the moderate smokers, who can take it or leave it. They derive little pleasure or none at all from smoking. They do it largely to be sociable.

With some excessive smokers, it has become a reflex to "reach for one." In a conference or at a party, lighting a cigarette and holding it gives them a degree of confidence out of all proportion to the significance of the act of smoking itself. No need to wonder why. Smoking is a distraction for them. They smoke, not because they like it, but because it lessens their inner tensions.

Smoking makes them part of the crowd. It saves them from fumbling with their buttons or otherwise being self-conscious. It gives their hands something to do. (Unless you are an actor or trained public speaker, you know how difficult it is to just let them hang by your sides without feeling as if you were standing with two awkward hams dangling there.)

So you see, we smoke either because we like it, tolerate it, or simply because it relieves nervousness. In the heavier smoker, it causes nervousness as well. One question a physician is bound to hear at least once every day throughout his entire lifetime of practice is this: "How about my smoking, Doctor? Is it harmful? Do I really have to quit?"

The easy way out for the physician is to say: "Smoking's bad for you. Better give it up." That forestalls tedious explanations of the whys and wherefores.

But such an answer is not quite fair—especially if the questioner is one of the many who can't wait for the morning so they can have their "first drag." I feel the question deserves more than a cursory answer. And I believe that I can give you an unbiased one—not only as a doctor, but as one who has had years of personal experience with nicotine and other tobacco derivatives.

For over thirty years I have nonchalantly made my choice between the cigarette, cigar, and pipe. (I have yet to experience my first chaw—probably I never shall.) Some days it was just cigarettes or a pipe. On others, two or three cigars.

My smoking has been moderate. Never more than a package a day. Never more than two or three cigars. Never a pipe continuously hanging from my lips. I am one of those who like tobacco, but never feel it is indispensable. And I have, at intervals throughout the years, proved it to myself. Every few years I renounce tobacco for a number of months. A day of oversmoking is usually the precursor of such drastic decision.

For example, some months ago, while under the exhilarating influence of discussing books with my publishers, I burned up more cigarettes and cigars than usual. The next morning I did without my regular after-breakfast cigarette—and stopped smoking for three months. It didn't hurt *too* much.

I have become autobiographical for a reason. I am privileged now to speak to you with authority; *if I can stop smoking without being told it is a necessity, then you can if you must.* There it is in a small package with great import.

If your doctor has made a diagnosis of stomach ulcer, coronary artery disease (angina pectoris or occlusion), high blood pressure or thrombo-angitis obliterans (blood-vessel infection and occlusion), he will, if he is a good doctor, insist that you give up the weed forever.

Remember that the sudden withdrawal of nicotine is not harmful for your system. If you say that you haven't the will power to stop suddenly, think of the thousands who have done it. If you wonder just how to stop—having at last made the resolution—remember that it can be accomplished.

Incidentally, *accomplish* is not the word for it. It gives the act of renouncing tobacco the unearned dignity and standing of a project. It is much simpler than that.

In writing of habits, Shakespeare said: "Refrain tonight and that shall lend a kind of easiness to the next abstinence." And James T. Mangan has re-enforced this theme: "The way to break a bad habit is to undertake the *first* abstinence. You may be smoking, drinking, or eating too much—and you admit it isn't good for you. How to stop? Refrain this once! Now dwell on this single act of abstention. Isn't it a great experience? This self-satisfaction contains more joy than the indulgence itself. You are now aware that you *can* abstain; you are stronger and more skillful at coping with the next temptation. A kind of easiness has been given you for the next battle, and your heart has come to know that there is more pleasure in destroying a bad habit than in preserving it."

The way to stop smoking is to do it the easy way. The best

way to drive a tack is with a small hammer—not with a sledge hammer. The best way to stop smoking is to do it without tensing all over, as for a supreme effort.

Just stop. Each one of us has brakes on our machine. All you need is the will to *want* to use them. It is the *willing* and *wanting* alone that require any energy expenditure. And the less the better.

Apparently, this sounds easier than it is. When I look back over the years, and think of the thrombo-angitis cases who would not give up smoking after warnings, and actually lost two legs by amputation; when I think of coronary patients who persisted in smoking two or three packages a day in spite of warning and who died prematurely; when I think of hundreds of ulcer cases who persisted in smoking and added gasoline to the fire of their heartburns; when I think of all these, I marvel how intelligent individuals complacently go about killing themselves.

We know much of tobacco and its effects and we know little of them. We only *suspect* that smoking causes throat and lung cancer. In a few diseases such as I have already mentioned, there are specific medical reasons against the use of tobacco. However, if you have none of these diseases, I hesitate to make the drastic and specific request that you stop smoking. We do not have enough proof that tobacco is a poison for everybody.

Nevertheless, I have the hunch that tobacco never did anybody any good. The minor reliefs from tension, the feeling of well-being induced by the after-dinner cigar or pipe, the sense of security that a cigarette affords before or after a period of stress— you must weigh how much these mean to you as against tobacco's potentialities for harm. Unfortunately, we have no test at present that will definitely indicate which of us may be harmed by tobacco.

If you should ask whether to smoke or give it up, I would say this: "If you have no definite physical condition in which smoking is injurious, then the choice is yours." We doctors, in the present state of our knowledge about tobacco, have no right to tell the healthy person that tobacco is bad for him. You must weigh the individual pros and cons in your own case.

Do you smoke? How much do you smoke? How much do you really enjoy it? Can you smoke a package a day without discomfort? If you enjoy every puff, I cannot advise that you must stop —or that you had better stop.

On the other hand, do you smoke only ten cigarettes a day or only two cigars? Shall you stop? Perhaps in your case, yes. Perhaps the tobacco habit is not worth it when you weigh it against the dizziness, throat irritation, loss of appetite and palpitation that even a few puffs cause.

You see, then, that if you are well, if your doctor finds no organic disease, you yourself are a better judge than he. You must make your own decision.

You should not deprive yourself of the pleasure of smoking in the present because next year—or fifty years from now—proof may come that tobacco is a sure poison, that it shortens life, for example, by contributing to the earlier beginning of arteriosclerosis.

Until actual proof is forthcoming (how can we say that it ever or never will be?), I believe you may continue to puff on your cigarette, grasp your cigar, fondle your pipe, to your great content and satisfaction.

I have little patience with doctors—especially those who have never smoked—who hand down the indiscriminate decision "no smoking" to every patient. This is being short-sighted and unscientific. Besides, it shows little compassion for or interest in, the daily small pleasures of their fellow human beings.

As for the relative destructiveness of pipe, cigar, or cigarette— that, is an individual problem. One pipeful will knock over the habitual twelve-cigar-a-day man and vice versa.

As for which cigarettes are milder, I suppose that depends upon the amount of money spent by the company advertising. The more money spent, supposedly the milder the cigarettes. Draw your own conclusion.

Chapter 32

The Truth About Liquor

ALCOHOLISM IS NOT A RECENT PROBLEM. If you would like
to see one of the earliest references to drunkenness, read the
description of Noah in the ninth chapter of Genesis.

Alcohol's medicinal use goes back to the Dark Ages. Before
the days of inhaling anesthetics, alcohol was used as a narcotic to
help patients withstand painful operations. Today, that would
be a waste of the various end-products of fermentation. Grape
and grain have other (and pleasanter) uses.

Although alcohol is not now an accepted ally in preventing
operative pain, man still uses it for many purposes: to allay
apprehension, for relaxation, for good fellowship, and as a
stomachic for good digestion. It has been estimated that there
are about fifty million "social" drinkers in the United States.

If it were possible for these moderate imbibers to remain
within the limits of this classification, then chronic alcoholism
would not be the great (and belatedly recognized) problem that
it is today. An ounce or two of hard liquor daily, or an occasional glass of wine or beer, if not exceeded as a daily dose,
unquestionably makes a contribution to the pleasure of living.

Still, many persons consider even the moderate use of alcohol
immoral. Many others believe it invites cirrhosis of the liver.
There is no factual proof that moderate drinking ever caused this

183

malady. In fact, according to the investigations of the late Raymond Pearl when he was at Johns Hopkins, if you are a moderate drinker the chances are that you will outlive your neighbor who is a teetotaler.

Although alcohol is not a cure-all for colds, snakebite or other discomforts—as some popular misconceptions would have it—it has its place in medicine.

In practice I have found that alcohol's chief value for most persons is in fighting tension. And anyone living in the present day needs no definition of what tension is—or what causes it.

There are few better ways of cutting the rope of tension that ties you to your work than taking an ounce of sherry or a shot of scotch or bourbon before dinner. A glass of beer also works as well for some.

Your cares will fall away, you will shed your fatigue, and your stomach will be ready to receive its nourishment. Your food will taste better, your conversation will be livelier and your outlook better and brighter.

Your wife should join you in this early evening ceremony because the "day over the hot ironing board" isn't conducive to evening good temper and equanimity either.

Hundreds upon hundreds of patients have told me, through the years (in all sobriety), how much the daily ounce or two of liquor has added to the fullness and enjoyment of life.

Nevertheless, doctors never forget that alcohol is a drug with powerful potentialities for harm. It is a two-edged sword: one edge dangerous, the other not. Even the layman knows that too many morphine, phenobarbital, bromide, or thyroid pills can be hurtful—useful as they are in small quantities when needed. And even an apparently harmless concoction like bicarbonate of soda and water is now known to be life-shortening for some heart and high-blood-pressure sufferers—if taken often enough. Likewise with alcohol. It can kill both the spirit and the body.

As a social drinker, if you don't control yourself, you may skate onto thin ice. If you ever become one of the three million excessive drinkers in this country, then you need to be still more cautious. If not aware of alcohol's inherent danger, you may fall through the ice and become submerged as one of the 750,000 chronic alcoholics this country has to contend with.

Just what is an excessive drinker? Oddly enough, he is not necessarily a chronic alcoholic. The distinction between the two is sometimes a fine one.

Briefly, here is a capsule portrait of an excessive drinker. John Smith is a successful businessman who enjoys the unenviable reputation of being able to drink most of his friends under the table. They are usually the first to yell "Uncle"—because Smith holds his liquor so well. He can take six or seven highballs at a party without getting too hilarious. And next day, instead of becoming temporarily allergic to the stuff and forswearing liquor for the day, he will down two or three martinis at lunch and perhaps have a few beers that night. Smith can follow this routine for weeks and still carry on proper business and social relationships. Although Smith enjoys a drink he is not a lone drinker. He likes it for the mellow effect it produces, not for its taste. He has never been on a "lost week end."

Smith can take it or leave it, *now*. But one never knows about *later*. At present, Smith is well adjusted in business and at home. Finances, wife, children, friends—all are "tiptop." But suppose the day comes when life increases its pressure; when things are not so free and easy as they have been. What will Smith do then? Will he need more and more to rely on alcohol? Will he be able to face misfortune without recourse to the anesthetic effect—the temporary forgetfulness—that alcohol provides?

If he does not require more alcohol, he will still be an excessive drinker—not a chronic alcoholic. But one never knows which class one will be in until the tensions increase. It is for this reason that I have always advised excessive drinkers to taper down, to become social drinkers. It is a long way from social drinking to chronic alcoholism. I say to the excessive drinker: "If a maximum of two ounces of liquor a day does not satisfy you, better give up alcohol entirely. Better forgo its benefits or you will become too dependent upon it." Two drinks or *no* drinks is a good rule.

So much for the excessive drinker. Really, the main difference between him and the chronic alcoholic is a matter of degree. The chronic alcoholic is sick—not weak or bad. He is a man running away from himself. Being able to run just so far without relief, he turns—and returns—to alcohol for forgetfulness. He behaves this way because he knows no other way to behave.

For centuries we treated the insane like outcasts whose only need, we felt, was imprisonment. In some places and times they were whipped, to drive the devils out of them. We now know they are not inhabited by devils—they are merely sick people. We call them "mentally ill" and treat their illnesses. With our new attitude and methods of treatment, the percentage of recoveries is high.

All this holds true of our approach to chronic alcoholics, too. Once they were the big jokes of the police courts. Befuddled, dirty, friendless, they were sentenced and thrown into jail. Released, it was not long before they ended up in jail again. They tried to break the habit, but were too ill to find their own way out of the maze of bewilderment and despair. The police and the courts could not help much. They did not even know what was the matter with these people.

Chronic alcoholism, I said, is a running away from life. It is a form of slow suicide. In fact, about 5 per cent of *all* suicides are chronic alcoholics. Many such alcoholics are psychoneurotic—afraid, dependent, frustrated. Some are psychotic, with bizarre patterns of personality change. Only recently have we realized these things. Only recently have we put our new knowledge to use.

Now, on all fronts, we are pressing the attack on chronic alcoholism. Our army is growing. Sympathetic judges, understanding social workers, enlightened physicians and psychiatrists, and investigators in chemical and biological laboratories who hunt new drugs like antabuse to fight this disease, are all helping us to win great victories.

Now we study the home life and job of the chronic alcoholic; we make a complete physical evaluation of him and complex personality studies. We provide medical and psychiatric treatment. The fifty thousand members of Alcoholics Anonymous lend their strength to rebuild the will and spirit of the patient. As he learns to stand on his own feet, he throws away the fatal crutch of liquor.

Despite the harm it can do, alcohol is not evil in itself. Like any other tool or thing we have, it is good when it is used to help, harmful when it is misused. But people often choose to see only one side of a subject. Why do you suppose the prohibitionists condemned alcohol? They concentrated on its bad effects, closed their eyes to its good ones.

Physicians, like alcoholics, use liquor as a crutch. But therapeutically, to aid the sick. I have found, for example, that alcohol is often invaluable in the treatment of anginal pains which grip the chest in patients with coronary disease. They require fewer nitroglycerine tablets and other medication if they take a few ounces of liquor a day. Many patients, you might expect, would welcome such a prescription. But not all.

I recall a minister's wife who was in my office with her husband one day. Her first words were: "I have something on my mind. It's liquor. And I'd like you to straighten out my thinking on it."

As she said this, she turned her gaze from me to her husband, a fine man of sixty. He settled back in his chair, his eyes wide with anticipation. You could see that he had been waiting impatiently for this moment.

She went on to say: "When we were here last year, before leaving for California, you told John to take as many nitroglycerine tablets as he needed for his chest pain. You also said, Doctor, that an ounce of whiskey once or twice a day might make him more comfortable—might obviate the need for his taking so many nitroglycerines.

"Well, his angina has bothered him so much lately that he has been dissolving about twenty tablets a day. That's why we're back again.

"Now here is what's troubling me, Doctor. I haven't let John take any liquor because it's against my principles—I was brought up more or less as a prohibitionist. Besides, his brother was a chronic alcoholic since his teens, and died of cirrhosis at thirty-eight."

Here was a fine woman in a common predicament. I said to her: "Frankly, aren't you really afraid that your husband may turn into an alcoholic?"

She was silent for a moment. Then she nodded slowly—and I was not surprised.

"I want to be sure," she said, "that I'm not keeping liquor from John just because I am afraid of it. If you think he really needs it, I'll go out right now and buy him a bottle of scotch myself. He suffers a lot. It's time his health and comfort came first."

When the interview was over she made good her words. That was months ago. Life has become bearable for her husband since that day. Fewer chest pains and fewer nitroglycerine tablets. Neither is he a chronic alcoholic now, and the chances are he will never be one.

For, in my experience over the years in prescribing alcohol to persons over forty, I know of not one case of chronic alcoholism that I induced. If there is no medical reason against it, I do not hesitate to prescribe some form of alcohol for patients past forty.

Before writing this chapter I wanted the latest scientific opinion on alcoholic habituation. I called a psychiatrist who has for years made a special study of the treatment of chronic alcoholics.

"In your opinion, how likely is a person to become a chronic alcoholic after forty?' I asked.

His answer: "I've just reviewed five hundred of my cases of chronic alcoholism. Only two in the entire series said they did not begin to drink until after forty. But on further questioning these two admitted they had been heavy drinkers since their twenties."

I felt better about it—and you should too, if you have ever feared you might become a middle-aged (or older) alcohol addict. Although the odds are better than 500 to 1 that you will not become a chronic alcoholic if you haven't been one before forty—better play it safe with a maximum of two jiggers a day.

And if you're under forty? My prescription is the same, but there's a further instruction—mix the recommended dosage well with a double dram of caution.

Chapter 33

There's Danger in That Bicarbonate

I RECALL A MOST COOPERATIVE HIGH-BLOOD-PRESSURE patient who nevertheless responded poorly to treatment. He willingly went on a diet and lost thirty pounds. He gave up smoking and drinking (not that all such patients *need* to). He rested for an hour after lunch. He increased his sleeping schedule from six and a half to eight and a half hours nightly. He took frequent vacations. He delegated much of his work to associates. He removed every possible constricting and enervating bit of stress from his daily living.

Yet, in answer to the question: "How are your dizziness and headaches?" he invariably said (even after three months of such cooperation), "Just the same. Not a bit better."

His blood pressure had not fallen appreciably. "Have you taken any salt?" No. He had followed the low sodium diet with this exception: he had overlooked the need for eliminating practically everything with sodium in it. He had been taking, he admitted, bicarbonate by the handful for the "acid in his stomach."

He stopped taking bicarbonate and within two weeks his dizziness and headaches disappeared and his blood pressure dropped markedly. Had he been aware that the value of even the rice diet lay in its low sodium content, he might have restricted his bicarbonate intake—and have been comfortable months earlier.

A similar case was a forty-five-year-old woman with rheumatic heart disease. She, too, was cooperative but overlooked the dangers inherent in taking bicarbonate of soda. It was there on the prohibited side of her diet list, but she had missed it.

For years her heart had carried her along without remonstrating. One spring she suffered a sore throat that did not respond to sulfa or penicillin. She contracted pneumonia, from which she finally recovered after the disease had run a stormy course.

Now her heart began to fibrillate (become irregular). She suffered shortness of breath on slight exertion, and ankle swelling. Her kidneys would not work properly. Although she was now on a salt-free diet, she did not respond to treatment. She needed to be propped up on three pillows for comfort at night; a month before, she had required none.

Although she felt better—at first—after taking digitalis and being injected with mercurials twice weekly, later her edema (swelling) increased. Only after she went off into a detailed description of her indigestion ("the only thing that helps me is taking baking soda"), did we find the leak in our defenses.

It was easily stopped. She gave up reaching for bicarbonate. Within the month there was striking improvement. Shortness of breath, cough and ankle swelling had practically vanished. She no longer needed to have excess fluid removed, as her kidneys had now returned to normal.

True, her murmur and her auricular fibrillation still persisted. But patients can live with these defects for many years. In her case, the heart condition was easily kept under adequate control by one digitalis pill a day.

Thousands of persons are unaware of the potential harm in taking bicarbonate of soda daily. The steady intake of small doses may add up to harmful consequences.

This drug, apparently innocuous, sits in the medicine cabinet or on the kitchen shelf of practically every home in America. Is there a man, woman—or child—who has not at some time had his bicarbonate? If not as a pill or powder, at least in his food? Even the small doses sprinkled on peas and other vegetables to bring out the "luscious green" often destroy vitamins C and D.

Then, there is another by-effect of too much bicarbonate: alkalosis. This is due to an imbalance in the alkali and acid levels in the blood. When the blood becomes too alkaline due to loss of excess carbon dioxide, symptoms arise. There may be numbness and tingling in the hands and feet, weakness, perspiration, difficulty in breathing and anxiety. As the alkalosis deepens, the symptoms become more marked; convulsions ending in unconsciousness may ensue.

One teaspoonful of bicarbonate every few days will not cause such symptoms; but reaching for the teaspoon and dipping it into the can of powder every few hours *may*.

"Nothing helps my ulcer so much as old-fashioned bicarbonate," says one patient. "I'm not one for taking the newfangled drugs." His ulcer being the cause of almost continuous discomfort, he doses himself with the drug quite steadily. And there is the vicious circle: the more he neutralizes the stomach acids, the more they re-form. This "acid rebound" demands more bicarbonate for relief. After weeks or months of taking it, may come alkalosis.

And think about how many persons bicarbonate keeps unaware they may have an ulcer. These patients go on smoking, drinking, overworking, undervacationing, eating improper foods. The bicarbonate masks their symptoms but doesn't cure them. The result? Their stress and strain in such living add up to a worsened ulcer. The possible results: hemorrhage or perforation of the stomach wall, with a chance of peritonitis.

An even worse consequence is the masking of the earliest symptoms of cancer of the stomach. In this disease, time is of the essence. Unnecessary procrastination in diagnosis and treatment usually spells catastrophe. Reaching for the bicarbonate may temporarily quench the fiery discomfort in the pit of the stomach. But, at the same time, it knocks out the alarm clock. The warning ring comes never—or much too late.

There are commoner problems than these. You cannot digest your food as well in a stomach whose juices are not normally acid. An older person, especially, should be watchful. The habit of taking bicarbonate may aggravate the condition of anacidity (absence of acid) that so many of the elderly have. It prevents efficient enzyme action on the food in the stomach. And then the food must pass through the intestines, a long trip for which it has not been properly prepared. Chronic, undiagnosed diarrhea is often due to lack of acid in the stomach.

Patients who rely on haphazard treatment of stomach symptoms often find easy, but strictly temporary relief. Shooting at their target in the dark, they rarely hit the bull's-eye of their disease. Bicarbonate is all right on your doctor's prescription—after X rays and other investigative procedures indicate exactly what is causing your symptoms.

At the risk of making you unnecessarily anxious (because, after all, there are such things as simple stomach upsets) I must tell you that diseases of the stomach and intestines are not the only causes of heartburn, flatulence, pain and other discomforts. I have mentioned heart disease and high blood pressure. Tuberculosis, kidney disease and involvement in any other part of the body may also give rise to stomach symptoms.

True, there is not always fire where there is the smoke of symptoms. But why take unnecessary chances? Even if it isn't cancer or ulcer, why suffer unnecessarily from an undiagnosed lazy gall bladder—or from one filled with stones? The trick is to know, rather than guess at, what you have.

I remember one patient who carried a decorative little box with him whenever he went out for dinner. It was filled with bicarbonate. He never ate without needing his bicarbonate.

One day he was rushed to the hospital with gangrene of his gall bladder. He developed liver complications and was fortunate to escape with his life. Since that operation he has never had indigestion. "When I think of how I took all that bicarbonate for years," he says.

Bicarbonate, then—for most of us—should be looked on as a

relic of the old days. Like sulfur and molasses. Of course, taken rarely, it is not a poison. Nevertheless it is a potential trouble-maker. It can be a petty thief or a killer—depending on how healthy you really are.

A good working rule is to find out, first. Have your yearly physical examination to evaluate your health efficiency. If it is all right, then an occasional pinch of bicarbonate is harmless. However, it is definitely to be avoided (unless prescribed by your doctor) if you have undiagnosed indigestion; if you have high blood pressure or heart disease: if you have alkalosis; or if you have vague, indefinable symptoms which might be due to a condition that the drug will harm.

There's danger in that bicarbonate! Stop, look, and listen before you dip your spoon into the can. It's not as safe—and pleasurable—as dipping into the cookie jar.

Part Six

———

THE DOCTOR DRAWS
A BATTLE PLAN
AGAINST ILLNESS

Chapter 34

A Little Knowledge

"A LITTLE KNOWLEDGE IS A DANGEROUS THING," we say, pigeon-holing the man who talks much but knows little. Still, a pigeon-hole has to be mighty big to accommodate a man. Knowledge, in itself, is not dangerous, as a rule. It's the use we put it to that is decisive.

Just how dangerous is the little knower and big talker?

He will read a digest of the international situation by his favorite columnist one day; and the next, he will hold forth in front of a group of friends as an oracle who knows all—not a little—about *which* country will next do *what*.

He considers himself an authority on Russia, having once heard a lecture on that country.

He *knows* England because he once spent a few days there.

He will talk about old civilizations as an expert, having once sat on a hot bench in the ruins of Pompeii; or having leafed through Gibbon's *Decline and Fall of the Roman Empire*.

Having caught a fish, he is a modern Isaak Walton; having read a book, he is an authority on modern painting; having the distinction of being the only one in his circle who can tolerate modern cacophony in music, he speaks with "full knowledge and understanding" on new trends in music.

"Little knowledge" in these instances is not "dangerous" to the speaker or to the listener—just boresome to the latter, and probably not fully satisfying to the former.

Whatever the knowledge, it is better than none—provided it is genuine knowledge, based on genuine facts. It is only when it is inaccurate, or used as the basis for a false conclusion, that it may become dangerous. Knowledge that is inadequate for the purpose to which it is applied may be dangerous, but not knowledge as such.

All of this is especially true, and vastly more important, where your health is concerned. Consider how necessary it is to have, for your own self-preservation, at least a "little knowledge" about illness and health. You will find it just the opposite of "dangerous."

If, because you are averse to being considered a hypochondriac, you stifle your natural curiosity about the facts of health and disease, you are letting your sensitivity to public opinion override your good sense. Wear your knowledge about health as a badge of intelligence rather than as an indication that you are a cowardly weakling. Constantly refurbish your health knowledge; keep the badge shining.

Your knowledge need not be great. For example, you don't have to know all a doctor knows about a ruptured appendix in order to save your life. The doctor, of course, knows more than you do about the symptoms, signs, pathology, and the treatment of the condition. Leave the "full" knowledge to him.

Let him be concerned about such things as pain, nausea, vomiting, rectal tenderness, fever, high white-blood-cell count, normal urine (or the evaluation of a few red blood cells in it).

Let him differentiate your attack from occasional right abdominal tenderness and pain due to rheumatic fever, a stone in the ureter, or diverticulitis.

Let his experience control the use of penicillin or other injections.

The "full" knowledge that your physician or surgeon has is surely not dangerous. *Neither is the little knowledge that you must have.* Without your little knowledge, the doctor's help may come much too late.

Even in these days of antibiotics, a ruptured appendix and peritonitis still can kill if you are not appendix-conscious when you get pain in the abdomen. You need to know only two things to have the necessary small equipment with which to fight appendicitis: One, never to take a laxative or physic for abdominal pain if your appendix is still *in*. Two, to reach for the telephone and call your doctor when you feel abdominal pain.

A little knowledge? Yes. Dangerous to reach for the telephone? No. You have only to compare last year's mortality tables for appendicitis with those of twenty years ago to learn, by graphic example, how many lives this "little knowledge" has saved.

The medical profession, the insurance companies, and other agencies have, for years, emphasized the dangers of the castor oil bottle in undiagnosed abdominal pain. Mothers now reach as casually for the phone (and the doctor) as they did in the past for the castor oil.

It is pathetic to think of the children who fought and squirmed as parents forced this "doomsday concoction" down their throats. I have also seen mothers, fathers, grandfathers, and grandmothers murdered by this false remedy when the real cure was close at hand.

Ignorance is a greater killer than war. These poor people were not aware of the need for even a "little knowledge" where self-preservation was concerned. Today, appendicitis sits low and dejected in the columns of mortality statistics, simply because preventive medicine agencies have forced a "little education" instead of castor oil down the unwilling throats of the populace. (I am all for self-treatment when it consists of doses of knowledge.)

What holds true for appendicitis is true of most diseases. The patient must—and can—help his doctor. All the advances in modern medicine are of no avail if the patient presents himself too late; especially if he has tampered with his machine before bringing it in for repairs.

I am not suggesting that you, as a layman, set out on a course of study that parallels your doctor's. You need not read works on physiology, pharmacology, pathology, diagnosis, and therapy.

You need only learn to keep an open mind to the fundamentals for self-preservation. You need only learn that your contribution to the prolongation of your life is as essential as the doctor's.

When you bring yourself to him as a wreck, you can expect only salvage even if you are made well enough to get about again. Procrastination is the prime cause of most human wreckage. This truth is overwhelming in cases of cancer. You know—or should, considering the literature on cancer which has lately flooded the nation—that what cancer feeds on is not only the body, but delay, fear, and indecision.

The little knowledge you should have is that in cancer the minor irritation or small lump today may become the fatal tumor tomorrow.

Early cancer can be cured. Thousands of lives are being saved yearly by the acceptance of this simple truth, just as countless potential peritonitis sufferers, following appendicitis, are being saved by the saying: "Reach for the phone instead of the castor oil."

Need you be an expert in cancer yourself? Need you know all the complexities of diagnosis and treatment? This is the expert's job. All you need to do is accept the little knowledge that early symptoms that may mean cancer should be investigated. That it is better to be cancer-conscious and live because your suspicions have been confirmed, rather than die prematurely because you are too frightened to see the little lump for what it may be and take it to your doctor.

What I have said about appendicitis and cancer is true of many other diseases to which man is heir. Heart trouble, hypertension, pneumonia, tuberculosis, ulcer of the stomach—to cite a few of man's enemies—generally retreat before early and sustained resistance. We shall look at these disorders in the next few chapters and see what we should know about them.

You, as the patient, should learn the fundamental truth that "a little knowledge is a dangerous thing" only when you attempt to substitute that knowledge for the doctor's full training and expertness in the handling of disease. When you use your little knowledge to complement his, it may be a life-saver.

Chapter 35

The Killers

I<small>N</small> <small>ONE RECENT YEAR</small>, these were the killers and the numbers they killed: Diseases of heart and blood vessels, 745,000; cancer, 209,000; accidents, 88,000; pneumonia, 47,000; tuberculosis, 34,-000; and nephritis, 29,000. Diseases of the heart and circulation are the Number One Bandit, taking almost twice as many lives as the combined toll of the next five leading causes of death.

According to a bulletin of the American Heart Association, examining mortality statistics by age groups, we find the leading five killers causing the following percentage of deaths in each group:

Ages 5-19

Accidents	39.5
Heart and blood vessels	10.2
Tuberculosis	5.9
Cancer	5.3
Pneumonia	4.7

Ages 20-34

Accidents	27.0
Tuberculosis	14.3
Heart and blood vessels	12.5
Cancer	8.1
Homicide	5.6

Ages 35-54

Heart and blood vessels	36.7
Cancer	18.5
Accidents	8.3
Tuberculosis	6.7
Nephritis	4.9

Ages 55-74

Heart and blood vessels	52.1
Cancer	18.2
Nephritis	5.6
Diabetes	4.0
Accidents	3.7

Age 75 and over

Heart and blood vessels	60.0
Cancer	11.2
Nephritis	7.5
Accidents	4.9
Pneumonia	4.1

Statistics can be nothing but cold, uninteresting columns of figures. It depends upon how much time you give to thinking of their implications.

For example, to me as a doctor, each single numeral—forgetting about the more than million deaths in this country each year—represents the end of the journey of the human being like you and me. It represents a sudden death or a lingering illness. It represents a person who has passed this way, never to do so again. It represents a loved one lost to a family who will never entirely forget the tragedy.

It behooves those of us who are aware that we only live once to sit back and coolly appraise the killers. They are constantly lying in wait to get us if they can. Our best weapon against them is knowledge. And, as I have said, a little of it is more helpful than harmful.

In considering the killers, let us first look at some in the lower echelon. We cannot close our eyes entirely to a private in the rear rank, like acute appendicitis, but we cannot give him the space we should reserve for a discussion of the five-star general: heart and blood-vessel disease. Here are some pertinent facts about the killers.*

APPENDICITIS

I talked about appendicitis in the last chapter. But not nearly enough. Until a few decades ago, at least twenty thousand persons died each year of a perforated appendix and the resulting peritonitis (inflammation of the abdominal membrane). One of the first patients "I rode ambulance on" was a new bridegroom writhing in pain. His young wife, sensing some sort of calamity, kept saying, "I asked Jim to please not take castor oil the night before last. But he said all he needed was a physic for his stomach-ache."

We rushed him to the operating room because his belly was already as hard as a board. Operation confirmed our diagnosis of peritonitis. The surgeon cursed to let off the steam of his chagrin when his knife point was lost in a gush of pus. The young man in his prime—another unnecessary addition to the fatality list of the year.

The combination of undiagnosed pain in the belly and a strong cathartic—and there you had death. And the same combination will produce it as easily today, even though we have our sulfa drugs and penicillin and their fellows. But in recent years the layman has been bombarded with literature and cautioned by his doctor so much against taking cathartics for stomach discomfort that appendicitis is no longer the major killer it used to be.

---

*Not discussed here at length are diabetes and nephritis, two killers your physician can readily diagnose. Nephritis, or Bright's disease, is an inflammation of the kidneys. Good general hygiene and regular medical examinations are the best prevention. Diabetes is nowadays well known. Its common symptoms are excessive thirst, appetite, and urination. Insulin injections and special diet can control this disease without difficulty.

Public education—and not increased surgical dexterity—has reduced mortality from this disease.

Remember these points: When a child complains of abdominal pain that persists for an hour or two, do not attribute it to "something he ate." Call the doctor—but do not expect him to make the diagnosis over the phone. If he prescribes over the phone for a stomach-ache, better call another doctor.

At times all the cardinal symptoms and signs of the disease are present: pain, vomiting, fever, nausea, high count of the white blood cells, and tenderness on pressure over the lower right abdomen at a spot called McBurney's point. At other times these danger signals may be absent. Everything may seem normal except for a type of rebound tenderness that only the doctor can elicit —and the diagnosis may often be made on this alone. So he must make the diagnosis in person.

The only treatment you may safely administer in the interval between your call for the doctor and his arrival is an icebag on the abdomen—and perhaps a few sips of water or a few pieces of cracked ice for the patient to suck if he is thirsty. No food, no laxatives or enemas, no paregoric or any other pain-reliever to mask the diagnosis.

What applies to the treatment of the child, of course, also applies to you, and to the other grownups in the family.

GALL-BLADDER DISEASE

"When considering the likelihood of gall-bladder disease," our medical instructors used to say, "remember fair, fat, and forty." That was a generalization good enough in its time. But experience has proved that the condition is more common in the overweight woman who has borne two or more children. That, like appendicitis, this disease may occur in the very young and in the aged. In fact, gallstones are commoner than people think. We find gall bladders "chockfull of stones" in patients who have never even complained of pain in the abdomen.

Nevertheless, indigestion is the usual symptom of the disease. Fullness and flatulence after a heavy meal (sometimes after only a few mouthfuls); nausea and occasional vomiting; pain and feeling of oppression under the right rib-cage, often extending around behind to the right shoulder blade or between the shoulders—these are the common signs. There is occasional jaundice. Sometimes this is the initial symptom produced by blocking of the large common bile duct by a gallstone. An acute blockage may cause sudden, severe pain and vomiting that are relieved only by an injection of morphine.

If you are overweight and approach the table with repeated daily apprehension because you know you will feel uncomfortable after eating, don't overlook the possibility that you may have gall-bladder disease. Your doctor can easily make the diagnosis by X-ray examination. He will decide on the need for operation or the more conservative management with a low fat diet. The mortality from gall-bladder operations is very slight. The disease is only a killer when you allow it to infect the pancreas, a neighboring organ; or when it indirectly causes the development or continuation of ulcer of the stomach.

ULCER OF THE STOMACH AND DUODENUM

The modern "man of distinction" is the fellow who sits with upraised glass—filled with milk and cream—for his ulcer.

The ulcer patient who has made a "success" in life, as measured by material evaluation, usually wears his ulcer as a badge of membership in a privileged inner circle. Unlike the patient who has other diseases, he takes his pills and powders in the open. He swallows them with an air of superiority.

"It's time for my milk and powders," he says to his secretary, who gets up in the middle of her dictation to bring them in. For a few moments you are witness to the performance of a rite that takes place two or three times during his working day. He downs the powder and milk, wipes the excess from his lips and begins at once to dictate where he left off.

In taking his medication he applies but a drop or two of healing balm to the fiery crater of his ulcer; in the normal course of living, however, he dumps what amounts to a gallon of gasoline on the ulcer, which is ever ready to flare up.

We doctors don't know the exact causes of ulcer, but we do know what helps bring it on and what aggravates the little quarter- or half-inch excoriation in the wall of the stomach or duodenum.

Some experts in the field of gastro-enterology have estimated that 10 per cent of the adult population in the United States have ulcers. Even one in twenty, as a more conservative estimate, is ulcer enough for this part of the continent. No doubt the competitive speed-up of modern American life and the constant alarms set off by a world divided are contributing factors. But, psychosomatically speaking, the fellow who "eats himself up" is the likely candidate for this condition.

As I wrote earlier, people are divided into two classes: those who give ulcers and those who get them.

Recently I stopped in for some gasoline, and the attendant— a thin, seemingly overworked, overworried, tense and driving individual, said, "I see by your license plate you're a doctor. Tell me, is there anything new on ulcer? I'm thirty-five and have had it for fifteen years. I'm taking banthine for it, which seems to help. But I guess, as my wife says, I'm my worst enemy. I let people get me. When they become unreasonable, I burn up inside. I wish I could blow up and tell them to go to the devil. But I keep my feelings locked up, and I can just feel the hole boring in my stomach."

There he had, if not the cause of his ulcer, at least the reason why it never healed. Some psychiatrists say that ulcer is the organic expression in an individual of his resentment against himself. He turns his hatred for others inward. They claim they can cure ulcer without medication by reorienting the mind and emotions of the patient. And in many cases, they can.

There is, at this writing, nothing new in the treatment of ulcers. As in high blood pressure, diabetes, hyperthyroidism, and other conditions in which the psyche (mind) has so much effect on the soma (body), the most important part of treatment is the acceptance of a new way of life—a new philosophy. It is necessary to plan and to practice it until you become proficient. You can't do it simply by wishing or wanting. It's like learning to play the piano or the violin—it requires perseverance, practice, and a telescopic view of the end result.

The drive for success must be harnessed, if not entirely overcome. Success must be evaluated, not only in terms of material, but in terms of spiritual, satisfaction. The ulcer patient must be content to live as Mr. Smith and not necessarily *up to* Mr. Jones. Envy, resentment, jealousy, the compulsion to beat the pack, should be subordinated to the wish for a satisfied and serene existence.

The ulcer patient must become the master of the telephone, the clock, and the daily pressure in his business or profession—rather than their slave. These are the fundamentals of ulcer therapy.

Thousands of ulcer patients have been able to "cure themselves" by this turnabout in personality. The doctor can only point the way—it is for the patient to follow or not. I have shown you the simple cure. It is difficult in the actual undertaking.

Next come the reserve forces that we bring to bear on ulcer: the pills and powders, the bland diets, the restrictions on tobacco and alcohol. All these are important. Sometimes a few weeks in the hospital are essential after other measures fail. As of today, banthine is the "ulcer wonder drug"—tomorrow there may be another. No medication is specific.

In case of bleeding ulcers, medical treatment is still the treatment of choice. An internist and a surgeon, in consultation, should decide whether operation is advisable. If repeated hemorrhages occur, operation on the stomach, perhaps with vagus nerve operation, should be considered. In case of perforation of the stomach by an eroding ulcer, immediate operation is required.

Ordinarily, ulcer is not so much a killer as an aggravator. But, in the few cases in which it perforates, the stomach should be closed within a few hours of the beginning of symptoms, which are unmistakable (excruciating abdominal pain, shock, vomiting, boardlike abdomen). Untreated perforation, after eight or ten hours, makes ulcer (like heart disease) a dangerous killer.

Ulcer patients are found everywhere. Ulcers are not badges of distinction. I have seen them in the lowly and the high. In all of these patients, there is one common denominator—they have not been able to come to terms with themselves and their environment.

If you have heartburn; boring unrelenting pain in the midsection under your ribs; if it is intensified by aggravation and relieved by milk or other food, only to recur again; if it sometimes wakes you at two or three in the morning and allows you to fall off to sleep again only if you have tiptoed to the refrigerator for a gulp of milk—the chances are that you have an ulcer.

You needn't guess. Let your doctor examine you and order X rays if necessary. If they show an ulcer, you must start a new way of life. Before long the ulcer will disappear—before the surgeon can get to it. The potential killer steals away to wherever he came from. We don't know exactly where.

PNEUMONIA

We have become overly complacent about pneumonia. We take the effectiveness of modern drugs too much for granted. We behave like the husband and wife in a cartoon: The wife says, "George, come out of the rain with your cold." And the husband answers, "That's why I am out here. You can't do anything for a cold. When I get pneumonia, penicillin will take care of that."

Any doctor who has lived through the pre-sulfa and pre-penicillin days will agree that much of the sting has been taken out of pneumonia. No longer do we wait hopelessly, day after day, for the "crisis" while the patient struggles with his disease: temperature over 105 degrees, toxic, wracked by uncontrollable cough and covered by uncomfortable chest plasters and turpentine stupes.

Admittedly, the pneumonia treatment of those days is now outdated. The sulfas, penicillin, and allied drugs knock the legs from under the high temperature, so that it drops precipitously from 106 to 98 degrees, within thirty-six hours.

But if you will look at the statistical table, you will note that between the ages of five and nineteen and over seventy-five years, pneumonia still causes over 4 per cent of deaths. And, more often than we realize, it snuffs out the lives of people in their prime. It is still a killer.

Your doctor will adequately diagnose and treat most pneumonias. As a patient, your greatest contribution is getting early and adequate treatment of the colds and grippe that often lead to pneumonia.

TUBERCULOSIS

For years at the head of the list of human exterminators, or close to it, tuberculosis no longer menaces us the way it used to. But you will still find it among the first five killers of persons between the ages of five and fifty-four. Streptomycin and other such antibiotics—and new operative procedures in advanced cases —have whittled down the mortality figures. However, the patient's cooperation is a large factor—as in many other diseases. Precautionary methods against its spread and a studied twenty-four-hour day of refusing to overdrive the human machine: these are the most important measures anyone can take to keep this killer at bay.

CANCER

Although heart disease is recognized as the Number One Killer, and we are doing much investigative work to combat it, at this time it seems that the sights of scientists and a fearful populace are more fully trained on cancer.

This is reasonable enough. The lay populace knows more about the symptoms of cancer, about the potential weapons to fight it with, and about the prolonged horrors of those struck down by it. Whereas heart disease may be borne for years in comparative comfort, cancer is a sadistic, unrelenting enemy.

Once cancer gets you in its grip and you allow it to hold on long enough, there is never release. Time is the crucial factor when you deal with cancer. It can be cured when diagnosed early; it will kill if the patient procrastinates.

I have great hope that very soon we shall discover the means of early diagnosis for cancer anywhere in the body. When that happens, cancer (like pneumonia and typhoid) will fall to the bottom of the list. But until then, the most important part of the treatment depends upon the patient. Procrastination negates all of the skill of the operating and radiology teams.

The patient who presents himself late might just as well be treated by an uninformed physician of the Dark Ages. The saddest words a doctor can say are: "If you had only brought him in sooner!"

Cancer has been known for thousands of years. Hippocrates, the Father of Medicine, knew it. He gave it the original name which was translated by the Romans into the Latin word *cancer*—meaning crab.

Some people think cancer is a disease of the aged. What are the facts? Examine our statistical table again and you will see that cancer ranks fourth as a killer of persons between the ages of five and thirty-four; and second (right behind heart disease) in the age group between thirty-five and seventy-five (and over). In 1942, over 450 cases were discovered under the age of four; and about 1,600 cases under twenty years of age. You see, cancer finds young as well as old to be juicy morsels.

We don't know what causes the disease. We do know that chronic irritation often precedes it. For example, skin cancer is relatively common in sailors, who are exposed daily to irritation of the sun and winds.

If we diagnose cancer early enough, we can cure three out of four cases. The American College of Surgeons has records of over forty thousand cancer cures. There are probably many more. When detected early, 90 per cent of skin cancers can be cured; late, only 25 per cent.

Cancer, I have said, is nourished by delay. Every day or week it goes unheeded, crablike it takes mortal hold on life. It grows and spreads and tightens its grip until it kills. In its later stages it can still be destroyed (by the knife, X ray, or radium), but only at the expense of the life of the patient. Cancer rarely relents when it has reached adulthood. It is stubborn against pleading. It can only be reasoned with, cajoled, and completely neutralized when it is still the youngest of infants.

Here are the warning signs cancer gives: unusual thickening or lumps, small sores that do not heal within a few weeks, unusual bleeding or discharge anywhere in the body. If you are over forty and you begin to suffer from indigestion that does not respond to treatment in a week or two, investigate (stomach cancer may be the cause). If a wart suddenly begins to grow and change color, beware.

Two hundred thousand deaths a year due to cancer may not seem many in a country almost 160,000,000 strong. However, it takes only one struck down by it in your family to make you realize how merciless and horrible is the disease.

ACCIDENTS

Are the statistical columns becoming more meaningful now? Are they more than ink on paper? Can you see each numeral, coldly set down in print, as really a gravestone over what was once warm flesh and blood; a human being now nothing but carbon and hydrogen and a few cents' worth of other chemicals: food for the plants and other life than ours? Then, perhaps, you are in the frame of mind to be awed and outraged by another look at the statistics.

You will note that accidents are the Number One Killer between the ages of five through thirty-four. In fact, accidents are three times as deadly as heart and blood-vessel diseases. And accidents are right up there among the first five killers all the way from age five through seventy-five. Be complacent about this if you can.

Only recently the newspapers recorded the millionth (just repeat it a few times!) traffic fatality since 1899. A man by the name of Bliss was, I believe, the first to die—of injuries in a streetcar accident. The one who had the dubious honor of being the millionth victim was a middle-aged school teacher struck down by a heavy truck.

When we consider the broken necks and backs, the decapitations, the fearful screams that died away into silence forever; the children, fathers, mothers, grandparents killed or maimed for life; the pain, the remorse—how can statistics stay cold?

We know autos are potential engines of destruction. But there are always fools who have too heavy a foot for the accelerator; fools who hold their own lives cheap, and those of others—until it is too late to do anything about it. The younger the driver, the heavier the foot.

I believe that if all states passed strict laws against teen-age drivers (and, incidentally, restricted licenses to those under seventy) there would be a sharp drop in automobile accidents. (I believe the reflexes of drivers over seventy are too slow.)

But cars are not the only causes of accidents. The apparently innocent stairs, bathtubs, ladders, unlabeled bottles of poison, knives, cigarettes in bed, match boxes within reach of small children—these are just a few of the commonplace things that take life if you do not see them as the hazards they are.

We speak with horror of heart disease and cancer but accept accidents as inevitable. Psychologists have proved they are not. Many people are prone to have accidents.

Sometimes they have the unconscious wish to die. They would laugh at you if you suggested it. But it is true. If you have had two accidents within the past six months—consult a physician (a psychiatrist if necessary) to see if anything is bothering you deep down. This is not funny. It is real, honest-to-goodness advice. It may save you from that third—and fatal—accident.

Chapter 36

Heart Disease—Real and Imaginary

I~N~ 1933, OUT OF 1,342,000 DEATHS in the United States, 39.2 per cent were due to cardiovascular (heart and blood vessel) disease. In 1948, according to figures of the National Heart Institute, 49.5 per cent of the 1,444,000 deaths in this country were cardiovascular ones. The greatest increase in heart deaths has been in persons between forty and sixty years of age. As a subdivision, coronary-artery heart disease is in the lead—as compared with rheumatic heart disease, which was ahead twenty-five years ago.

I have devoted other books to a full consideration of heart diseases. In one chapter I could not possibly explain their diagnosis and symptoms, and give you specific advice for each type of heart disease. Here my purpose is to evaluate our common enemy in a general way. Not to give you a detailed picture of him, but to describe him and his characteristics in an over-all manner—so that you will really recognize him for what he is.

After observing so many persons who have been concerned about their hearts, I believe it is essential for the doctor—and the patient—to make a distinction between *heart trouble* and *heart disease*. All cases of heart disease deserve the label heart trouble. However, the reverse is not true.

You may have heart trouble and yet have a strong, willing

healthy heart doing its best for you. Perhaps this sounds like a contradiction but it isn't. I think a good definition of heart trouble should include two subdivisions: (1) real heart disease; (2) imaginary heart disease.

The definition of real heart disease is self-evident. It includes all those types of actual organic heart involvement in which the doctor has made an unequivocal diagnosis of heart disease. For example, rheumatic heart disease, congenital heart disease, arteriosclerotic and hypertensive heart disease, coronary disease (coronary occlusion and angina pectoris), thyroid heart, endocarditis, and others. Run your eyes again over this partial list of real heart disease and forever throw out the generally accepted belief that the term heart disease covers, like a blanket, *one* definite group of causes, symptoms, pathology, and treatment.

Nowadays, when everybody is to some degree heart conscious, for our own peace of mind it is well to know that heart disease is not a single entity. If you have an organic murmur and your neighbor dies at twenty-two of rheumatic heart disease, it should reassure you to know that no two cases of heart diseases are alike; any more than two voices are exactly alike. *Your* murmur may not prevent *you* from reaching seventy.

There are many reasons for being more optimistic about heart disease now than we were twenty-five years ago. Special examinations by fluoroscope, X ray, electrocardiograph, ballistograph, heart catheterization, and dye injections for better heart visualization, help us make the diagnosis of heart disease less of the conjecture it often was years ago.

A quarter-century ago a diagnosis of coronary occlusion (in which a heart artery is obstructed) was considered a diagnostic feat if made by one other than a heart specialist. Today, the general practitioner in the smallest town can make the diagnosis as routinely as his father diagnosed pneumonia years before him. Many unusual murmurs in congenital heart trouble—the type some people are born with—remained large question marks in our minds until the process of cardiac catheterization became an accepted procedure. Now the investigator can, with routine casualness, perform what must have been an exciting experiment the first time it was tried on a human being: Cut a vein in the bend of the arm, insert a tube and, by gently exerting pressure, slip its end into the cavity of the heart itself. In this way, chemical analysis of the heart's blood at its source is possible.

One feels a deep thrill and excitement when one thinks of the marvelous operations now being performed on the heart itself and the brilliant new methods of treatment. Thousands of coronary patients have been saved by treatment which thins their blood, prevents it from clotting too readily (by means of dicumarol, etc.) . Investigative work is going on in laboratories throughout the world in search of the key that will unlock the mystery of aging and the causes of heart disease.

Arteriosclerosis is still the "great problem" but we are surely —if not too quickly—learning about what makes A's arteries harden sooner than B's. Cholesterol studies have us hot on the trail of some great revelation. In the past, we used to throw up our hands when confronted with cases of high blood pressure. We didn't have any idea what caused it: we could only guess at what to do for it. Now we have physiological indications that a "pressor" substance formed by the kidneys may be the causative agent. If and when we can actually isolate this substance, the antidote will follow. Already, lives have been prolonged and patients made more comfortable by sympathectomy, an operation on the nerve pathways that improves the function of the smaller blood vessels.

Medicine and operation accomplish wonders for the overactive and underactive thyroid heart. Subacute endocarditis (an involvement of the heart valves) is being brought under control, although for years it was almost impossible to save even one patient out of a hundred stricken with it. Now? Penicillin and other antibiotics bring the majority of these patients back from the edge of the grave. When you consider the great strides medicine has made in fighting these diseases, perhaps you will not be so dejected when ever you think of your heart.

Having lived through the twenty-five-year period in which the management of heart diseases has made greater progress than in all the thousand years past, I believe I have a right—on scientific grounds—to feel optimistic about heart disease.

In view of the tremendously increased efficiency in diagnosis, treatment, and laboratory investigations, it's not too much to hope that next year or twenty-five years from now we shall have the answer to arteriosclerosis and high blood pressure. When we have this, life will be prolonged. Eighty-year-olds will have the vigor of present sixty-year-olds. Coronary disease will not cut down our great men in their prime. High blood pressure will not inflict its discomfort on the relatively young: perhaps on none.

I am not being pollyannish. I speak on the basis of what I have seen. Twenty-five years ago we gave a man who had just had a coronary attack a "year or two." I have personally treated one patient, apparently unable to survive even his immediate attack, who lived for eighteen years and died of a disturbance other than in his heart. Medical literature offers numerous reports of "coronary" patients who have survived their attack by at least twenty-five years.

I am not so pessimistic about the outcome of angina patients as I used to be. There is no question that the danger of angina pectoris should not be too easily discounted. Nevertheless, I have seen many patients live out long lives with only mild discomfort if they lived within their limitations of exertion. I have seen many who couldn't "walk a block without stopping," who—with perseverance, calmness, and acceptance of a new way of life—gradually overcame their restricted existence. Their pain ceased, apparently forever, because over the months and years of careful living they had given the heart opportunity to form life-saving collateral circulation. Many smaller vessels had formed and interwoven into an efficient network to take over the work of the narrowed or completely occluded large artery.

Years ago a systolic pressure of 170 would frighten patient *and* doctor. Today we know that the height of the pressure is not the final index of health or disease. Much depends upon how the heart, brain, kidneys, and blood vessels throughout the body have withstood the increased load. I have in my files charts of patients,

still living, whose notes reveal that they first came under observation over ten years previously with pressures around 200. Many
of these patients never even complained of headache or dizziness.
There are a few charts with pressures over 200 (some around
250) for five or ten years without any evidence of cerebral or
heart involvement.

For those of you who are blood-pressure-conscious, it should be
reassuring to digest all this and remember that you may be healthier with a pressure of 180 over 80 than your neighbor who has
160 over 100. As for low blood pressure, if you have it, accept it
with thanks. Insurance companies know you are even a better
risk than the fellow with "normal" pressure. And yet there are
still thousands of healthy persons who subject themselves to medication, special diets and injections to bring *up* their pressures.
That is as senseless as tinkering with a new car when its innards
are in good working order.

Only a heart specialist who has lived through the advances in
treatment can realize the increased satisfaction that comes in
caring for the heart-sick nowadays. For example, we used to stand
by helplessly and watch the water-logged cardiac gasp out his last
few breaths begging for water. Now we know that water may be
given, even though the patient is water-logged. There is no need
for him to die of thirst as well as of heart disease itself. Many died
prematurely because we knew too little about the value of sodium
and salt restriction in cardiac edema (excessive fluid collection in
the tissues) . We did not have the mercurials, one injection of
which can remove extra quarts of edema fluid. In pill form, these
drugs—in conjunction with digitalis—often add years to life.

Now, one would believe, with so many recent contributions in
the care of the heart, that most of our population would not be
unduly concerned. (When there are effective weapons one usually
does not feel so disconcerted and fearful in the face of danger.)
Nevertheless, the nation is just "plain scared" of the very word
heart.

Statistics showing heart diseases as Number One Killer contribute to this fear (but there are more heart deaths because we

are living longer). Another cause is the annual heart drive, which makes us all conscious of the little half-pound muscle beating within our chest. Newspaper headlines about famous men succumbing, attacks of heart disease and invalidism in friends or a member of the family—all these contribute to the fear.

And fear it is. In my experience and in that of colleagues who do not limit themselves to cardiology, the majority of frightened patients are those who come in concerned about their hearts. Of course, we see patients who have cancerphobia; who are afraid they may have infantile paralysis; who are sure they have an ulcer; but heart worry heads the long list in healthy patients who are convinced they are sick. These worried individuals range from the one who is mildly interested in a fleeting left-chest pain to the confirmed hypochondriac who dies a death with each innocuous heart skip.

All these are the patients who suffer from heart trouble, or to use a more descriptive term, imaginary heart trouble. I have elsewhere written, in a book devoted to these people, that three out of four patients who come to the doctor thinking they have heart trouble really haven't.

I estimate that at least fifteen million persons in this country have thought, do think, or will think, that they have heart trouble —*and yet do not have it.* And still their suffering is very great; actually, I believe it is greater than in persons who have the real disease. Don't think that I take the pain and invalidism of genuine heart diseases lightly here; but one cannot discount mental torture, which so often outweighs the physical.

Imaginary heart patients often die a death a day. For example, one patient says: "Doctor, how can you sit there calmly and tell me that my heart is all right when it's literally turning over in my chest? How long can it keep this up? I'm sure that even if I don't collapse here and now, I'll pass out in my sleep tonight. How can you tell me it isn't heart trouble?"

That poor man is suffering what only one who has experienced chronic, recurring fear can fully appreciate. Daily existence for him is like going "over the top" in World War I days; like looking up at the skies for a potential blockbuster raid in World War II; like waiting for the first atomic blast—wondering when and where it is going to strike—in World War III. A missed heartbeat is as fearsome to the imaginary heart patient as the whine of an enemy bomber is to the civilian who has already experienced a series of bombing runs. In each case, the imagination paints the picture of horrible imminent destruction.

Why do people get imaginary heart trouble? Earlier, we talked about hypochondriacs. The personality of the so-called neurotic, we saw, is so delicately balanced in relation to his environment that almost any disturbing factor may tip it down on the side of ill health, supposed or real.

Take the case of one man who had not slept well for weeks, nursing an invalid wife. Yet he was obliged to rise at six every morning to be off for a hard day's work. Inevitably, the result was chronic fatigue. This mounted insidiously day by day. (Put enough feathers on a scale and they will tip it.) But still he did not show it, so that his friends marveled at his stamina. They thought he had almost incredible untapped reservoirs of strength. Then after months of his soul-tearing schedule, came the first indication that his endurance was at an end.

One night, having returned to his bed after getting his wife some water, he lay stiff and immovable, waiting for his heart to beat. It had indeed actually skipped a beat. Since this was his first experience with what medicine calls extrasystoles or premature contractions, he thought the next beat never would come. His face was as wet as if he had thrust his head under a shower.

That one episode of irregularity made a cardiophobe (one anxious about his heart) out of him. For weeks he was sure he was going to die of a heart attack. Not until he was prevailed upon to get away from work for two weeks—his wife had sufficiently recovered to be up and about—did he show improvement.

When he returned, rested and rejuvenated, he said to me: "You know, Doctor, a man's state of mind can't be good if he is exhausted." This was a simple statement of an important truth. The only thing that had saved him from complete nervous exhaustion was the fact that he was basically a well-integrated person.

This man told me that now, even if his heart "skipped all over the place," he would not become so frightened as he was the night he lay immovable, flat on his back. All he had needed was rest and reassurance and he was well. His imaginary heart trouble had vanished.

There are many like him who come to the doctor. There are others who come complaining of various symptoms that direct their attention to the heart, who are "cured" by one office consultation. A mere O. K. by the physician after a thorough investigation is all they require. They leave the office saying: "That's all I wanted to know. I've forgotten about my heart already."

What else makes people unduly heart conscious? There are many causes. For example, tactless physicians often are responsible for imaginary heart diseases. (The technical term is iatrogenic heart disease—heart disease caused by doctors.)

A doctor can instill unreasonable heart fear by the manner in which he examines the patient. A lifted eyebrow, a *mm-mm,* a shaking of the head, an oracular "You have a murmur, my good man," or a forthright statement: "If you don't take care of yourself, you can drop dead"—such are the poisonous seeds that doctors can plant in fertile soil.

Sometimes an insurance examiner will hint to a patient that his blood pressure is bad or his heart not working well. I remember a girl who wanted to take swimming lessons at a "Y." She came running, frightened because of her "murmur," which an examiner had told her about. Examination revealed a murmur that was functional (not due to disease of the heart).

Palpitation frightens some persons. Others, a stitch in the left side. Left-shoulder pain and gas influence others to believe they have heart trouble.

I have found that once the seed has been allowed to flower, even the opinion of half a dozen qualified physicians often will not remove the fear of heart trouble from highly introspective and nervous patients. They remain cardiophobes for the remainder of their lives. They think they live on borrowed time. Needlessly, they throw away their tennis rackets and golf sticks. They give up bowling, gardening, and any unnecessary exertion. They are sick healthy people.

They are as useless to themselves and society as is a good house that has the reputation of harboring ghosts. It stands empty when it might otherwise be filled with living. Since I know what organic heart disease patients suffer, naturally my full sympathy goes out to them in their trials of discomfort and pain. But I have enough left for the imaginary cardiacs. Their friends and family cannot realize how greatly they suffer. On their backs they carry a cross that is invisible but nonetheless heavy.

I never tell such a patient to "forget it, it's just in your mind." That would leave him more helpless, with nobody to turn to. If his doctor doesn't understand, then who can? He needs patient understanding, constant encouragement, and practical advice to strengthen his nervous reserves. Sleep, sedation, hobbies, vacation, change of work, and repeated reassurance that the heart is normal —these will work miracles in many imaginary heart patients. Some need the sympathetic understanding of wife and children, who may ignorantly minimize their discomforts.

There are a number who need psychiatric guidance before they can emerge from the tenacious morass of anxiety.

For the physician practicing internal medicine, as in other branches of medicine, there are deep satisfactions. I have known what it is to deliver a baby. I brought my quota into the world as an intern. I have known the satisfaction of removing an inflamed appendix and thus preventing peritonitis. I have felt the peculiar thrill of amputating a gangrenous leg and saving a life. I have known the inner feelings of recompense in bringing a patient out of a deep diabetic coma, of pulling another through pneumonia or by prompt measures bringing a would-be suicide back to the living.

I could never express in words the satisfaction I have felt in prolonging the lives of children and adults wih rheumatic hearts; and making an early diagnosis of a coronary occlusion and having a live patient years later.

Nevertheless, none of these satisfactions quite outweighs the one I have felt after accomplishing the seemingly simple—yet often quite difficult—feat of convincing a patient his heart trouble is imaginary, and seeing him live accordingly.

Chapter 37

Everybody Gets Arteriosclerosis

Practically everybody is scared of arteriosclerosis. This formidable word—it means hardening of the arteries—sounds like the crack of doom to many. The layman views arteriosclerosis much the way he does the mushrooming atomic blast. "I figure one or the other is sure to get me in the end," a patient told me recently.

Before we let anything scare us, we should find out more about it. Maybe it won't be so frightening once we have the facts. In the first place, just what is meant by arteriosclerosis or hardening of the arteries?

Arteriosclerosis is the laying down, in the smooth elastic tissue of the blood vessels, of yellow mounds of undigested fat. The doctors call it cholesterol. This gradually becomes infiltrated with lime salts (calcium). As a result, the artery walls may become almost as hard and rigid as a piccolo—but not so smooth.

Once the artery walls get hard and calcified, their ability to expand and contract easily is cut down. They thicken, too, and the blood flow diminishes. Tiredness, shortness of wind, occasional dizziness, pounding of the heart, less zest—these are a few of the symptoms you may feel.

Yet all this is quite normal. It is merely one of the effects of aging. Remember that *everybody gets arteriosclerosis*. That is, if he lives to be old enough. Smith may have it at fifty; Jones may not have as much as Smith until he reaches eighty.

People appear to dread hardening of the coronary and cerebral arteries in particular. What are the real facts here?

If you have hardening of the coronary or heart arteries, that is no guarantee you will have a coronary attack. The diminished size of the arteries may cause gradual changes in the heart muscle. But you will be able to live within your limits. Perhaps less golf, fewer stairs, decreased working hours—but life can still be enjoyed if limitations are accepted rather than fought against.

If you have generalized hardening of the cerebral or brain arteries, you may be plagued with dizziness—which becomes more pronounced in your seventies and eighties. Change of position exaggerates these feelings. You may complain of poor memory. This is all another name for "getting on in years." Such artery hardening will not necessarily kill you early—especially if your blood pressure is normal.

In severe cases, this hardening may affect the smaller arteries of the kidneys, of the brain, or the coronary arteries. In such cases you hear of one man having chronic kidney disease, another having cerebral thrombosis. Sometimes localized hardening of the leg arteries causes marked interference with leg circulation. But these are the grave, advanced cases of arteriosclerosis that do not depend upon age as such. Most arteriosclerosis is not so serious. Many people overcome the limitations it imposes on them, and make much of the increasing years.

Modern medicine is making great progress in the fight against arteriosclerosis. I can visualize the day—not too far distant—when men and women of eighty will have smooth, elastic arteries. In the past we have said: "You can't prevent hardening of the arteries any more than you can wrinkles or gray hair." That's old-fashioned stuff nowadays. Still, to speak frankly, there is much we physicians need to learn about the cause, prevention, and treatment of the disease. For example, here is what we don't know:

1. Why is it possible for some teen-agers to have a greater degree of hardening of the arteries than some sixty- or seventy-year-olds?

2. Just how sure are we—yet—of the effect that eating foods rich or poor in cholesterol has on the production of arteriosclerosis? (Cholesterol is found in eggs, cream, butter, and animal fats.)

3. Because early hardening of the arteries is often associated with low thyroid function, is it true that thyroid trouble plays a part in producing it?

4. Is the generalized arteriosclerosis that comes on in the fifties and sixties definitely life-shortening?

I guarantee that if you ask these questions of a dozen medical men you will get answers—but what kind? Will they be the same? Will the doctors agree? No.

Some will be as definite as can be that eggs, cream, butter, and other cholesterol-rich foods are sure poison for the man who has had an attack of coronary occlusion. Others will say: "Prove it." (The truth is, we are not quite agreed upon it—yet.)

Some of the twelve doctors will say arteriosclerosis is a disease of old age. But the others will ask: "Then how do you account for the cases in the early decades of life?" And there will be guesses about bad teeth, tonsils, or infected gall bladders causing the early degeneration. But that's what they are—guesses.

One doctor will say: "I give my older patients thyroid medication. I think it prevents arteriosclerosis. No one has ever explained away the association between a subnormal thyroid and arteriosclerosis." The other doctors say: "You may be right, Jim. Some day a thyroid pill a day—alone or with something else—may be the answer. But prove it." Jim can't. Neither can the rest of the profession.

You see that we doctors are intensely interested in this question of arteriosclerosis. We are not standing on the side lines—watching you worry and suffer unnecessarily.

For instance, there are certain things we have learned about the problem. Here is what we *do* know:

1. Hardening of the arteries does not parallel the calendar line in advancing years. Many a seventy-year-old has less arteriosclerosis than a fifty-year-old. The cause is something in the metabolism—the way the body makes use of food. We're pretty sure of that. The warm trail of cholesterol studies may lead us there.

2. The degree of arteriosclerosis is not so important as its location. We used to feel a man's arteries at the wrist and try to roll them under our fingers. If they were thick, we'd say: "Hm-m. Pipestem arteries. This fellow has severe degree of hardening. He's in a bad way."

But that thinking has been changed. We know now that you can have rigid arteries at the wrist, or have tortuous, wormlike arteries at your temples, yet have nice, soft, elastic coronaries, kidney arteries, and brain vessels.

Many a person we examine with what appears to be evident widespread arteriosclerosis is shown, by examination, to have normal youthful vessels in back of the eyes.

3. At least as many persons are as frightened of high blood pressure as they are of arteriosclerosis. They say: "I may get away without hardening of the arteries hurting me but it will cause high blood pressure—and that is sure to get me." We know now that arteriosclerosis does not cause high blood pressure. It is usually the other way round.

4. We know that if you are fat you are more likely to develop arteriosclerosis early.

So you see, we doctors know some things about arteriosclerosis but don't know others. But where we have it over you—the layman—is in knowing what we don't know. Your trouble lies in thinking you know certain facts about hardening of the arteries —but these "facts" are often only guesses or outdated folklore.

Here are some pointers to help you overcome or at least reduce the problem of hardening of the arteries. It is especially important to follow this regime if your family's history indicates its members have a tendency to early arteriosclerosis:

1. Present yourself to your doctor for a yearly physical examination until age sixty; twice a year after that. Preventive medicine

is still the cheapest and most satisfactory investment for good health and long life.

2. If you are obese—lose weight. Extra poundage taken off guarantees an extra day—week—month—year (perhaps decade) of life. It is as simple and as important as that.

3. Whether or not you should continue smoking and drinking depends entirely on your doctor's decision.

4. Low cholesterol diet? That is also your doctor's problem. If you—or any member of your family—have had coronary disease, perhaps you had better omit from your diet (or cut down on) eggs, cream, butter fats, fatty meats, oils, etc. Perhaps laboratory examination will indicate that your blood cholesterol is not adversely effected by high cholesterol foods. Better not experiment with diets. Let your doctor decide.

5. And the last suggestion? It is this: Don't be concerned about arteriosclerosis. It isn't a killer unless you live in such a way as to invite early extinction. Stay slim, live moderately, and avoid stress. Follow these rules and you will look forward to being able to complain about arteriosclerosis in your eighties—rather than worry yourself sick about it in your forties. Remember that everybody gets arteriosclerosis—if he is so fortunate as to grow old enough.

Chapter 38

Diet or Die?

MAHATMA GANDHI, THOUGH NOT A DOCTOR, stated an important medical fact when he declared: "True happiness is impossible without true health, and true health is impossible without a rigid control of the palate."

People are coming to be aware of this, but not enough. Obesity is still a respected member of the community. Fat is funny rather than fearful. People look upon overweight in themselves or their neighbors with complacency. They say: "I'm getting too fat," and laugh.

But therein lies the danger. Obesity is an assassin in disguise. Although it masquerades as an amiable and harmless fellow, it holds a dagger ready under its cloak. It does not kill at once. Its methods are slow and stealthy.

We know that overweight shortens life. We have evidence that there is a close association between obesity and disease of the heart and blood vessels; that high blood pressure is more common in fat people. Eight out of ten with diabetes are overweight when their illness sets in. Cancer and gall-bladder disease are more frequent in the fat than in the thin. Arthritis, appendicitis and arteriosclerosis are more common.

If you are fat, you are prone to have more trouble when you

undergo surgery or even bear a child. Remain obese and your chances of dying by your own hand are greater. More fat people than thin people commit suicide.

It has been my own experience—and it is borne out by insurance statistics—that weight reduction definitely improves a person's health if he has organic disease. If he has none, normal weight often prevents it or forestalls it.

Consider these statistics from the Metropolitan Life Insurance Company: For people 5 to 14 per cent overweight—22 per cent above normal death rate; for people 15 to 24 per cent overweight —44 per cent above normal death rate; for people 25 per cent or more overweight—74 per cent above normal death rate.

Small wonder someone has put it this way: "The risk grows with your waistline."

Still, many people refuse to recognize fat for the killer it is. A man with a tight collar prefers to blame the laundry—rather than the bakery. We rarely part with old habits cheerfully. When an overly fat person comes into my office for the express purpose of losing weight, I know from experience that what seems like a simple problem will often prove complex.

The case of Jim—a former patient of mine—is very much in point. He came to me with a blood pressure over 170. He showed electrocardiographic and other evidence of insidious heart muscle weakness. He weighed forty pounds too much.

"Jim," I said, "I suppose you have been reading and hearing about the ill effects of carrying around too much fat. Well, you're nominated. Take off those pounds or your pressure and heart will be getting you into trouble. And better start today."

You wouldn't say that Jim hadn't been warned. Neither would you say that he had been unduly frightened. Jim knew about his heart and pressure. Jim neatly folded his prescription and diet list and put them into his pants pocket. And Jim left the office resolving—at least so he told me—that he'd be back in two weeks weighing six to eight pounds less.

I said I hoped he would. But I crossed my fingers—for Jim, his wife and two children. Jim was forty-eight. My hunch was that if he didn't melt off those forty pounds, he might not be around to celebrate the half-century mark. I had reasons for having doubts about Jim: He was only one in a long line of hundreds and hundreds of similar patients I had seen over the stretch of years.

Jim returned to my office three times at two-week intervals. Then he stopped coming because he was ashamed to face me. He had gained seven pounds in a period of six weeks although he had resolved to lose twelve to fifteen pounds during that time.

At his second visit, when the scales showed he had gained two pounds, Jim smiled sheepishly and offered this excuse: "I went to Baltimore last week. My brother's boy's wedding. You can't travel that distance and sit down to a celebration without celebrating. I'll make it up in the next two weeks." For most persons every day of dieting is as much fun as taking a hot shower in winter— with the water-heater out of order.

At the following visit there was another pound of butter distributed throughout his frame. No excuses this time, except that it was a shame he had spoiled a good dinner by filling up with those little knickknacks whose names sound so different from the way you spell them.

I reminded Jim that he was on the fence—if he jumped the wrong way, he would land in eternity. He renewed his resolution.

The next and last visit: a two-pound gain. For Jim it signified the beginning of the end. He had fought it out with himself and the forces of destruction within him had conquered.

What was it that made Jim give up? Why would a man knowingly endanger his future and his family's happiness? Jim was intelligent. He had read statistics about the life-shortening effects of obesity. For example, he knew vaguely that fifteen million persons over thirty are 10 per cent overweight. That being 20 per cent over the ideal weight is pathological, and that there are at least five million Americans in this category—in the popular phrase, digging their graves with their teeth.

Years before, an insurance company had denied Jim a policy on the basis that he was overweight. He had ample warning that he was committing slow suicide. Still he could not help himself. It was as if a force—as sure and powerful as gravity—was pulling him to his doom.

Jim died a few months after his fiftieth birthday—in an attack of coronary occlusion.

I have seen too many Jims die before their time. I have heard their widows cry out: "Why didn't he listen!" And I have wondered again and again why people will not admit to themselves that they may harbor a force of self-destruction. Admitting it, we can better cope with it. Blind to it, we let it sweep us to our death.

We recognize that eating is an urge. We also know that habit can make it more than an urge. It can be a compulsion. The nightly trip to the refrigerator for cheese and crackers, to be washed down by a glass of beer—or for a glass or two of milk and a slice of apple pie—this is habit, if you are not hungry. If you are not hungry, and you have been repeatedly warned you are dangerously overweight, but still continue to eat more than you should, your act is irrational. This we may call compulsive over-eating.

What is the tinder that sets off the fire of appetite? It lies superficially or deep within us. Now that we know our mind walks hand in hand through life with our body—an integral part of it, leading it and being led by it—we perceive that some people over-eat to compensate for chronic apprehension and fear. Sometimes overeating is due to boredom. Some eat as others reach for a cigarette. It is not harmful unless it is excessive.

If Jim had gone to a psychiatrist as I had wished, we might have learned why he preferred certain extinction to giving up food and drink; why he used food as a daily narcotic to relieve conflicts in his unconscious mind. Or, perhaps his trouble wasn't unconscious. Perhaps he was aware that it was the constant worry over an invalid son that "drove him to food." In any event, the psychiatrist might have helped him to resolve his fears and conflicts and save his life.

We are all not Jims. Dieting is simple for many. We need not depend upon brute force of will to remove excess weight. Some of us do not realize we are overweight until we are brought up short by our mirror, a weight scale or the inability to get into last year's suit; knowing we are overweight, we make a resolve to lose and, presto, there it is: The weight has diminished.

Such patients are a pleasure to work with. Personally, I derive great satisfaction out of taking thirty pounds off a patient. In medicine there is as much sense of accomplishment if you can prevent—or delay—diabetes, high blood pressure, or a gall-bladder attack, as there is in curing it. Weight reduction is often the same as disease prevention.

There is another type of patient who says she hasn't been able to gain an ounce in years. She weights ninety-five to one hundred pounds. She may be stylish as far as clothes are concerned, but she is frail, anemic, and actually scrawny. "I assure you, Doctor," she says, "I put in as much food as my stomach can possibly take. I actually force it down." That is probably true, but the poor, neglected stomach—by now shrunken and unvigorous with disuse —gives forth a belch after a tablespoon of nourishment, whereas it formerly accepted a full-course dinner without audible evidence of discomfort.

You have seen such women. If you follow the food itinerary of one of them for a day, you will observe her at a drugstore fountain drinking coffee and smoking a cigarette while she reads *Vogue* or *Harper's Bazaar*. She sips her breakfast through a straw, stoking up for the morning with a coke. Comes lunch, perhaps a cup of black coffee and a small mouthful of what passes for a sandwich. At night? She nibbles at a full-course dinner if invited out. At home? Perhaps she takes nothing but a glass of skim milk or a few tablespoonfuls of soup because "I'm not a bit hungry tonight."

Why does she eat this way? Is she at the mercy of style? Has she become inordinately weight-conscious? The quick, superficial answer often is not the right one.

My experience with such people is that sometimes they are the thin counterpart of Jim. They are busy running themselves down into some chronic illness for a reason that is hidden deep inside.

I remember a girl of this type who was the daughter of a drunkard father. She had wasted her body from one hundred and thirty-six to ninety pounds. Her three sisters were of normal weight.

Questioning elicited the fact that she had been the only one who took her father's side. Her mother and sisters had long ago given him up. She told me it "killed" her not only to see what was happening to her father, but to have to sit around a table with an apparently heartless family who had lost their sympathy for him.

"How could they eat while Dad was in the next room vomiting up his bile?"

Sympathy and habit drove her away from the dinner table. Only her father's death, and moving to another city—to a new environment away from her family—saved this girl from herself. But not completely; underneath, she probably felt guilty because her father was dead and she was alive, and so she was slowly starving herself to death.

These cases I have cited are not extremes. We see people who weigh 350 and others who weigh 60 pounds. Each is a diet problem. Weight must be slashed from the first group and actually tablespoonfed to the second.

Weight reduction and weight addition are now being accepted by doctors as serious medical problems. It is about time. Insurance companies have been stressing the importance of weight control for years. But the medical profession, like most others, is a slow, lumbering, collective mentality that is often too busy with other problems to grasp and accept the simple truths in front of its nose.

We know now that it is often necessary to treat the mind before we can affect the poundage. We know now that often the psychiatrist succeeds in a patient's weight manipulation where we have failed. We know now why some persons lose readily yet in a few months regain the lost poundage: Their fear or chronic anxiety has returned. For them, nibbling becomes the tried and previously proven anesthetic.

If you are overweight, in most instances you can lose easily if you remember these points: What you eat and how much you eat are matters of habit. You can change your habits if you make an intelligent and continuous effort. It is not hard to stop nibbling between meals. You can eliminate nightly ice-box snacks. You can do without those extra calories: the nuts, cake, pies, bread, potatoes, candy, ice cream, soft drinks, hard drinks, and fats of all kinds. You can cut down on foods, you can substitute low-calorie foods for high-calorie foods.

Don't fall for newspaper ads on "new" reduction cures. Don't be misled by fancy one-day or thirty-day diets. As for taking thyroid and benzedrine for reducing, remember these are only crutches. Rarely does thyroid medication in itself take off poundage. Benzedrine is only of use, perhaps, to start you on the long, tedious trail of reduction. It decreases your appetite for the first few weeks. Later its effects wear off. Then we increase the dose, or take away the crutch altogether. The important point is: You will not be taking appetite-killing medication forever. You must rely on yourself after a while. The only way you can be successful is by changing your eating habits. You should learn to be satisfied with the food a proper diet dictates, or you will fall into your old habits again.

Never tell anybody you are on a diet. The surest way to get the finest morsels and second helpings: Tell your hostess you are reducing and simply insist that you will not go off your diet. Remember that you can't be fat and fit.

The value of exercise in weight reduction? Let's not go into that again. The only satisfactory way to control your weight is to control the amount and kinds of food you eat.

Dieting is only a question of mind over matter, of substituting a good habit for a bad one. But remember that—although it will work wonders for your conscience—a saccharin pill with your coffee won't make up for a helping of pie à la mode. Don't drink to forget your diet worries—alcoholic beverages are loaded with calories.

And let me tell you, as patients have told me: "There's as much satisfaction in taking off thirty or forty pounds as in building a bridge or composing a song." Losing weight—and keeping it lost —is no mean accomplishment. You may be destroying pounds—but you are adding years to your life.

Chapter 39

The Annoyers: Virus—Colds—
Allergies—Headaches

A FEW DECADES AGO, the term "colitis" was in fashion. It was, in general, not supposed to be too grave a disease, and it served as the convenient medical (and lay) label for many disorders—understood and misunderstood. Patients with acute appendicitis died unnecessarily because they thought "all I have is an attack of colitis." Others came too late—even as now—for their treatment of cancer of the stomach or bowel.

"Rheumatism," too, was once a convenient label (or, if you prefer, filing cabinet) for many related and unrelated conditions. Now we are more specific. We say—depending upon the category—rheumatic fever, gout, rheumatoid arthritis, menopausal arthralgia, and so on.

In the last few years another term of equally vague scope has come into common usage: virus. (Good old-fashioned grippe seems to have disappeared from the face of the earth.) With newer bacteriological investigative techniques, we are learning more about virus infections—but we are still more or less stumped about their true nature.

Otherwise we should know the exact viral causes (and cure) of

poliomyelitis. We should be certain whether or not (as some suspect) a virus is tied up with the cause of cancer. We should know
more about the treatment of certain obscure pneumonias, for
example, that are completely unaffected by penicillin, terramycin,
and the sulfas. Aureomycin is thought to be more effective, but
isn't always.

We know enough about viruses to be moving in the right direction in overcoming them, but we haven't yet found the road which
will lead definitely to our diagnostic and therapeutic destinations.
Undoubtedly, the time will soon come. I am optimistic that a key
will be found to open the vault containing specific information
about viral infections.

The next time your doctor says, "It's a virus," bear with him.
The fact that he (and his fellow workers in the laboratory) are
virus-conscious, presages well for suffering humanity in the future.

The common cold is probably "Annoyer Number One" as heart
disease is "Killer Number One." Everyone has read statistics about
the millions of man-hours lost each year because of the common
cold. Many a two-hundred-pound steel worker is confined to his
home one or two times yearly by a sore throat, cough, and generalized malaise. Many an office is run by a skeleton staff because
most of the employees are kept in bed by colds.

Where these infections come from—and what to do about them
—is the continuing mystery that baffles the brightest minds in our
profession. Some patients insist that "preventive cold-shots," taken
before the winter season, protect them. And perhaps in many cases
they do. But we have no specific remedies that are absolute proof
against the infection.

Hundreds of remedies, over the years, have been suggested to
fight the common cold. There is an axiom in medicine: Whenever
more than one or two drugs are suggested for the treatment of
any illness, probably we have not found the specific cure.

For example, there is no guesswork about giving quinine for
malaria, digitalis for heart failure, arsenicals or penicillin for

syphilis, colchicine for an attack of gout, insulin for diabetes, liver extract for pernicious anemia—to name only a few antidotes to diseases.

In the treatment of colds, however, if you were to take a random poll of twelve doctors or laymen, you would find numerous pet remedies not based on scientific fact. One doctor will insist on bed rest and old-fashioned aspirin (and perhaps be as right as any). Another—less patient and more impulsive—will reach for the shot of penicillin. A third will swear by aureomycin. Sometimes they hit it—sometimes they don't.

If you have a cold, depend upon it that you will receive—whether you asked for it or not—advice from the soda-jerker, the man sitting next to you on the bus, or from your good old friends. Each hands down his procedure as if it were a pontifical utterance. Each self-appointed physician is either "selling" grandma's favorite recipe or handing out the advice received from another self-appointed physician who happens to be an excellent carpenter. (You will find me hammering at these home doctors again and again—I simply cannot stop trying to put them out of business.)

"Sniff a bottle of iodine a few times a day," or "Take a drop or two of iodine a day," is one form of newfangled therapy I have been hearing lately. Another reverses an old-time remedy and suggests it is better to starve a cold rather than feed it.

One of a group at a social gathering singled me out and said, "You know, Doctor, I've discovered the magic cure. The best treatment for a cold is to get yourself to sneeze even more than the cold is making you do. Sprinkling pepper around the bed will break up a cold faster than anything—ten times out of ten."

Being helpless in knowing the specific cure, what could I do but smile as a father does in listening to the whimsicalities of his child?

At present, the most sensible way to consider a cold is that it is usually a self-limited infection. The doctor's job is to make the patient as comfortable as experience has taught him how; and to be on the lookout for complications.

As I have said elsewhere, the lowly cold—if underrated—may lead to more serious disease, like pneumonia. The cold that is stubborn for more than a few days, deserves the attention of a physician. Working with a cold is unfair to your co-worker—whom you may infect—and to yourself because you perhaps invite a more serious malady.

Books have been written on headaches and allergy. It would be futile to attempt here to give these troubles the space they merit. Nevertheless, they are high on the list of annoyers, and deserve mention.

The patient's headache is also the doctor's. A symptom rather than a disorder, it often defies the most careful investigation. If it recurs regularly, it is like a Scarlet Letter—the patient is branded and often must learn to accept and live with his discomfort. Sometimes psychiatry helps.

Allergy is a disorder nowadays almost as well known as the common cold, and frequently just as misunderstood. In fact, doctor and layman alike often mistakenly label a cold as an allergy and vice versa. For this reason, recently, the heavily advertised antihistaminics have been used by millions with the hope that here —at last—was the specific cure against colds.

Like many of our other early enthusiasms, the delight at the discovery of this treatment has been tempered by disappointments. True, in those colds that have an admixture of allergy, these medications have been of some help. But we still know too little of colds *and* of allergy to have definite cures. Allergy means the sensitization of the body tissues to a "foreign agent" with which they cannot cope. We call the sensitizer an "antigen"; the protective agent that the body attempts to manufacture against it is called an "antibody."

For example, if you break out in hives after eating strawberries; if you get a headache after taking a bar of chocolate; if you have indigestion and vomit after eating pork—these are indications that you have been sensitized to these foods.

If you sneeze, ache and suffer all the other torments of hay fever, consider yourself as having become sensitized to ragweed, or any of the many other pollens. This sensitization is a matter of capillary wall (small blood vessel) disturbance that coincides with the manufacture and outpouring of large quantities of histamine. Histamine is the substance that initiates the various allergic discomforts.

And the antihistamine tablets have been, in a way, the "small wonder" drugs that temporarily relieve these discomforts. Sometimes they help in asthma, sometimes they don't.

A modern specialist has been born into the medical profession to treat these hundreds of allergies. His job is (by skin tests and other means) to determine the nature of the sensitizing agent. If he is able to discover it, he proceeds to "desensitize" the patient. He does this by injecting—over a period of months—gradually increasing doses of these antigens until the body has become able to produce antibodies in plenty, and to build a strong wall of resistance against the antigens.

This is the reason why so many hay fever and asthma patients are nowadays better able to live with their diseases: Their discomforts are lessened because the formerly helpless body can, with help, learn to resist these sensitizing agents. Sometimes injections are not essential. If the allergist discovers that shellfish or chocolate is the source of your allergy, you may find complete relief simply by avoiding these substances.

As much as we have learned about allergies, we are still on the threshold of knowledge. The possibilities in this field are unlimited. It is not beyond likelihood that the study of allergy may open the door to the better understanding of rheumatic fever, poliomyelitis, tuberculosis, and cancer. One must keep an open and optimistic frame of mind. It is not beyond possibility that our study of the "annoyers" may show us the way and the weapons to destroy the "killers."

Chapter 40

Murder by Advertising

I HAVE SOMETIMES WONDERED how well the chairmen and boards of directors of some large companies sleep. Is their rest undisturbed by the harmful effects of their advertising? Are they really naïve enough to believe that their products live up to the promises they splash over papers and periodicals?

Think of the mouthings of announcers over the radio (how the ads must vex some of these announcers). And now there is television, with its power to unite both sight and sound to beat against the inner ears and retinas of millions of easily suggestible people.

Will this bombardment ever end? Never, unless you and I and the next fellow are cognizant of the irreparable hurt such advertising can produce. Some of the most disreputable characters on the American scene have been the medicine hawkers or barkers in side shows and circuses. Perhaps the only justification for not comparing some heads of modern business with these fellows, is that they believe so much in their products that their conscience doesn't prick them.

And yet one wonders. It is difficult to imagine that the president of a large company that advertises a twelve-way tablet that's guaranteed to cure a cold—it is difficult to picture him taking or prescribing his own medicine for himself or his family.

Only if he does not call his doctor, but takes his own medicine, is he an honest man with scruples; if he hotfoots it for his telephone and the doctor, he is not even one notch above the level of the medicine-show barker. In fact, because of his position in the community, he really falls far short of the barker's level.

However, I am not attempting so much to place the guilt for this cold disregard of human welfare as I am trying to point out the existence of such a menace in our midst.

Advertisers continue to send out will-weakening shock troops of copy that dog the American in his home via radio and television; in the office via trade magazines; in pullmans, in planes and wherever he happens to be, via periodicals, papers and other printed matter.

Man cannot make a free and easy choice. The promoters tell him how to live. Buy this cigarette and it will help your sore throat; buy that cigarette and you become the equivalent of first cousin to a Turkish count; inhale the other cigarette and your voice will be only a few notches below Pinza's.

Use this soap and you nullify the obnoxious effects—social and otherwise—of B.O.; use another one because it floats and is easy to catch; and another because it sinks and is fun to go looking for beneath the surface of your bath. Here is a soap for a he-man; there is a scented, fragrant soap that will ensnare the he-man.

For heaven's sake: Don't use soap just to keep clean—use it because it smells, floats, entrances, is nonslip, is pretty—and for a dozen other reasons the ad men devise.

"I don't care how you say it, but keep saying it about the product" seems to be the watchword of the sponsors of most advertising. So the air and the printed page are cluttered for millions to hear and read the moronic, soporific, conscienceless sputterings and mutterings of ad men, who devote their hearts and souls to the concoction of senseless and, most often, damaging fictions that influence the lives of millions who are naturally uncritical.

I suppose the advertisers go on the principle: "Let the buyer beware. If there are enough morons to buy, we may as well hand out what they will easily believe."

All this may be innocuous enough where health is not concerned. If people want to throw away their money on foolish things, that is their prerogative. But when we let advertisers get away with misrepresentations that endanger your life and mine, we are guilty of criminal negligence.

Recently I had occasion to read a newspaper that was published a hundred and fifty years ago. The local and national news filled only a small amount of space; the rest was splashed with advertisements that guaranteed to make you healthy if you were sick, and better if you were fit.

The advertisements aimed at a large audience. The nostrums they promoted were supposedly as efficient for the cure of asthma as they were for the seven-year itch. One pill promised cure for thirty diseases—take your choice. Apparently anybody with the price of an ad could concoct and promote a wondrous, special antidote for anything and everything under the sun.

I guess life was cheap in those days. Human beings and human rights were not so highly prized; medical science was not advanced as far as it is now—and the fact that "it was in the paper" lent a semi-official stamp to the quality of the products.

Times have changed, but the human being (emotionally) is not far removed from the 1800's or A.D. 10 for that matter. Papers and magazines carry more news today, but advertisements of medical nostrums are still far too numerous. For a generation that is so conscious of its health and the proper way to keep it, we are remarkable for our blind acceptance of the promises put forth in ads. Like our antecedents, I suppose the fact that "it was in the paper" is enough to convince us.

The government, the American Medical Association, and many state organizations have attempted to abolish these false promises. They have tried to wipe out phony health dispensers; they have insisted that the ingredients of a bottle of medicine be correctly set forth.

In my opinion, we are still too far behind in the measures we take against such unnecessary hazards to our national health. For the protection of its citizens, the government should, with one wide sweep, abolish all medical advertisements—from periodicals and papers, from the air and elsewhere.

If this can be construed as interference with the right of free expression, then something is wrong somewhere. If you are an advertiser who believes in "let the buyer beware," it is well to remember that you are influencing the lives of humans and not simply trying to sell a product.

As one whose daily work is dedicated to preventive medicine and the treatment of the ill, it is hard for me to conceive how people themselves will allow this nefarious advertising to go on. I suppose, there again, unconsciously crops out the urge to self-destruction. Otherwise how can one explain this widespread acceptance of such advertising?

If a night club burns down, community wrath demands immediate investigation and inspection to prevent such an occurrence in any other night club. If a hospital or hotel burns down—whatever the size of the community—the entire nation rises up in horror. It demands stringent regulations and immediate inspection of all such institutions. But soon these, too, are forgotten—until the next catastrophe.

Unfortunately, there is never any concerted rise of indignant public opinion against medical advertising.

How is one to know whether ten thousand or a hundred thousand die needlessly every year because of foolish, advertisement-induced self-treatment?

How is one to know whether Aunt Fannie died of TB only because she took "that wonderful cough medicine" for two years —instead of seeing her doctor?

How is one to know whether Grandma died of diabetes only because she kept taking that tonic to gain weight?

How is one to know whether the soothing ointment for piles may have helped Uncle Willie's piles but disguised the rectal cancer underneath?

How is one to know whether the little sore on your nose is not

a cancer; that the ointment advertised for just such a sore is healing the outside while the cancer buries itself crablike under the
skin?

It is too bad we don't know. The trouble is that not just the
doctor's mistakes are buried with us—many, many more of our
own are, too. I have no doubt whatever that mass medicinal advertising produces mass murder. There are no atom bombs, knives,
actual poisons or guns involved—but death is death for all that. Yet
we sit back and thumb the magazines or papers; we read the arti-
cles and stories and glance at the ads.

*Our tire is the best tire. Our coffee will not keep you awake!
Our breakfast food will make your boy a champion. Our mat-
tresses will wipe out all your troubles in sleep,* and so on ad
infinitum. Harmless and amusing—exaggerated, but sometimes
highly readable and entertaining . . . so far.

But continue to glance through the pages you hold. Like the
ads in 1800, here's one that promises that one type of pill (if
taken regularly) will cure any of more than twenty symptoms.
Another is a sure cure for indigestion alone and another for that
obstinate cough; another is surefire for your liver—or kidneys—
or nerves—or rundown condition.

All of these ads act as soporifics that dull any mental acumen
a person may have. It's simpler and less expensive to reach for an
ad and cut it out, than for the phone to make an appointment
with the doctor.

People are lulled into a sense of safety. It is easier to convince
a person of what he wants to believe is true. For example, even
when a man visits two doctors, he will usually take the advice of
the one who says "you don't need X rays," as against that of the
one who suspects ulcer and says he does need them. He will follow
the cue of the doctor who says that operation is unnecessary;
and not the advice of the one who advocates early excision of a
suspicious-looking mole on the arm.

And so these ads offer the easy way out. Especially for the fearful, who can't face the possibility of an alarming pronouncement

by a doctor. If millions of such persons were not possible buyers, would the sellers pay advertisers hundreds of millions every year to illuminate the virtues of their products?

Think of the millions radio reaches. It pounds their ears while they eat, talk, read or drowse. Most persons can't stand commercials. Yet they must bear up under them if they hope to hear their favorite programs.

The announcer shouts to high heaven of cigarettes that doctors prefer; of cigarettes that will actually cure your cough or sore throat. When one cigarette advertiser admits that his cigarette is "a treat and not a treatment, we are tobacco men and not medicine men," we breathe a sigh of relief. Here at least is honesty; although its purpose also is to sell cigarettes. One wonders if the advertiser might not have used another slogan if it was equally good. I know of no manufacturer, of any product, who thinks first of the buyer and secondly of his profits.

Cigarettes are not harmless, yet nobody can furnish indubitable proof that they are universal poison. Whiskey ads (at this date) are not allowed on the radio. Perhaps the owners of the stations have a holier-than-thou attitude about liquor. Perhaps the church would fight it. Perhaps it's due to regulations.

Banning liquor advertising on the radio is not as important as lowering the final curtain on the tragic drama of medicinal advertising. If you were a doctor, you would agree you had seen many cases who died because their disease went untreated while they took the radio-advertised cures. Announcers, of course, all add a footnote: "See your doctor if not relieved." But it is buried somewhere in the announcement so that you pay no attention to it.

Subtly the advertisers call on physicians to stand behind their false promises. "Doctors say that these cigarettes—" "Doctors say that vitamin B—" "According to a survey among doctors, our product—". They confuse you by means of an ancient trick: using the voice of authority. They seek out men of distinction for magazine ads, athletes for cigarette ads, housewives' testimonials; anything to sell the product, to pour it down into the many throats of a million-headed animal called believing man.

Headaches, backaches, worries, weight loss, weight gain, indigestion, cough, sleeplessness; there are thousands of complaints. Name one—and there is a promised cure on paper for you to see, or on the radio for you to hear. Television? One shudders at its potentialities for destruction.

The American Medical Association and the government have been remiss. On the one hand we fight cancer, heart disease, poliomyelitis; on the other, we calmly stand by and allow countless numbers to die prematurely because of the blandishments and false promises of the modern side-show medical barkers. (I do not refer to the large ethical drug houses.)

I suppose the answer to this acceptance of catastrophe is that life en masse is still cheap. Only when tragedy hits you personally do you awake to what is going on under your nose.

Chapter 41

Slow Suicide by Self-Treatment

WE DOCTORS HAVE millions of self-appointed assistants.
(Maybe you are one.) It has always seemed remarkable to me
that so many intelligent people—untrained in medicine—have the
temerity to tinker with human machines. Yet they do. Not only
with their own, but with yours—if you give them the chance.

One day, as I sat at the far end of a drugstore soda-fountain
counter (near the prescription department) I saw the head of a
large industrial concern walk up to the pharmacist and heard
him say: "I've been having a lot of gas—and heartburn, too. I
know what started it: a veal dinner I had on the train a few
months ago. I haven't been the same since. Let me have a large box
of that good old-fashioned bicarbonate my grandmother used to
prescribe. That will fix me up."

And fix him it did. In six months he was dead of an inoperable
cancer of the stomach. I heard of it from his doctor. His death was
front-page news. An expert in his own field—inexpert when he
assumed the duties of a physician.

I ask myself, why will people, supposedly intelligent, keep
doing this? There are a number of answers. One is: the unconscious desire for self-annihilation. The unconscious mind lies deep
—so deep that most of us cannot even conceive what is going on

249

way down there. I go along with Sigmund Freud, the Father of Psychoanalysis, in believing that in the unconscious there is a continual tug-of-war—a fight for supremacy—going on between the urge for self-preservation and the urge for self-destruction. I see it all about me in practice. Self-treatment is one of the great means to such self-destruction.

Another cause of the common but frequently deadly practice of self-treatment is muddled thinking, pure and simple. If you are a clear thinker, before you take any action in most matters, you look at the facts. The better your knowledge of them, the more appropriate is your action likely to be. But you must start with facts—real facts—not assumptions, hunches, guesses, or intuition. Yet, how often have you reached for an aspirin or asked for a "good cough mixture" without really knowing the facts about your symptoms—what it was you were troubled by beyond an obvious pain?

Granted that usually a headache is just a simple headache, that a cough is due only to a cold or bronchitis. But in many cases the headache or cough may be a symptom of underlying serious disease that an untrained person cannot diagnose—disease that requires immediate attention.

At the very least, self-treatment causes delay. Delay allows serious illness to get a runaway start. Taking cough mixtures for months may allow ordinary TB to "gallop." On more occasions than I like to recall, I have seen patients with bilateral (in both lungs) tuberculosis who had treated themselves by emptying gallons of inefficacious cough syrups. Early diagnosis might have prevented calamity.

You reach for the aspirin. True, no doctor would expect you to come running every time you have a headache. He would probably agree that you were being oversolicitous about your health. Nevertheless, repeated headaches that prevent sleep, or are otherwise disabling, certainly deserve investigation. They may be due to sinus, eyestrain, or overwork; yet, there are always more serious possibilities.

When you diagnose, you guess; when you treat, you fumble around with probabilities. When you turn your problem over to your doctor, however, you are dealing realistically with the facts —he has been trained to discover illness and to eliminate it, if possible. I believe thousands upon thousands of Americans die needlessly each year because they are unaware of the danger of tinkering.

Would you tinker with the instruments on the dashboard of a strange plane before you took off? Would you fly it at all, knowing only that a plane is something that has an engine and wings? (You would think more of your life than to try that.)

Would you tinker with the motor under the hood of your car if you knew little or nothing about the difference between clutch, brake, and differential?

Would you attempt to take apart—or put together again—the movement of a fine, expensive wrist watch—not knowing the difference between a mainspring and the second hand?

Would you rock the boat in a storm? Well, that's actually what you do if you treat yourself when you are sick.

Your body, even in health, is a delicately precisioned and balanced machine. When sick, it is even more easily thrown off gear. Sometimes self-treatment is excusable: during an emergency, and when you are forced to live the life of a Robinson Crusoe. At all other times, the choice is still yours—but it can have far graver consequences than you may have realized.

Ailing people put off seeking medical attention for a lot of reasons, all of them shallow when you consider how much may be at stake. Making an appointment with the doctor is a nuisance; enduring long, thumb-twiddling hours in his waiting room intensifies the dislike; and paying a fee tops it all off. It is much simpler to treat yourself; to listen to the suggestions of your neighbor (a plumber, perhaps), or to put yourself into the willing hands of your druggist, who is just around the corner. Why consider that your cough may be due to tuberculosis or cancer; that your indigestion may be due to ulcer or heart disease; that your rundown feeling may be due to a blood impairment! (Most of us prefer to shun such unpleasant thoughts.)

You almost have to be more than human, if you have intestinal pains, for example, to shut your ears to such friendly words as: "Bill, I've got just the thing for that gas of yours. My boss had *the same thing* and these pills cured *him*. Try them. Even if they don't help, *they won't hurt*."

The italics mark the fallacy. A double one.

In the first place, remember that no disease is ever "the same" because no two patients are ever the same. You might find two cases of pneumonia with pretty much the same degree of lung infection, but think of the difference in the patients. One might be fat, the other thin; one might be thirty, the other fifty. One patient might not recover even with the help of penicillin; the other might withstand three separate attacks of pneumonia without the help of any drug. So, when your friend suggests that what helped his boss will cure the *thing you have,* always remember that is one of the greatest fallacies about illness.

Your friend's boss's gas may have disappeared so quickly because the pills relieved a tense stomach. Your gas may be due to a gall bladder piled with stones, that only an operation will help.

The second misstatement in your friend's remark is his inference: "Even if they don't help, they won't hurt." Of course, most medicines that you can buy without a prescription are inert and nonpoisonous. But where they can hurt you is in being the cause of time loss. While taking the medication, you put off your visit to the doctor.

It is such procrastination that often causes the doctor to throw up his hands and say to the family: "He has an inoperable *this* or an untreatable *that*. If he had only come in to see me earlier."

There are so many persons who are not guilty of muddled thinking, ignorance, procrastination or any other of the faults that I have mentioned. Their only reason for delay in seeking a doctor's help is this: Their complaints are not urgent enough. They don't want to take up the doctor's valuable time. They want to save him for "really sick people" who need him.

But this is another misconception. The modern doctor will not underestimate your complaint. He will not "laugh it off"—at least, he shouldn't. When my patients have prefaced their request for an examination with the remark that they felt foolish taking up my time for such a little thing, I have invariably answered: "I'd rather have you walk in here under your own power than wait until you were sick enough to be carried in on a stretcher."

The beginning of the most serious illness may be silent and unrecognizable to the layman. Cancer begins without pain and discomfort. Heart disease may first show its presence by a slight cough or indigestion. Hundreds of other conditions start behind an impenetrable curtain unless you call in the doctor to lift that curtain—or at least peek under it.

Preventive medicine is less dramatic, yet more important, than any other kind. It's true that more people will come to the burning of a house than to the building of it. Likewise, it is more dramatic to be in an operating room and have a ruptured appendix removed than to catch your own right hand with your left as you reach for the castor oil for an undiagnosed bellyache. What's more important, the prevention of the peritonitis or its cure?

Resolve never to treat yourself. For long, at any rate. Don't lose time! And the next time a friend suggests a "tested" self-treatment, ask him which medical school gave him his degree. (Or, if you are a carpenter and he a plumber, just try to advise him on how to plumb. He will catch on.)

And if your corner druggist suggests a very good tonic or an excellent cough mixture, thank him by all means, but turn from the prescription department to the soda counter and ask for an ice cream soda instead. At least such self-treatment is not out of order in a drugstore.

Chapter 42

Dimes Against Death

M AN MUST BE SAVED FROM HIMSELF. Saved from his fears and procrastinations; from his muddled thinking and his unconscious will to die. Have you seen the coin boxes that are scattered about the city when a community health drive is on? To save you from yourself, we plant these in drugstores, factories, and department stores. Wherever people pass or gather in great numbers, you will find these tiny reservoirs of cash.

The pennies, nickels, and dimes (and occasionally quarters) you contribute are not charity. If the drive is against TB, your own lungs may be benefited someday. If it's heart disease, these coins may be the insurance against your own heart failure. If against cancer, you may be the fortunate one to live on because of a few pennies. Perhaps someday you will read and do something about a small lump described in a cancer leaflet or a magazine those pennies paid for.

More often, though, you will do nothing about it. You may become ruffled. You may be frightened. You may become too cancer- or heart-conscious. You may blame the medical profession and health agencies for making you overaware of disease. You may express the thought audibly, or keep it to yourself: "I think they're overdoing this health education. They are scaring more people to death than cancer or heart disease can kill."

Clarence W. Lieb, M.D., has made the statement: "As psychosomatic medicine develops, it may well be proved that more people have died of the fear of cancer, and the effects of that fear, than of the disease itself."

Now, when a doctor utters such oracular words, how can we blame the layman for saying the same thing?

Attempting to save man from himself is the most difficult and thankless job there is. Preachers will tell you that. Doctors will concur. So will social workers and all other members of the professional and amateur armies of workers who fight against inconceivable odds to save your health and life.

Someday man will take sides with those who are on his side. At present, though, I rate the health I.Q. of the human race as very low. The general intelligence of those of us who waste money, energy, and effort in strewing these little piggy banks all over our cities is not one bit higher.

We should slay the modern Goliath of disease, not with pebbles and rocks, but with atomic-bomblike contributions. It could be done, and in relatively short order. First, however, people would have to realize how important the problem is. Few do.

I have seen a well-dressed man drop a dime in the slot with such a flourish you might think he were slaying TB single-handed. Once I called on such a man for a contribution. What did he say? Without a guilty flicker of an eyelash, he answered, "Sorry. Good cause. I just made my contribution this morning." (He would not give another dime against death.)

I suppose we should be thankful for these ten-cent contributors. About $2,500 was raised in an intensive heart drive, two years ago, in a city of about 250,000 population. That averages about a penny per capita. The publicity director said, when the returns were in: "Well, I'm not disappointed. After all, it's not the money, it's the education of the public that counts."

I could not see how he had educated the public against the fight to overcome heart disease when one penny apiece was all the public thought it was worth.

Man, in many ways, is a phlegmatic animal. It is difficult to arouse him. Still, he often responds to forceful argument; he has to be rudely awakened.

I wonder if we, in our public drives against disease, have not been too hesitant, too fearful of instilling anxiety in our lay brothers. Common sense dictates that we go whole hog or none. In our endeavor to educate you against disease we should not hesitate even if you are easily frightened.

It is wiser to frighten a man, because a live man is an asset to his family and community. A prematurely dead man is a total and unnecessary loss.

The success of a drive against heart disease in any community should be measured in dollars per capita, not in pennies. The fear of cancer, polio, and heart disease likewise should be counteracted by public response in sum proportionate to that fear. Since human nature is such that you don't contribute to what does not interest you, our job is to interest you even at the cost of causing you apprehension.

I have found, in treating people who have chronic disease, that the patient who takes his disease seriously is likely to live longer. Often he has read about the grave eventualities; at other times, he has learned about them from hearsay. Whatever the source of his knowledge, he was wise enough to accept his disease and live with it; not laugh it off as something exaggerated by medicine men.

A number of years ago an article in *Reader's Digest* graphically illustrated the dangers of careless driving. The article was as horrorful as it was graphic. It painted grisly pictures with words. Reading it you could visualize the blood, bashed heads, broken spines, and sightless eyes of the victims of the road.

Suppose, of the millions who read the article, that a few hundred became unduly frightened. Suppose they swore never to enter a car again. Weigh those anxious souls against the hundreds of thousands who resolved to be sane drivers.

Whenever I press too hard and long on my accelerator, my mind races back to that article, "Sudden Death." My recklessness is soon counterbalanced by concern. Then follows sensible driving. Is it important that I was momentarily anxious or perturbed? What is important is that I acted on good advice.

And so for the diseases of the heart and lungs; of cancer and diabetes; of poliomyelitis and stomach ulcer; isn't it better that you live, with some degree of anxiety, than die early in ignorance?

The medical profession has a bigger job ahead than the one it has done. We have only nicked the surface of public education. We have hampered our progress by submitting our evidence in a namby-pamby way. We have been afraid to make you unduly afraid. The problem is this: Do or do we not want to show you how to live longer—and in better health? If we do, then we should allow nothing to interfere with our message. As Aldous Huxley has said: "Ignorance is a bliss we can never afford."

Once I suggested to a newspaper publisher the great contribution he might make to the community by inserting free full-page ads weekly on preventive medicine. He answered, visibly hurt and astonished at my suggestion: "Do you know what you are saying? Do you realize how much a full-page advertisement means? How much it adds up to in dollars and cents?"

I let it go at that, but I don't think that you, as the public we are trying to educate, should dismiss it without further thought. The next time the drives come around, recognize them for what they are: an important part of our war against disease. Not any disease—but the disease that may strike you.

Don't contribute coppers, nickels, and dimes. Pay for your welfare in greenbacks. Your money will be well administered. It will find its way to laboratories of scientific investigation and to clinics, as well as to other avenues for the dispersion of public health knowledge.

If you contribute enough, you will be your own sponsor. Instead of listening to cigarette and soap programs, perhaps you will hear heart and TB programs. Twenty-five minutes of jokes and a five-minute weekly commercial on the heart would sell a lot of healthy hearts throughout the year. Weekly space in papers and periodicals would do likewise.

Are you concerned that we may all become a breed of hypochondriacs? Well, perhaps we may. But having considered the pros and cons of this problem for years, I have reached and retained this conviction: A live hypochondriac at seventy-five means more to himself and the world than a dead superoptimist at forty.

Part Seven

THE DOCTOR LOOKS AT
DOCTORS—AND PATIENTS

Chapter 43

Doctors Are Human Beings

Aᴅᴏᴄᴛᴏʀ ɪs ɴᴏᴛ ᴄᴏɴsɪᴅᴇʀᴇᴅ an active and experienced member of his profession unless the magazines in his waiting room are at least six months old. Some medical students in my day used to raise a mustache before they ever raised a stethoscope, so they might have that aged-in-the-wood appearance when they hung out their shingle. These days, however, the "mature look" does not seem to be so necessary a part of the doctor's equipment. Some people want a "young doctor" because they believe he has the latest medical discoveries at his finger tips; others want the older man for his experience (or, often, only call him by force of habit). Most will settle on any doctor as long as he can put a stethoscope in his ears without wincing.

The physician is one of the most peculiarly oriented members of human society. Both his work and his patients make him so. He is a combination of big man and little god. Big man in the sense that a person becomes an outstanding individual when he is one of about 200,000 physicians that serve a country of close to 160,000,000. And little god because his patients are prone to deify him in time of catastrophe.

In reality, he is far from being either of these. He is first, as

I stress, a human being. Second, he has the most misunderstood job (as seen by the laity—and sometimes by himself) that a human can undertake.

Please bear in mind that what I write here about doctors is written by a doctor. I am not in the sunrise or sunset of my practice. I am at the point (after twenty-five years of practice, and being just over fifty) of midday, or at least the early afternoon hours. Being neither green nor overripe in my profession, perhaps I can give a relatively clear and unbiased opinion or judgment upon it. But remember, if I praise doctors, I praise myself; if I condemn them, being one, I condemn myself. I shall not hesitate to do either.

Why does the youth decide to become a doctor? Does he sense a call? Is it because his father and his father's father were doctors? Is it because in the profession he may not find the restrictions often encountered in the world of business, banking and insurance? Is it because he has been interested since childhood, in bandaging the legs of stray cats and dogs?

Why are any of us what we are—or hoped we would be? I think chance is the greatest factor. Circumstances, many or few, known or unknown, inside and outside us, persuade us to select one direction out of many. No man can ride all roads at once. When he is at the fork he can only guess (in spite of the views of those who have traveled the roads) how he will enjoy the journey.

I recall many a boy who "knew" he would be a doctor when he was yet a youngster, because his father had it all mapped out for him. He would grow up to take over the practice when the old man began to slow up. The Mayo brothers are a household name in point. But there are countless other factors that play a decisive role. Most of us have become doctors as others have become firemen, engineers, or the policemen most children dream of being someday. I have asked many of my colleagues and their answers substantiate this.

I remember how my own decision came about. When I was

quite young, I joined the Boy Scouts. My interest in bandaging
was perhaps a bit more intense than that of some of my fellow
scouts. For a week or two I felt the early stirrings of the desire to
be a doctor someday. It disappeared as it had come. Not until
my senior year in high school did I actually stand at the fork
in the road. Up till then, I had only occasionally and vaguely
thought of medicine as a career. I had no special leanings in
that direction.

Came the day when our futures were to be inscribed in our
graduation book and I had to indicate some sort of anticipated
goal. The only thing I could think of was a three-year course at
a musical institute in New York. That decision is what ultimately
appeared under my photograph as a member of the graduating
class. Yet my violin instructor had told me only a few weeks
before that I would never be a Fritz Kreisler or Mischa Elman—
my idols at the time. I felt frustrated. I had forced myself to
choose a field in which I had already been labeled mediocre.

A few weeks before graduation I walked home from school with
two friends and the entire course of my life was changed. A
block from home, we stopped on the corner and one of my friends,
now a prominent New York pediatrician, said, "Why do you want
to go into music? You don't seem to be cut out for it. [He, too,
had heard me play!] Why don't you take up medicine? *I'm* going
to be a doctor." And I can still hear the girl with us saying: "Sure.
Why don't you be a doctor like Sammy? You don't want to carry
a violin case around with you for the rest of your life, do you?"

My friends had confirmed my violin teacher's views—that was
enough for me. My decision was now made. With the reassurance
of my father and mother (who, incidentally, were elated at my
choice), the help of their two-hundred-dollar backlog of savings
and their weekly checks, my working in the summer, and the
passing of the college and medical school years, I at last became
a doctor.

I have been ever thankful for the privilege of being one. First
to my parents and second to the little boy and girl on the corner

who said in effect, "Aw c'mon, be a doctor," as if they had been inviting me to come out on the street and play ball.

You can see, then, that the doctor is not a "special kind of being." He is a little boy who has grown up to make a choice of careers. Having chosen medicine, he has submitted his living material to instructors and professors, to be shaped into the mold of the physician.

The doctor-to-be is introduced to the anatomy and physiology and pathology of existence by successive stages. He dissects fish— even as you do at the dinner table—but more minutely and with serious thought, because ultimately he will be examined about the spinal column and nervous system of fish. He studies worms and their eliminative organs, a far cry from studying the future patient who presents himself with problems about constipation. The medical student draws cats dripping from the formaldehyde bins and dissects and ponders over them; and slowly begins to muse and marvel at the wonderful intricacies of the animal.

Then the "stiff": that cold label of the human being that was. Our first body resisted being turned on the dissecting table, as if angered at being denied the right to rest in peace. There is the memory of four of us "working" simultaneously on each body. We followed the origin and insertion of all muscles; we traced the course of veins and arteries; we studied the fibrelike endings of the glistening nerves. We removed the brain and were amazed at the network of convolutions and puzzled that these should be the center of all human contact with the outer world. We examined every working part of the heart, the lungs, the kidneys, the liver, and all the rest. After a few months the "stiff" was ready for the wastebasket; perhaps in death having made greater contribution to mankind than in life.

I remember the microscopes and the new worlds they brought to view. The chemistry labs stinking with H_2S gas which we ourselves manufactured. I remember how all of us feared the final exams each year—exams in anatomy, physiology chemistry, pharmacology, medicine, surgery, obstetrics, gynecology, eye, ear, nose, and throat, dermatology, physical diagnosis. I remember the pots of black coffee we drank to stay awake. I remember the first patients in the clinics and on ward rounds—the admixture of privilege and awe I felt in being one of the group around the bedside. I remember the four of us who started in the freshman year and lived in one room; and the two of us who survived the faculty probings with sufficient grades to get our M.D.'s.

More than anything else, how all of us (the best students and the worst) lived with the constant fear that we might never make it. As we looked at each other during graduation exercises we wondered how it was possible that each of us could still be blond, black-haired or red-headed. Gray hair should have been the inevitable outcome of our years of work and worry. But youth can take a lot of punishment. It took still more in internship training and preparing for the state board examinations.

In a sense, all these trials had been minor. Now came the real test. If medical school is potentially a source of gray hair, what is actual practice? It may be either the fulfillment of your wishes— or your nightmares.

First, unless you become associated with an established physician, there is a deadly vacuum while you, as a young M.D., wait for your patients. The change from a busy internship with its twenty-four-hours-a-day contact with patients, to the loneliness and dejection of a private office is uncomfortable and frightening. It is like being without food and water after you have grown accustomed to a life of plenty.

After days, or weeks, the first patient comes. Then a member of his family or a friend to whom he has recommended you. The weeks pass and the months, and the young doctor can look forward to seeing at least a few patients every day. The question mark of survival becomes gradually smaller. After a few years the physician has established his practice. For many it is still true that "The average physician never gets bread till he has no teeth to eat it."

I have lived through it all and am still a part of it. I know the outstanding doctors and the mediocre, the good and the bad. I

have a definite opinion (as haven't we all?) of what is right or
wrong with the profession of medicine. Before I appear to castigate
or overly praise the members of my own profession, let me tell
you that—in one respect at least—I admire every practicing member in good standing.

Forgetting for a while that the physician practices in the
expectation of earning a living for his wife and family, think of
the kind of life he leads from day to day, in all the days that are
allotted him. Basically, his is one of the most unselfish of exis-
tences. Others come first, he and his family second. Often he
does not get a full night's sleep; his examining table, the top of
his desk, or the kitchen table bears many a reheated dish of taste-
less food. He is hemmed in by the clock and by the telephone for
twenty-four hours every day—including Sunday. He is always at
the summons of the sick and bereaved. He works when tired and
ill and when beset with his own troubles.

He is the witness of daily recurring suffering and tragedy. He
listens to tales of scandal, misery, marital discord, and adolescent
pitfalls that would serve as gossip for countless tea parties and
bridge games; but what he hears he keeps locked within himself.
Often he knows you better than does your own husband or wife.

For this dedicated sort of existence I look up to every fellow
practitioner. But there are many pros and cons; many ifs, ands,
and buts. Being human, and not a super-race of supermen, doctors
are subject to the weaknesses and the strengths of mankind in
general.

There are conniving lawyers, and plumbers paid by the hour
who wilfully forget their tools; there are carpenters who can't
drive a nail and painters who botch up a simple job; there are
teachers who need themselves to be taught, and men of God who
would find their natural element in the field of business.

Doctors, too, can be fits or misfits. Unfortunately, medical men
do not deal in contracts, pipes, boards, wills or the color of your
kitchen wall. The stuff they work with is health and life itself

In spite of this grave responsibility, doctors sometimes reveal a childish side. As a class, they are chauvinistic. If they graduate from a "name" school, they wear their noses high when "just another" medical college is mentioned. They speak much of "medical background." "What's this fellow's background?" they ask concerning another practitioner.

They forget to ask about his "foreground." What has he done since graduating from medical college? I know quite a few men from name schools, with good internships, who have been so imbued with the importance of their background that they have made it their stock in trade. Advances in medicine have gradually passed them by. Disdaining to develop a present in keeping with their past, they neglect medical meetings and the reading of the medical journals which are indispensable for the prevention of professional rust.

I know excellent doctors—as judged by the standards of scientific knowledge—who nevertheless are wanting as good practicing doctors. They know the science and not the all-important art of medicine. I have seen them make rounds of the patients' charts rather than of the patients themselves. They are more interested in an obscure laboratory finding than in whether or not the patient is in pain or has slept well. They are tactless and often seem indifferent to human misery. The bedside manner is not for them; they abhor the term and what it stands for in its best sense. Kindliness, reassurance, cheerfulness, instilling faith and hope in the immediate future—these seem unnecessary to many men in practice.

Doctors run the gamut of humanity. There are the overtalkative and the quiet ones. The well-dressed and the slovenly ones. The cheerful and the morbid; the impressive and the pallid personalities. As far as success in practice is concerned, there seems to be room for them all. No one can ever predict with certainty that Beau Brummel with fine bedside manner will make as great a success as gruff Baggypants. The formula for success is a varying one. By and large, however, sympathy, conscientiousness, and hard work seem to be necessary ingredients.

By the nature of their occupation, doctors are, or should be, genuine humanitarians; a scalpel never draws a color line. To the physician deeply concerned with the next human being, the yellow or black of a patient's skin has no bearing on the practice of good medicine. Like many of my colleagues, I have a particular warm spot for colored patients; the colored were the first people I examined and treated in the clinics of the University of Maryland Medical School; the first baby I delivered was a twelve-pounder in the colored section of Baltimore. The doctor who deserves the name draws no distinctions between the patient he treats after climbing four flights to reach a windowless bedroom and the one surrounded by butlers and maids. This, too, is often the true test of his fitness for his work.

There are smaller tests that are not always true ones. As I have suggested elsewhere, the real bane of the doctor's existence is the night call. Although he welcomes all the calls he can get (night or day) when he first begins practice, the energy depletion of his job wears him down perceptibly after fifteen or twenty years. The doctor who has spent a hard day, and looks forward to a good night of rest and rejuvenation in preparation for another trying day tomorrow, finds that the jar of the telephone bell at 3 A.M. smites his nervous system like a hammer. To go, to send a younger man, to lay oneself open (by refusing) to the ready rebuke of an "old" patient: such are the grim questions that must be answered by an exhausted body and mind before the receiver is put back on the hook.

If all night calls concerned matters of emergency, this early morning self-examination would not be necessary; night calls or not, most doctors would gladly (except for the natural human protest) be on their way to the patient. But so many calls are far from being urgent. Firemen are not the only ones who get false alarms.

If you have a doctor friend you will know how physicians feel about interruptions during an evening out. The usher will tiptoe down during a performance at the theatre and call the doctor away at the climax of the play. Or he may be summoned off the floor at a dinner dance. And as for dinners themselves, many a hostess has sighed and said, "Now don't you worry, Doctor. We'll keep your fried chicken so it will be as good as new when you get back. Don't hurry." Despite her optimism, it is well if the doctor is not overly fond of fried chicken.

What I am writing is not completely in the nature of complaints. All this is a part of living; it makes its contribution to the fullness of the doctor's life. But it becomes wearing when, as must sometimes happen, his energies are not equal to the demands of practice.

Every so often we read in the papers about a community's turning out to honor a seventy-five- or eighty-year-old physician who is still in practice. I wish I could join in such celebration (though, as I said earlier, I should not want to be the cause of it). A man who has survived so long in so exacting and beneficent an occupation should be a supremely thankful person. No greater monument is necessary to such a man than the life he has lived.

Follow the average doctor around for about a week and you will wonder how some physicians ever get to be in their seventies so they can have such a celebration. If you would learn to live, observe your own doctor carefully—and don't do what he does in his daily life.

Doctors do not practice what they preach, but this is more an occupational than a personal failing. Some will gulp their food— always in a hurry. Most of them are human smokestacks; their cigars, cigarettes, or pipes give forth a steady stream of smoke. Some drink too much. Some vacation too little. Few have time for hobbies, but the few that have are often surprisingly proficient in painting, sculpture or music. And as for sleep, we have already discussed how irregular are the physician's hours. Often there is little time for play with his own children.

As for his wife, she needs to be a trusting, understanding, unselfish person. The supreme test of womanhood is to marry a doctor.

Lately, everybody, from the top echelons in Washington to the "little people" in the rear ranks in the smallest of towns, has become medicine-conscious. This awareness has been hastened by the advent of state medicine in Great Britain. People want their medicine, but they want it cheap. And one can't blame them. In these days of high prices and high taxes, a prolonged illness can wipe out the financial reserves of many a white-collar worker or laborer.

The problem is there. What to do about it? Retain private medicine as it is? Institute government medicine? Or find some halfway measure of relief? At present there are many suggestions but no one solution.

Basically, what is wrong with the practice of medicine is the fee system. I think it far from civilized to expect that human health should be tossed about as a commodity to be bartered and bought. That is what makes for the fee splitters; for the pill slingers; for the "injectors" who have patients come again and again for their "shots" that might, just as efficiently (and more cheaply), have been taken as tablets or liquids; for the unnecessary laboratory tests; for the removal of healthy tonsils and adenoids; for other unnecessary procedures that cost the patient money and bloat the pockets of the unethical medical man.

Some surgeons know how to get on your right side—if you still have your appendix. Some medical men can always find a spot in either arm, or thigh, or buttock that will take another shot. I can only be thankful that such "practitioners"—who do not even deserve the name of quacks—are a small minority of the small body of men in our society who are giving so much of themselves to you.

I used to have a professor who would say: "If I had an enemy, I would send him to a surgeon for a tonsillectomy, and pray that the doctor would throw in a hemorrhoidectomy for an encore—on the same day." I know a few doctors, practicing as I have indicated, who might deserve this double-barreled or double-ended treatment.

Some formula must be found to remove the dollar sign from medicine. Government will have to be out of it and in it at the same time. Politics as such must never have a hand in telling the doctor what or what not to do in the actual treatment of a human being.

I think what is at the root of the faults I have mentioned in the practice of medicine is financial insecurity. The doctor is an "earning machine" when he is well enough to treat his patients. But unconsciously he keeps asking himself, "What will happen to my wife and children if something happens to me?" The ethical doctor stills this worrisome question by having faith that his machine will not break down. But the member of the minority says, "I'll get mine while the getting is good"—and proceeds to do so. The unsuspecting patients en masse soon become the suspecting ones; there is unrest; the politicians, with their ears to the ground, hear it; now begin the rumblings for the socialization of medicine.

There are arguments for and against both private and government medicine. Neither is perfect; there needs to be a true blending of the two. To help out medicine, as it is practiced now, on a completely ethical basis, I firmly believe that every doctor should be assured—by the government—of a small annuity at a set retirement age (or after twenty-five years of practice).

The policeman on the beat, the fireman, the worker for the city or the state, know what a great comfort it is to look forward to such security in old age. If the government could provide for doctors the same way it does for civil servants, I feel it would put a powerful prop under medicine and the public welfare without interfering politically.

Immediately, there would be better medicine practiced. Not perfect—but better. There would be more reasonable fees, less extortion and a generally healthier medical scene. The medical faddism that flourishes in the land would wither, over-specialization would diminish, and patients would have an opportunity to unburden themselves of their problems and worries, which are often the gravest part of their ailments.

Doctors, I hope we are agreed, are human beings. Like most of us, they have their weaknesses and their strengths. More than most of us, they do lead a dedicated existence, and deserve well of us for their devotion. Be thankful that, as a group, physicians know they have a special calling whose work cannot be measured in dollars and cents.

In this labor-union-minded world, God help the millions in the United States if the few hundred thousand went on strike for a month.

Chapter 44

About Patients

H AVE YOU EVER RUN ACROSS the kind of person whose mere presence in a room seems to light it up? The kind with the quick, sunny smile which is eager to please? It appears to gain courage from your approval, and broadens and brightens and takes on a life of its own. Such a smile cannot be developed with practice—an honest-to-goodness smile is there or it isn't. Well, of all the patients I can think of at present, one with such a smile stands out more than others.

He is a little grocery storekeeper and quite deaf. I can also vouch for the fact that he is very much henpecked, for I have seen his wife with him on a few occasions. You might think that her presence would make his cheerfulness vanish. It does. But only in the sense that a flimsy white cloud hides, for a moment, the bright rays of a hot midsummer sun at high noon. You feel that the heat of the sun is lessened but you know that it is only for a very short time; that the cloud can obscure it just so long and no longer.

In his wife's presence, any questions I may shout at him are not answered immediately. He looks at her obediently for instructions, reminding me very much of a batter looking at his manager at third base before daring to take a cut at the next pitch.

When he comes to the office alone—that is the time to observe him with satisfaction. He is very short, has a fat little belly, and bounces around like a friendly but clumsy puppy before he sits down. His face is highly colored, his cheekbones being pink in contrast to a surprisingly white and stubby small nose which he pecks at.

His eyes are small and dark, set way back in the sockets, each surrounded by a web of wrinkles. They are quite playful, yet observe intently.

Whenever he looks for a specimen of urine, which he always brings for examination—he has diabetes—he can't seem to hunt in enough pockets at once. If he had three pairs of hands, they would all be busy. This is for him the only serious part of his visit, finding his specimen bottle. After much fluster he locates it and hands it over with a feeling of pride, as if he had made a rare discovery.

If sugar shows up in the specimen, I get very serious in order to make a lasting impression on him. He listens intently as I point out, for the hundredth time, the dangers of breaking his diet. He answers that he has followed it carefully; and looks up at me when he senses my doubts. Then he breaks me down with that contagious smile before admitting that it is awfully hard to keep up a diet; that a fellow's got to eat *something*.

I've had him in the hospital twice; the last time he was bordering on coma, and he escaped death only with the aid of insulin. He swore to me after that experience that he would always watch his diet, but now he is back to his old tricks. Some soda pop, an extra slice of bread, a small piece of pie and here he is in the office again, urine full of sugar.

He looks hurt when he gets the bad news, but only for a moment. A serious expression seems out of place on his face. He smiles again and says: "Well"—as if to imply that he deserves what has happened to him, but what does it matter anyway.

He cannot read, so directions must be shouted at him. To see him concentrate his gaze on a spot on the floor while he cups his ear to listen is the most diverting entertainment.

I can't get angry with him. I keep telling him that he will always have to be careful with his food. He looks at me, seems to take in all my directions and shakes his head up and down as if to emphasize again how much he agrees with me. But the next moment he says: "I've got a very good appetite but it doesn't do me any good. When can I eat lots more, Doctor?" Then he beams all over.

He often forgets to take the cheap little specimen container with him when he leaves. Unfailingly, he returns in fifteen or twenty minutes. His face looks rosy and happy, he smiles, and invariably chuckles as he takes the container. "Ha-ha, I'm glad I found it, or else I'd be using up all the bottles in the city."

I have often mused about this patient and the thousands I have known intimately in the past twenty-five years. For the most part, I consider that it has been a privilege to have human contact with so many people. In the final summation, this intimate human contact—and not fees—is the physician's real reward for his labors.

In the course of a quarter-century, the average physician comes in close personal contact with at least a hundred thousand patients. As a student, as an intern, in the medical wards, in his office, and at the bedside, he has listened to all these hearts and their reassuring life-thump. He has tapped various chests, felt the lean and fat abdomens, searching for possible growths or malformations. He has seen his patients behind a fluoroscopic screen, has taken blood tests for laboratory examination, examined their urine and taken every conceivable diagnostic step to ferret out the cause of their discomfort.

But of all these maneuvers to outwit disease, none has been more important than the study of the patient himself. The knowledge of human nature is one of the most important parts of the doctor's armamentarium. And no doctor who practices can escape becoming steeped in such knowledge unless he is absolutely void of receptivity.

Is it any wonder that some of the greatest contributions to the world's literature have been made by men trained in medicine or brought up in a medical atmosphere? For example: Schiller, Goethe, Dostoievsky, Ibsen, Flaubert, Chekov, Sir Thomas Browne, Tobias

Smollett, Oliver Goldsmith, William Osler, Oliver Wendell
Holmes, Sir Conan Doyle. And coming closer to contemporaries:
Somerset Maugham and A. J. Cronin.

The successful novelist may depend to a good part on intuition
for his work, but it must also be based on actual experience and
observation. What greater laboratory for the study of man than
the clinic, the hospital, the consulting room? If the rather indefin-
ite expression "life in the raw" brings any picture to your mind,
you might apply it to what the physician sees with his patients.

The pretty woman you met at a social gathering the evening
before is now oblivious of her appearance; *sans* lipstick, fetching
frock, or perfume, she is but another human in sudden need of
relief from pain. You see her and talk to her and listen to her
and gather insight about her that nobody at the party could possibly have obtained.

And here is the great banker who the day before sat behind
his desk waving an occasional greeting to a passer-by, as a king
might condescend to recognize a subject or member of the government. You help him out of a "lost week end" which even his
closest associates do not suspect, because it happens only once
or twice a year and he is a total abstainer between times.

Every possible action and reaction of the human being at some
time comes into the direct line of vision of the doctor. For the
doctor, more than most men, does the curtain of good manners
and artificial behavior rise to reveal the true character of people.

After so many years of observing patients, I have come to the
conclusion that they are not basically smarter today than when I
began my practice. Although medical information spread by periodicals, books and the radio have made many people more aware
of the proper way to care for their bodies, the greater segment of
the population is still basically misinformed or uninformed.

I have also learned that the great financier, the judge, the
teacher, the philosopher, and the intelligent white-collar worker
are not more health-aware and health-intelligent than their fellows
who are uneducated. A brilliant person may be a stupid patient;

a moron may get well because he blindly follows the doctor's directions.

True, no doctor can help but admire the fortitude of the human being in illness. It wrenches your heart to see the terminal cancer patient manufacture a feeble smile and pat your hand as evidence of his appreciation of your efforts, when you are sure that he knows he is dying and that you will be unable to do anything about it. You would have to be made of iron to remain indifferent when you see him attempt to keep his tearful family cheered, worrying more about their feelings than about his own discomforts.

How can you tell he knows he is dying of cancer even though he has not asked you and you have not told him? You see it in the tragic look of his eyes as he greets you when you visit him; you see it in his feeble wave of the hand in bidding you goodbye.

Courage takes many forms. The man who plunges into a river to save a drowning person; the man who rushes into a burning building to bring out a helpless child; the boy who steels himself not to run away in battle—these are examples of fortitude that show great human strength. But they do not compare to the fortitude of the man who submits to the daily, weekly, monthly (and often yearly) trials of the spirit that disease inflicts. To have to bear protracted pain and discomfort is a fearful experience. To bear them without complaint is almost more than human.

Of the evidences of such courage in the fight against disease and death, the doctor is a privileged beholder. It renews his faith in man as man. Whatever the patient's weaknesses as a person, a doctor can afford to disregard them in the presence of this evidence of man's inherent greatness.

Nevertheless, patients have weaknesses that at times try the physician's understanding. It is disheartening to bring to a patient all our modern illness-and-death-defying machinery, only to find that often he throws into it the proverbial monkey wrench.

Warn the high-blood-pressure patient to lose weight and decrease the intake of salt, and he will proceed to gain weight and protest that he cannot stop taking salt with his food. A diabetic will eat sweets when he knows he shouldn't. A heart patient will climb stairs or play tennis against orders. An overworked business-man will persist in working himself into a breakdown of some sort simply because "I just haven't the time for a vacation." These cases are common, and I have spoken of them earlier, but the shame and waste of them haunts me.

For years the doctor had the reputation of being "the magnificent liar." He would not reveal that you had heart disease, or any other condition, because he was afraid to frighten you. Or perhaps the family requested secrecy. Now the doctor is a more forthright individual. We are beginning to believe that the man or woman who comes for diagnosis and treatment has the right to know the score. Otherwise the patient is driven from pillar to post by distrust and lack of faith, and the physician defeats his own purpose. Too many patients, even when assured that the verdict is the true one, still disbelieve. They think the doctor isn't telling the truth because "he doesn't want to frighten me." Although the forbidding goatee, striped trousers and cutaway coat are out of style, people are still scared of doctors.

As it is, the doctor is appreciative of the patient's faith in him. The wonder is not that the liver pill will find the liver, and the heart pill the heart, but that the patient has faith that they will.

One of the most difficult jobs the physician has in his daily rounds is to convince the patient that bed rest is essential. Patients hate to stay in bed. They are in a hurry to get well, so they can quickly return to the daily routine of hating to get out of bed every morning. They seldom realize that rest may be as important as medicine in their recovery.

There are many ways to lose a patient. Not long ago a woman patient whispered to me: "Is there anything more trying than a woman with laryngitis?" I jokingly answered: "Yes. A talkative woman *without* laryngitis." She smiled as she waved goodbye to me—most likely forever.

Some patients are quick to change doctors. They are prone to get on what I call the medical merry-go-round. They are the habitual shoppers. They spend their money and get little return in health. A high-blood-pressure patient, for example, cannot expect to be relieved of his headaches, dizziness, or other complaints overnight, yet many such patients will become discouraged after one or two visits and try another doctor that a friend suggests, because this doctor is said to have a "new treatment."

When a patient takes a train to see a physician, the patient is probably on the way to consult a "professor." Genius never lives right around the corner! I have often wondered why, occasionally, patients come all the way from the West Coast and the South to seek a doctor's advice. It costs some patients hundreds of dollars of plane and train tickets (not to mention consultation fees) to discover that there are probably a half-dozen excellent physicians within a one-mile radius of the city hall in their home town.

Patients should choose a doctor with great care. If you need one, inquire of the medical society for a list of men who are recognized specialists in their fields. If you are looking for a good general practitioner, you can likewise find out his standing from the medical society. Having found a satisfactory one, stick with him unless you develop a personal dislike for him or lose confidence in him.

Many patients are appreciative; others are not. They feel all the doctor needs is his fee. They will call him at the dinner hour even though it is not an emergency; they will get him out of bed in the early morning hours because they have a temperature of 100 degrees, not realizing that a wait of a few hours would make little difference in the outcome.

Some patients place too great faith in Mother Nature. They pay five dollars for the prescribed bottle of medicine, then watch it gather dust on the shelf of their medicine cabinet, unopened. Others become angry because you will not allow the drugstore to refill a bottle of medicine that you prescribed for them months or years ago; they expect you to diagnose their condition over the telephone. They attribute your reluctance against long-distance diagnosis and treatment to irritation at loss of an office visit, rather than to your conviction that that is no way to practice medicine.

Some time ago a patient called up about his son's bellyache. "I guess it's due to the hot dogs he had at a party last night. No need for you to see him, Doctor, so what do you advise?"

After convincing this woman that the *one* condition I would never treat over the phone was a bellyache (especially in one who still had his appendix), I called on the boy. He was in the hospital within the hour and a hot, fat, ready-to-explode appendix was out before you could stutter Jack Robinson. Telephone advice, however innocuous, might have killed him. Waiting until morning would have been equally fatal.

I have found that when a child is sick, his parents will leave nothing undone to get him well. Yet when parents become ill, they often put off treatment to the very last. They rarely stop to think that they owe it to their children to be healthy for their sake.

I have frequently been asked who makes the better patient— a man or a woman. In general, it has been my experience that woman is less the groaner and complainer. The sick man around the house is more demanding. He becomes a little child again. Any woman who has had around her neck for a few days a husband healthy in all respects beyond his attack of grippe or virus, will perhaps agree. The difference between sick men and sick women is this: Women just keep on making the beds (sick as they are) but the men just crawl into them. This custom is deeply rooted in our patriarchal civilization, which still, in many ways, treats woman as a slave.

Many people excuse themselves when they come to a doctor's office with minor complaints. It seems they think the doctor is interested only in salvaging human wrecks. As I have already pointed out, the doctor prefers in this age of preventive medicine to prevent a fire or put out a small one, rather than be called late when the blaze is beyond control.

Too many patients have become addicted to pill taking. Although vitamins have been scientifically proved as specific antidotes to some diseases, it is true that millions are taken unnecessarily. This is also true of sedatives, tonics, and other medications. In these days of multicolored pills, the colorblind patient is at a disadvantage. He misses much aesthetic pleasure when he takes his medicine.

Although "earphones" for the hard-of-hearing are coming more and more in evidence, patients still have an aversion to wearing them. On the other hand, patients will accept the need for glasses without question. In fact, one of my friends, an ophthalmologist, has told me of numerous cases in which glasses were not needed, yet the patients bought elegantly fashioned and colored frames with window glass because glasses were stylish.

But not so with patients who have developed faulty hearing. They return year after year with some lame excuse as to why they have not yet bought hearing aids. Without realizing it, they are the most selfish of persons. Their family and friends literally wear out their larynxes in trying to make themselves understood. But the person with hearing impairment is perfectly willing to cup his hand over his ear and ask over and over again, "What was that? I didn't quite hear.".

If your ear doctor says a hearing aid will help, don't delay in visiting a "hearing-center" for advice about purchasing such an apparatus. If everyone who needed one bought it, hearing aids would soon enjoy as great a vogue as glasses.

Regarding misunderstandings about fees, the patient is often at fault as much as the doctor. Mindful that there are some doctors who will take advantage of too-trusting or unsuspecting patients, the patient should inquire in advance how much an operation will cost; about the fee for an X-ray or laboratory study; about the cost of a series of office visits; or the charge for the delivery of a baby.

The honest doctor will welcome such questions. It is true that the difference between a bill and a pill is that the bill is something harder to swallow. But it is also true that if you have been given an estimate of cost, the bill will be easier to swallow because it will not be unexpectedly large.

You see, then, that in the patient-doctor relationship there is room for improvement in either partner. As the patient, you should remember this. The doctor cuts the pattern of existence for his individual patient. This includes advice for the mind and the body, to carry you on your daily round. You, as the patient, must accept this pattern. If you are a good and sensible patient, you will wear it whether you think it is becoming to your way of life or not. You must have implicit faith in the designer. Only in that way can you find your best opportunity for survival.

Your relationship with your doctor may endure over the years or be terminated as quickly as you can snap your fingers. It is invulnerable or precarious, depending as much upon you as upon him. I have had the opportunity to observe—and be affected by— the reactions of innumerable patients to their physician's ministrations. These reactions are sometimes the boon, at others the bane, of a doctor's existence.

There is an axiom among doctors that many patients are "floaters." The older man tells the worried novice: "Don't worry so much that Mrs. Smith has left you for another doctor; Mrs. Jones is probably on the way from his office to yours. The gains eventually wipe out the losses."

However, as he calmly goes about reassuring his fledgling colleague, the experienced physician feels like the oracle who says a lot but knows little. No matter how many years a physician is in practice, he cannot get over the wonder that there is a practice at all. He thinks of all the forces, almost as strong as the pull of gravity, that are being exerted on his patients. He marvels at the loyalty of Mr. Z when everybody from A to Y is trying to get him to another doctor. He thinks of the bridge clubs and afternoon tea tables: those battlegrounds of opinionated rumor and gossip where a doctor's name rarely escapes untarnished. Although nine may be for him there is always the vote against. And that vote against, if delivered with cobra-like venom and animosity, can very well turn two or three of the nine from Dr. Quick to Dr. Quack. A doctor's reputation depends not alone upon his successes.

I asked a doctor the other day: "What is the outstanding example of a patient's lack of appreciation?"

"I don't have to think hard to recall," he said. "About ten years ago I was called out at night to treat a woman who had taken an overdose of sleeping tablets. She was pretty close to an intimate chat with St. Peter. After I had worked until daybreak with stimulation and stomach pump, she came to.

"For ten years I treated her family faithfully. I brought her husband through pneumonia and her daughter through appendicitis, and hovered over her father like a mother bird as he lay dying of cancer. If ever a doctor might consider patients as being loyal, I would surely have nominated this family.

"But there was one thing I hadn't considered. Why were they loyal? I found out it was because I had never let them down. I was always at their beck and call. They were gracious and appreciative when I came during my dinner hour or at midnight. They paid their bills promptly. I thought the patient-physician relationship was as perfect as anybody could expect.

"Then one night, at about three, the phone rang. I could hardly answer as I had a high fever—had been in bed for a few days fighting it—and my throat was like an inflamed sponge. It seems that the husband, who had been working all day, felt achy. He couldn't sleep, and got up at three to take his temperature. It was about 100 degrees. He didn't want his wife to, but she insisted on calling me.

"I gave her some suggestions over the phone but she said, 'I'd rather you came over, Doctor.' When I told her that I was ill in bed but would be glad to call a colleague and send him over: 'Oh,' she said, 'never mind, I'll let you know.' Would you believe it? They have never used me since. I tell you, I'm trying to pass it off lightly, but it hurts."

I tried to give him balm for his hurt by offering advice. "This philosophy has helped me," I said. "It never fails. Here it is: Never, in speaking of patients, say 'my patient.' There's where the trouble lies. Doctors unconsciously think they have a first mortgage on each patient they treat. I may have believed so early in my practice, but a few experiences like yours cured me. I never say: So-and-so is *my* patient. He is no more my patient than I am *his* doctor. The relationship is not like that of marriage."

Divorce between doctor and patient should be made easy. The patient need present no incontrovertible proof that his doctor is guilty of practicing poor medicine or that there are indisputable reasons for dislike. And the doctor need not present reasons why he no longer wishes to take care of his patient—as long as he procures suitable medical attendance before he resigns from the case. It should be as easy as that. The tie that binds patient and doctor should be one fine strand of silk. This will prove strong or weak depending upon how soon either of the two snips it.

What should you expect of your doctor? What does your doctor expect of you? Your doctor should be qualified to do a good job. He should be conscientious. He should be sympathetic. These three ingredients are essential. Any two without the third indicates there's something lacking in your physician. He may be well qualified to treat you, and conscientious. However, if he has not enough sympathy to regard you as another human being who is in distress; if he handles you as impersonally as if he were working on a piece of board or treating a guinea pig, then you are not receiving good medical attention.

If he is unqualified to remove your gall bladder or treat your stomach ulcers, there's no question that he's not the man for you. There are good surgeons and mediocre ones, good physicians and bad ones. Your job is to spend time *before* you call him, to investigate his professional standing. If he is conscientious, you will expect that he will treat you to the best of his ability at all times; that he will be honest; that his fees will not be outrageous. These three characteristics are about all you need in your physician.

What does the doctor expect of you? One, that you put your full trust in him and appreciate what he is trying to do for you. Two, that you be cognizant of the fact that he himself is a human

being and not an indestructible machine. Three, that you pay him
for his services so that he too can buy his bread. Many a physician
has carried poor patients for years without charging them. Still,
most doctors are allergic to the patient who can afford to pay but
is a confirmed "dead beat." Your part of the contract is to pay your
doctor his fee as promptly as you pay your landlord his rent, or
the city its taxes.

Treat your doctor the way you want him to treat you. Don't
regard him as an obedient robot. Some patients not only feel the
doctor should always be at their beck and call—he must always be
cheerful as well! I remember a patient, a few years ago, who called
me to say that her son was greatly disappointed at his last visit to
my office. "He's been a patient of yours for fifteen years. You've
always smiled at him. He said you didn't yesterday. Fact is, he
wonders if he'll ever want to come in to consult you again."

The morning in question, I was on my way to the dentist; a
throbbing tooth had me down. I suppose I should have smiled
during the patient's visit. I am sure I wasn't discourteous or
abrupt. But he had grown to expect a cheerful countenance and
felt that I had let him down. (This boy obviously depended too
much upon the approval of other people. If you failed to smile, he
interpreted it to mean you did not like him. He was too self-
centered to realize other people had their own problems!)

I suppose, with doctors as with people of the theatre, the show
must ever go on. But I think that it is because patients grow to
depend so much upon their doctor that lack of consideration becomes a problem. If you stopped to think about it at all, you would
realize that your physician, like you, can get hungry, tired and
disgruntled. He can suffer pain and get sick, and he likes his
night's sleep undisturbed, if possible. He appreciates any evidence
on the patient's part that he is accepted as one human being trying
to help another. He does not want to be thought of as a tireless
machine.

One day, a number of years ago, a nice lady was in my waiting
room, on time for her appointment. Now, I have always reminded

myself that a patient's time may be as valuable as my own. Therefore, my hours have been arranged on that basis: no rush, no hurry,
sufficient time for each patient so that the one in the outer office
can be ushered in on time. This lady had been a patient of mine
for ten years. In all that period—she admitted it to me later—she
had never had to sit in the waiting room for more than a minute
or two beyond the time of her appointment.

Well, this day the patient preceding her had fainted after a
sample of his blood had been withdrawn for laboratory analysis.
A big fellow, he lay stretched out, pale, sweating, and temporarily
dazed after he came to. I was with him an extra half-hour. As he
left, I ushered in the lady I speak of.

Her first words were: "Doctor, you've kept me waiting a half-
hour!"

At first I thought it was a circuitous way of showing her appreciation for the ten years of prompt reception. But I happened to
glance up as she sat down opposite my desk and was momentarily
confused by the look on her face. I could not believe that she was
as hurt and insulted by my tardiness as she appeared. But she was.

Now it was my turn to be upset. The achievement or trait in
which we take the most pride often becomes our tenderest spot.
For this woman, forgotten were those days when I had rushed to
the office without lunch in order to keep an appointment with
her, forgotten my reputation for protecting her time allowance.
One unpreventable failure, and there was the reaction of discontent—the all-too-common viewpoint of "But what have you done
for me lately?"

I devoted the first fifteen minutes of our consultation to a discussion of the weaknesses of human nature. When the lady left,
it was with the understanding that she had better find herself
another doctor—or be content to await her turn patiently the next
time.

The following day I received a box of fine cigars. The attached
note read: "From a devoted patient."

And she has been, for the last fifteen years.

Chapter 45

Making Rounds

MANY DOCTORS, I HAVE HINTED, object to the so-called "bedside manner." Somehow, they'd rather their reputation rested on being scientific than artful.

When a patient says, "My doctor has a wonderful bedside manner," the physician should consider it a great compliment. It is a simple way of saying: "When my doctor walks into the room I begin to feel better right away. He calms me. He reassures me. I'm not so frightened when he holds my hand and says everything will be all right."

The treatment of the patient's psyche is as important as that of his body. The patient needs a sense of security—full knowledge that there's always someone he can lean on and trust. And the doctor can supply this only when he is unhurried and keeps forever before him the thought that the patient is a helpless, fearful human being who craves the promise of recovery.

The bedside manner is perhaps most important when the doctor is treating patients to whom he is a stranger; particularly those ward patients who have no choice of physician. They have to take what they are given. For this reason, patients in the ward feel more insecure than "paying patients" who have their own doctor.

To help you to understand my view on the bedside manner, I

am going to invite you to walk through the wards while two doctors on service make their daily hospital rounds. Most laymen do not know what it is all about, this being "on service." Let me tell you about it before we reach the hospital.

There are, in most cities, a number of hospitals which administer aid to both private and ward patients. The accommodations for the former are on varying scales of luxury (hotel comfort), depending upon the means of the patient. The private patient who can afford it, may have one of the best private rooms with adjoining toilet and bath; the choice of his own physician; and three nurses (around the clock) who serve him with as great fidelity and attention as any sultan or rajah might expect to receive when in health.

A buzz and here comes the bedpan; another buzz for a massage and rubdown; another buzz and here is a nice cold fruit drink; a push of the button, and anything inside—or outside—the hospital is brought up to the room to satisfy the private patient's whim (provided, of course, that the doctor has not left specific orders to the contrary).

The private patient's room bill may run between $200 and $300 a week, his nursing charges between $150 and $200; various laboratory fees round out the hospital expenses. Then, when the patient has recovered sufficiently to withstand the shock, his private physician tenders *his* bill.

There is another classification: the semi-private patient, who does not have quite the comforts of the private patient. More patients in the room, fewer frills, just as many pills. But he has his own doctor and receives considerable attention, relatively speaking.

Now what about the ward cases? These are the ones treated by the doctor "on service." "Making rounds" means working in the hospital wards, visiting and treating ward patients free. Usually such a "service" runs three months a year. During this period the doctor and his assistants visit the hospital daily. The doctor's job is to get the ward patients well; an equally important part of it should be to try to convince them, by his manner and approach, that they are as important to him, to themselves, and to the community as are his wealthiest patients on the hill.

The test of a doctor, I have suggested, is his humanity. It is most conspicuous in his behavior while making rounds, while treating patients who bring not one penny of financial reward to him. The beggars, the old chronic alcoholics out of gutters, the unknowns, the have-beens, the humble—but always the poor. No chance for big fees; in fact, for any fees. No future buildups or praise sung at bridge parties after a brilliant diagnosis or cure. Just the run-down Madam X's and Mister X's—and no future favors for the doctor.

Now, let us follow our two doctors on their separate rounds, treating the poor—and afterwards you can tell me whether the bed-side manner is nonsense or good sense.

There is the jangle of the elevator door as it swings back and out walks Doctor Number One. Head nurses greet him, leaving whatever work they are engaged in, to be at his beck and call. Student nurses glance sideways while carrying trays of food, in the hope of getting one little smile of recognition. Interns hang on his every action. If he decides to read a chart and it takes ten minutes, there stand the nurses and interns until the God of the Wards asks a question, tells an ancient joke or says, "let's go."

They start down the hall: the chief, two interns and a nurse. "I'll start on the female side this morning." The hospital is going full blast. It is overcrowded and some of the patients' beds are in the hall. There are about forty female and the same number of male medical beds. The attending chief and his entourage must enter and leave many wards before rounds are over.

The clock ticks away three hours. You watch closely. What do you see? Shiny discs of the stethoscope in and out of the chief's ears. Glasses on and off, looking at and away from charts; an occasional kneading a belly or thumping a chest or throwing back the bed covers without regard for sensitive feelings. And, very rarely, a direct question to a patient: How are your bowels? How is your appetite? Impersonal. No smile. No cheer. The Almighty consenting to talk, but too great to waste words. (And this is no tirade against one doctor because of any personal dislike; it is a composite I am talking about.)

So from ward to ward. A few changes in treatment here, a new diagnosis there, a problem, a question, an admonition to an intern, a *mm-mm,* an order to a nurse, and out he glides, the superior being. What has he accomplished today? Nothing that his interns might not have done.

If this doctor would come around some day when his service is over for the year and observe the next man on service he might perceive wherein he had failed. But he won't come back for such an insignificant purpose. After all—what more is there for him to learn? Unlike him, let us peek in on the second doctor, also a composite.

Here is Patient Number One, first one on the right as the physician enters. An old woman, her face a meshwork of deep and shallow wrinkles. The intern says, "G-I series shows Ca of the large bowel."

So the poor unfortunate has cancer of the bowel—six months or a year left. The physician thinks. She's probably seventy-five if she's a day.

How different this physician is from the earlier one! He doesn't go into a diagnostic trance, and thump the patient's dry, shrunken belly so hard she squirms. He knows what the hard mass will feel like to him; the interns have already examined her. He quickly feels her abdomen and verifies the diagnosis. Why put her through the mill? Not he.

His examination consists mainly of pinching both her cheeks and getting a surprisingly bright smile out of her by saying: "Granny, see you at the dance tonight" (probably for the first time in years sending the rusty machinery of her brain whirring back to the happy years when a remark like that was a promise) .

Patient Number Two is a young girl, about eighteen, olive skinned and pretty. She would be a decorative partner for "that dance," but is just as helpless as the lady four times her age. She had rheumatic fever eight years ago for "just a few days." Long enough, however, to come down with an involvement of her heart valves known as mitral stenosis. She also has auricular fibrillation, a heart irregularity, caused by the rheumatic fever of years ago.

Just this morning, one of the interns drew off a pint of fluid from one of her lung sacs and a few quarts from her abdomen. Her breathing is labored, her lips are blue, and she is in evident distress.

Nevertheless, she has sufficient courage and spirit to smile faintly when the attending physician says: "I'll have to talk to the superintendent and complain about the way they are treating you. I understand all the patients around here are being served as much orangeade, lemonade, and water as they want, while you have to beg for a few sips of water. As if that isn't enough, they've been sticking needles into you to take away what little fluid you have. I'll see about that.

"But there's one privilege you are going to have this afternoon that the others won't have—a chocolate ice cream sundae." And he turns to the head nurse with instructions that she be certain to get that ice cream, even if she has to go out to the corner drugstore for it herself.

You may ask, "What was so wonderful about that?" My answer is that only when you yourself have experienced cold, impersonal handling will you understand how essential a part of good medical care is the treatment of the human spirit.

Let's not leave this doctor yet. He is about to interview Patient Number Three.

He sits down on the bed of a middle-aged woman. For fifteen minutes he listens to her story of "how they are taking away my home from me." He knows she is being transferred to the psychiatric service later in the afternoon. Yet, she is not too unbalanced for him to take the time, during a busy day, to hear her fanciful story. About how the city is foreclosing and that very hour is removing her furniture and other belongings.

The doctor calls for the social worker. He doubts it, but wants to be sure there has been no slip-up in the investigation. He learns, as he suspected, that her fears are a delusion. Nevertheless, he remains with her until she is sufficiently relaxed to fall asleep. He pats her hand, shakes his head slowly and continues to the next patient.

Rounds like these are being made all over the country right now. Vertical human beings are treating and nursing horizontal sick ones. Both of the doctors you have accompanied are among them. Each is an excellent scientist, but one is a better human being. I somehow feel that he is a better healer, too. Fortunately for the sick, the intensely sympathetic doctors greatly outnumber the occasional "guinea-piggers."

Doctoring, as I have remarked elsewhere, has its advantages as a profession. The spiritual rewards are immense, however. I am not trying to hold myself up as a great-hearted St. Bernard of mercy—most doctors are as human as I am—but some of the richest satisfactions of my life were experienced in the wards.

I hadn't been practicing medicine very long when I received a compliment that moved me as deeply as any that has ever been bestowed on me. It came from a gray-haired, shriveled little Irish lady. Flat on her back in a hard, unyielding plaster jacket for two months because of a fracture, she had lately come through a complicating siege of pneumonia.

"Doctor," she said, "I'm going home tomorrow, as you know. Before I do, I want to thank you. Not so much for the fact that you saved my life—you need no thanks for that, that's your job. What I'm thanking you for is that you treated me like a lady—as if I had a million—not like an old fool that hasn't got a penny and is tomorrow going back to live in her hole in the wall."

And her last words were washed away in a rivulet of tears that dropped down from red rheumy eyes. I patted her cheek and winked to the head nurse as I walked out in an effort to pass it off. But I felt better than I can tell.

Chapter 46

Visitors Are Bad Medicine

THE SCENE IS A HOSPITAL ROOM; the leading character, a widowed young mother. Time: the second night after her operation.

Enter the villains: a roomful of visitors. The patient lies there hoarse, her neck held stiff by a large, tight-fitting post-operative bandage. She can't turn her head; her eyes still have the scared look that identifies so many of these patients.

She had looked forward to her operation and the hospital. Suffering from an overactive thyroid—exhausted by the care of her three children, and having lost forty pounds—she had told herself that at least she would have a few weeks of quiet and rest.

But here are unexpected complications: oversolicitous friends. Smoke and chatter fill the room. All attention is focused upon her as if she were holding court.

You can see the appeal—almost animal-like—in her eyes. She wants to shriek, to ask them to please let her rest. But the tragedy of it is that she cannot even bring her voice up to a whisper.

No experienced physician will question the fact that—in her case, at least—visitors are jeopardizing her convalescence and her recovery.

I have likewise known terminal cancer patients and others hopelessly ill who could not even die in peace: their room, a daily meeting place for visitors who discoursed on bridge and canasta, on new shows and new frocks—altogether forgetful that here lay one dying the slow death.

Some time ago I visited (for ten minutes) a physician friend who had come home from the hospital the day before. He had had his gall bladder out. He looked as if he had been put through the proverbial wringer. He was not only tired—but mad!

"I know why I look and feel the way I do. Visitors! Visitors! Sometimes a fellow wishes he didn't have so many friends. Would you believe it—six visitors were sitting in my room staring at me while I was still suffering the after-effects of the anesthetic. You'd think they came to see a performance.

"Believe me, I've learned something first-hand. My patients are going to have a better and more understanding doctor from now on. I'm going to build barricades for them against visitors."

The DO NOT DISTURB card that swings from the outside knob of the hotel-room door is only a convenience; but the DO NOT DISTURB or NO VISITORS card tacked to an invalid's door is most often a *must*. You have no choice but to respect it even though it is not prefixed by the word POSITIVELY.

Recently I was called by a nurse who sounded highly excited. She was in charge of a hospitalized patient who had suffered an occlusion of the coronary artery three days previously.

"Doctor," she said, "a man has been visiting Mr. Jones for three-quarters of an hour. He came in while I was down to lunch. I can't get him to leave."

"Keep him there. I'll be right over," I said.

And I stepped on it. I know that every such visitor is a potential menace to the sick one. When I arrived, I walked straight to the patient's room. As I turned the knob, the NO VISITORS sign was conspicuous by its absence.

There sat the visitor chewing on a dead cigar. The room was overladen with heavy nostril-and-eye-irritating fumes. The patient was having a paroxysm of coughing. The nurse's eyes were red-rimmed and she was blowing her nose. The visitor seemed completely oblivious to any discomfort within range of his sight or hearing.

I nodded "hello" to the patient, and bent a forefinger a few times at his friend, who followed me out the door. No sooner were we in the hall than I saw him calmly pin up the NO VISITORS sign. I sought out a quiet nook in a corner and we sat down.

Before I could introduce myself or learn who he was, he began: "Doctor, I'd say you are angry about something. Probably about me. Let me explain.

"Being an impulsive fellow, when I heard last night that my old friend Henry had had a heart attack, I made reservations on the next plane to get here fast. I've flown five hours, twelve hundred miles, just to see him. We were one hour late because of a storm and, let me tell you, for a while I was probably sicker than Henry here.

"I took the cab right to the hospital and the first thing that greeted me was this sign on the door. I took it down and put it in my pocket. No piece of cardboard was going to keep me out after a twelve-hundred-mile hike.

"So I went in. I was surprised the nurse wasn't there. I had a nice long talk with Henry. When the nurse came in, she got excited. She asked me to leave. I said, not by a darn sight is any nurse going to tell me I can't stay for a few minutes after such a long trip. The next thing I know, you walked in, Doctor."

It would be fruitless—except to expose my extreme impatience with him—to tell you what I said and how I reacted. I can only say that the patient died suddenly later that night. Considering it fairly, no doctor would say definitely that Henry's well-meaning friend had inadvertently hastened his end. Nevertheless, my hunch is that the visit *didn't do the patient any good.* With rare exceptions, most visiting harms a sick person rather than helps him.

In these days of crowded hospitals, when one must go begging for a bed, the chances are that the majority of the patients are really ill. Few people reserve a hospital room for a few days, as in the past, just to get away from business and the telephone. There's no place in the hospital of today for fashionable rest cures or week-end vacations.

My contention is that sick patients deserve protection from hordes of visitors—some well-meaning and others not. Let us reconsider the specific case of Henry who died on the fourth day of his coronary attack. What do we know about it?

We know that when a coronary artery is occluded suddenly, that within twenty-four to forty-eight hours a part of the heart muscle —bereft of its circulation—becomes useless. The heart and the patient require complete rest for the next six to eight weeks (especially the first two) to allow the muscle to heal and the circulation to rebuild itself.

This is so important that I write these standing orders for the first few days of treatment:

1. Complete bed rest; no turning to bathe.
2. Nurse to feed the patient.
3. Patient not even to reach for liquids.
4. No unnecessary conversation with the nurse.
5. No radio, newspapers or magazines.
6. No visitors except the immediate family (only two members, coming together, twice daily for ten minutes morning and night).
7. And sufficient sedation so that the patient does not mind being alone so much.

Rather drastic curtailment you think? Perhaps it is. Some doctors are not quite so strict about it. But experience has taught me that you can't err on the side of being too careful with a coronary —or any other very sick patient.

After the first two weeks—when the heart muscle has started to heal—I allow an increase in the number of, and length of time for, visitors. But I still limit them. I don't just say, "Stay only a short while"—that may mean five minutes to one visitor and two hours to the next.

What has the patient lost by his imprisonment? For two or three weeks we have kept out his eager friends. Perhaps the patient, too, has been eager to have visitors. What has he gained by doing it the doctor's way?

He has had uninterrupted opportunity to rest and restore his heart and system with new energy. The frayed rope that held him to life has been reinforced. The patient has been rather lonesome for a few weeks; but the peace and quiet have strengthened the foundation of future months and years of life. Not a bad exchange.

A patient should take visitors as he takes his pills, just so many a day—and at certain specified times. A doctor cannot consider the gratification of his patient's friends and family. He can only hope that they have tact, understanding, and real sympathy for the sick one. Otherwise, they are potentially poor visitors.

The best time for visiting is after the patient has left the hospital. Time enough for bedside chatter when the patient is stronger and convalescing at home. Someday (soon, I hope), doctors and hospitals will wake to the need to curtail—or abolish—visitors. Formal visiting hours are old-fashioned. Hospital corridors and elevators become as cluttered as a department store during the Christmas rush. And this excitement overflows into each room where a patient fights for health.

Think of it—in one recent year about 17,000,000 patients were admitted to 6,430 registered hospitals in the United States. The average daily census was 1,242,777 and the total patient days for the year were 453,613,605. Visitors ran into the tens of millions!

Many persons are habitual visitors of the sick as others are habitual funeral goers. They derive—probably unconsciously—a sadistic pleasure in observing unfortunates. It makes them feel good to be perpendicular while the next fellow is horizontal.

Others visit in a spirit of curiosity. But afterward they tell their friends, "I saw Mabel today. She looked awful!"

Or, they say to the heart patient: "I hear Minnie just died of a heart attack. But I don't suppose yours is anywhere near as serious."

And to the patient who is to undergo surgery: "Just how good is this doctor you have, Jim? Pretty young to be taking care of a serious condition like yours, don't you think?"

And so do friends inadvertently spread the gloom they shouldn't. If you must visit; if you have an overpowering compulsion to go to the hospital; if you "just can't wait to see Eddie," then it might be well to remember the importance of these qualifications when visiting: tact, common sense, compassion, and a feeling for the passage of time.

Be cheerful. Say you've come only for a short while—and prove it. Leave within ten minutes. Don't smoke. Don't mention any outside catastrophes. Don't discuss the patient's doctor. Don't discuss the patient's illness. Ask about the nurses—then switch the subject to yourself. Talk about what you have been doing and plan to do. And try to inject plans for a proposed interesting schedule with the patient when he recovers.

But better still, visit by proxy. The ideal visitor and *friend* sends his card with books, flowers or candy. He restrains his impatience and makes up for his absence by being a home visitor instead of a hospital visitor.

Take it from Shakespeare:

> *Unbidden guests*
> *Are often welcomest when they are gone.*

Chapter 47

The Medical Detective

I HAVE ALWAYS BELIEVED that any good detective who becomes an M.D. would make an unusually fine diagnostician. And that any doctor who forsook medicine for the detective force would be its shining light. In a sense, Sir Conan Doyle, a doctor, proved this in his Sherlock Holmes stories.

To a certain extent, a physician's job and a detective's are very much alike. The work of both requires learning the identity of a culprit, tracking him down and later doing something about him. The M.D. after your physician's name might just as well stand for "Medical Detective."

Your doctor dotes on solving problems. In fact, he has to like being a medical detective because his success in diagnosis and treatment depends on his ability to ferret out the cause of disease.

The physician's days and nights are dedicated to solving a never-ending series of mysteries. A headache or pain in the side, a cough or sudden weakness: These are but a few of the many clues to underlying disease processes which he must track down.

The criminals a doctor hunts are masters of disguise. As I've indicated, no two people react to the same illness in identical fashion. And no one person reacts in exactly the same manner to an illness if he happens to get it again.

Everyone has had more than one cold. Picture your own experiences with this relatively harmless, yet exasperating pest. One time, a splitting headache is the outstanding symptom. Another time, the sniffles. Another, the scratchy throat or cough. Or all of these symptoms together. And yet it is easy to diagnose a cold. You don't have to study in physiology or anatomy classes to be able to recognize one.

But how about some of the thousand other ailments that are catalogued in the medical books? It is not so easy to track these down. The difference between success and failure in diagnosis depends on the doctor's talent and thoroughness in assembling a likely looking completed picture puzzle out of a jumble of seemingly unrelated lesser symptoms and signs (clues, if you prefer).

Here is an authentic example of how diagnostic results depend on thoroughness:

Agnes M., a girl in her early twenties, was well until about two months before her admission to the ward service of a well-known hospital. She had put off hospitalization for that length of time because her complaints were not particularly bad. There was a feeling of tiredness early in the afternoon, followed by exhaustion so marked that she had to get to bed about seven o'clock in the evening. As her strength returned morning after morning, she attributed her state to overwork. However, her symptoms became more exaggerated and fever entered the picture. So she came in for study and observation.

Soon she held the unenviable position of being the chief diagnostic problem of the hospital. She presented a few clues like fever, rapid pulse, and slight anemia—but nothing else. These symptoms could be fitted to any number of diseases. The staff drew up its differential diagnosis (the list of diseases in which the offender might be found) but the solution of the mystery was just as far away a few weeks after her admission. The trail was cold.

There were many suspects—none could be singled out. In her case the logical possibilities, not probabilities, were: typhoid fever, undulant fever, Hodgkin's disease, tuberculosis, malaria, and a low-grade infection of the kidneys. At the bottom of the list (like the unsuspected murderer in a mystery story) was a condition called subacute bacterial endocarditis, which is a blood infection due to involvement of the heart valves.

Well, all of the more likely suspects were exonerated. You might say that they had been fingerprinted and that their innocence had been proved. X rays, blood tests, cystoscopic examinations (studying the bladder and kidneys) were all negative.

As for the innocent-seeming party called endocarditis, the staff had practically exonerated him on the grounds of insufficient evidence.

The diagnosis of that girl's condition remained a baffling mystery. What caused her fever? Her tiredness? Her loss of weight and anemia? The attending physicians had to admit temporary defeat and made a note on her chart: "Patient has fever of undetermined origin."

But the case was not closed. Careful attention day after day not having revealed anything new in evidence that might help, a general consultation was held. About a half-dozen of the hospital's medical men came together to discuss this unfortunate girl's condition.

One of the physicians, a professor of medicine with a reputation for many brilliant diagnoses, refused to admit defeat! He asked the intern, "Does her blood culture show any streptococci?"

"No, sir."

"Has she ever had red blood cells in the urine?"

"No."

"Any murmurs at any time?"

"No, sir! We have examined her daily."

"Does she give a history of rheumatic fever, sore throats or St. Vitus's dance?"

"No."

He asked all these questions before he approached the girl. He then went over, smiled at her, patted her hand to reassure her. Then he picked up her well-manicured hand and asked whether she would mind if the nurse removed the nail polish. "I'd like to get a good look at your nails," he said.

The groups soon became expectant. One could sense their tenseness as the professor peered closely at her nails. Having searched the rest of her body themselves (eyelids, eyes, chest, fingers, toes, back) and found nothing, they knew what he was looking for. The one place they hadn't examined, because they thought it a waste of time to track down a perfectly innocent party, was now under close scrutiny.

He finished looking (it had taken about ten seconds) and then asked for a stethoscope and listened to her heart.

"Gentlemen," he said, after leaving the bedside, "this girl, as you know, is an unusual case. She has no murmurs, her blood cultures are negative and she *had* no petechiae [small spots, livid or crimson in color, often found in subacute bacterial endocarditis]. It is impossible to make a diagnosis of subacute bacterial endocarditis with such slim evidence but—she now *has* petechiae. They are the sliver type, under the nail of the right forefinger. In my opinion, subacute endocarditis is the diagnosis and one of these days or weeks blood cultures and examination of the heart will prove it."

He was right. The diagnosis was confirmed one week later when a murmur appeared and the blood culture revealed streptococci in her blood.

This has been but one example of how a doctor has to run down clues. I am sure that any good detective with medical training might have found the telltale sliver.

But the ways of the doctor and detective part here. The officer gets his man and turns him over to the proper authorities. There ends his interest in his case. The physician's work just begins. Having cornered his man, he must now treat him.

This may be easy sometimes, hard at others. But even when the treatment is simple, it is really quite difficult to administer because the doctor is always so busy. He solves one mystery, and fifteen or twenty more that day may also require solution or other disposition.

Every doctor's office is a miniature F.B.I. headquarters in that there is always some problem awaiting solution.

Does your boy like mysteries? Does he want to be a detective when he grows up? Tell him that is fine. But also ask him if he would like to be a *super-detective*. If his eyes shine and he says yes, send him through medical school later and he will come out a detective with an M.D. after his name.

Your doctor is not born with an inquisitive bump, but before he has been in medical school a few weeks, he becomes conscious of the need to develop an insatiable curiosity.

Earlier I mentioned some of the things the doctor-to-be must study. Their detail is almost infinite. Anatomy offers up to him the working parts of the human machine. Physiology stirs his imagination. He learns how the kidneys act as filters; how the brain receives and sends messages; how the pancreas regulates the body sugar; how the liver accomplishes dozens of life-giving syntheses; how the heart beats and what blood is for and why the human being has been called the most wondrous chemical factory ever created.

Perhaps for the first time he is formally introduced to the unseen world. He peers through a microscope and wonders what makes this bug innocuous and that one a sure killer. Bacteriology opens up this incredibly complicated world from which science has long since driven some of the mystery.

As the months roll by in school, the student is introduced to physical diagnosis. He meets his first patients. He taps the chest and abdomen. He listens with his new, shiny stethoscope; he examines the patient's excretions and blood; he studies X rays and electrocardiograms. He has nourished in him a passionate desire to track down and eliminate disease.

Later he studies pathology. He examines the dead heart and wonders what stopped its beating. He removes the cranium that houses the brain and muses on its millions of cells and the electrical contacts that made for pleasure, anxiety, and grief.

If the young medical student is an impressionable person—and who would not be impressed by this new, enticing world that unfolds day after day—there grows within him this bump of curiosity without which he will never be a good doctor.

When he graduates and begins his internship he soon realizes that he has not been trained to be an impersonal mechanic—an expert in tinkering with and repairing broken-down machines. It is human beings that he is being thrown together with.

Machines, nevertheless. But the most unusual, distinctive and baffling machines a man can ever hope to see.

So the doctor learns to be always on his guard. He learns to be as distrustful of apparently innocent symptoms as a detective in the house of murder is of every apparently unimportant clue. The doctor does not predicate his findings on appearances. He examines, tests, checks and double-checks. Later on, experience and intuitive diagnosis enable him to make many short cuts in diagnosis. Even then, too many short cuts may lead to improper evaluation of illness.

As the years go by, every physician unquestionably comes to this conclusion: No method of investigation is more satisfactory than getting a complete health history from the patient. True, X rays may furnish a diagnosis of fluid in a lung sac even though we have never actually seen the patient. But they do not tell us the cause of the fluid. That we must know if we are to provide adequate treatment. The prescription we make when the cause is a lung ailment is not the same as when the fluid is the result of a heart ailment. And one of the most valuable means we have of tracking down the cause is talking to the patient—finding out how he feels and has felt, as well as a host of other facts that may mean little to the patient, everything to the doctor.

That is why the doctor must get a full history from the patient. Sometimes it may seem endless to you. As you listen to the questioning, you are amazed at the doctor's persistence and almost insatiable curiosity.

When were you born? How much did you weigh? Are your parents alive? What did they die of? Did your grandmother, grandfather or anybody else live with you when you were a child? Did they have a chronic cough? Are your brothers and sisters well? How is your wife? What sicknesses have you ever had? Any operations? Have you gained or lost weight in the past year? How much? Do you get easily fatigued? How about your appetite? Do you suffer from indigestion? Yes? Describe it. Do your ankles ever swell? How long have you coughed? What do you expectorate? Ever any blood in your sputum? Do you have chest pain? How do you sleep? Are you more comfortable on a few pillows? Have you been having any trouble with your urination? Any burning or blood? Do you pass your urine more often—and at night? Do you feel achy in the afternoon or evening? Do you feel warm as if you have fever? Do you perspire and complain of being warm when everyone else in the house is chilly? Are you nervous and upset? Or are you taking the cough in stride?

Here you have only the partial bony skeleton of the history-taking. For example, the question: "Do you suffer from indigestion?", when elaborated upon, would delve into: How are your bowels? Do you have constipation or diarrhea? Do you take laxatives? Do you have heartburns? Have you ever had X rays taken of your gastro-intestinal tract? Do you have pain in your stomach? Is it made worse or relieved by food? Does it ever wake you about 2 or 3 A.M.? If so, what do you do? Take bicarbonate or a glass of milk? Does it relieve you?

I could go on and on. The art of history-taking might well fill a book. Some doctors realize its value at the outset and never forget it. Others, when pressed for time in a busy practice, hardly do any history-taking at all and spend the few minutes available on cursory examination.

If I had to choose between becoming a cross-examiner of the patient and a layer-on of hands and instruments, I would choose the former. Just by sitting with hands folded, I sometimes can accomplish more than when I only tap and feel. Fortunately, we do not have to make a choice; both methods of investigation are open to us.

I can understand why patients have more fun at the theatre than at a doctor's office. And I realize why so many put off making appointments for examination. And, incidentally, why the urge to cancel appointments becomes strong as the hour draws near for the investigation.

The reasons are many, and we looked at some of them a number of chapters back. Here's still another: Nobody relishes having the doctor pry into the dark corners of his life. Nobody likes to bring out the family skeleton, even for a doctor.

Yet it is because so many patients are hesitant to confess what is troubling them that they inadvertently throw a roadblock across the avenue of diagnosis and slow down their treatment and recovery.

Remember that the doctor is inquisitive merely because he wants to help. He is not looking for the latest in gossip. Like the medical detective he is, the doctor is interested only in solving a mystery. He wants to know not only how you are suffering but why you are suffering. Having discovered the answer to these questions, he is then able to treat you efficiently.

Answering the doctor's questions helps the patient as well as the doctor. How often has a patient left the office feeling 100 per cent better because (for the first time in months) he has been able to lower the dam, to let the repressed anxieties, fears, and hostilities pour out of him—and consequently find relief from inner pressure that has been mounting and complicating his ailment.

I am discomfited by a woman's tears—more so by a man's. But when a patient indicates by the forming tear at each inner canthus of the eye, that he wants to let go, I encourage him to forget his dignity. The sobbing, chest-convulsing cry is a heart-lightener, a salve to the wounded spirit.

When we were in school years ago, although our instructors used to stress the need for a complete, thoroughgoing history, they said little of the interlocking of the mind and the body. They knew only a fraction of what we know about psychosomatic medicine today.

We were not taught, in seeking the cause of a man's stomach symptoms, to consider that they might be due to the frigidity of his wife. Or to her fear of pregnancy, which caused him to practice withdrawal at the climax of sexual intercourse . . . making him "sick to his stomach."

We were not taught that stomach ulcer might be caused by tension and business stress; that diabetes might be hastened by the arguing and tension between husband and wife; that high blood pressure might be caused by the daily frictions between two partners in business; that coronary disease is often the price of relentless work without relaxation and vacations.

But now we know these things. Still, we cannot discover whether they are responsible for your troubles unless you give us the clues. A doctor simply must be inquisitive if he is to help you. And you, as the patient, must be frank, cooperative and as truthful as you can possibly be. If he asks, "Are you happy at home?", say no if you are not. He will want to know why not and you will have the opportunity to explain. This, in itself, will make you feel better. And, as one who looks at your problem calmly and dispassionately, the doctor will be able to advise you better than you can yourself.

Certainly you feel a natural hesitancy about revealing your deep hurts so that even one other human being may be witness to them. But that way lies salvation. Talking it out acts as an emotional catharsis or release as surely as a dose of salts produces results by evacuating a constipated stool. The employment of mental catharsis to rid oneself of dogged fears and unhappy problems is an essential part of all treatment.

The next time you consult your physician, resolve to be open-minded, free and easy, and completely relaxed in his consultation room. What may seem to you to be a singularly unusual revelation is probably something he has heard over and over from various patients.

Try to think of your doctor as a medical detective. You come to him to report a robbery of your health. You want it back. If you expect results, better not withhold any clues—distasteful or otherwise.

Chapter 48

Medicine Has Its Miracles

Hᴉꜱ ꜰᴀᴄᴇ ᴡᴀꜱ ʟɪɴᴇᴅ ᴡɪᴛʜ ʟᴇᴀᴛʜᴇʀʏ ᴡʀɪɴᴋʟᴇꜱ that ran up and down, crossways and around. All seemed to empty, like the tributaries of a great river, into the deep groove which fell from each side of his nose to the corners of the wide mouth. His hair was as white as this paper, and just as smooth.

While talking, he would blow away a wisp of unruly hair from his eye with a sudden gust of breath from the puckered-up corner of his mouth. Then he would pass the back of a gnarled hand over his face rapidly, as if trying to brush away a bothersome fly.

He still had his original teeth, but they were worn down to the gums.

His eyelids were red and the lashes were almost all gone, but there was not even faint evidence of "arcus senilis," the telltale white circle in the eyes of the aged. On the contrary, his eyes, clear as a child's, were filled with twinkles.

Why bother telling you about this old man? Let him answer the question himself.

"Doctor, I suppose you wonder whether it's any use tinkering with an old wreck like me. To put you straight, I'm old, but I'm not ready for the junk-heap yet. Life is still sweet. You can go all out with repairs. I have faith that I'll pull through."

He had a bad heart. He had lost forty pounds in the last four months. "All I have is a little indigestion," he said. The X ray report, on my desk, contradicted him. His daughter and son, who were with him, knew what it showed; probably cancer of the stomach with involvement of the head of the pancreas.

If what the X ray seemed to indicate was true, it was a death warrant. What should I do? For a younger patient, I would have insisted on an exploratory operation—even if the outlook seemed hopeless. For an elderly patient, often he or his family must make the choice.

This patient made it when he said, "You can go all out with repairs." The surgeon had him on the operating table—bad heart and all—for about four hours. He found a gall bladder bound down by adhesions, and a large chronic duodenal ulcer whose adhesions had pulled the end of the stomach to the pancreas. All of this had simulated a cancer on the X-ray plates.

The gall bladder was removed; also about three quarters of the stomach. He had no post-operative complication and he is alive today—about three years after his operation. His eye-twinkles have increased in number and intensity.

Every physician can turn to his filing cabinet and pull out case histories like this one, cases that lift up his spirits. In his daily struggle to stave off sudden disaster, he has to remember these cases with the unexpected happy endings. He meets plenty of the other kind.

For example, there is the simple matter-of-course operation which develops unpredictable complications—a clot forms in the blood, pulmonary embolism results, and death comes swiftly. Or the heart patient who shows every sign of getting better, then skids downhill to extinction. Or the child who develops an incurable disease almost out of nowhere. We watch, helplessly, as his life fades away.

This is the physician's daily fare. It is often the reason for the disquietude that dogs his days and his nights. Commonly referred to as "hard-hearted" and "case-hardened," the doctor never quite gets used to human suffering.

Personally, after many years of practice, I am more affected by the patient's discomforts and the family's losses than I was as an intern. Instead of steeling the doctor against human suffering, I think years of practice soften him.

His outward "coolness under fire" is but the measure of equanimity which he has developed over the years. Sir William Osler recommends this as the necessary trait of the good physician. The physician, at least, must remain calm during the sudden squall or the prolonged storm—otherwise there is danger that the patient and his family will be blown away by lack of confidence and loss of hope. And hope and confidence are requisites for recovery.

I remember another patient whose case was like the old man's —and remember the night of his trouble. It was sweltering. I had been reading in bed because I couldn't fall asleep. I looked up. The hands of the clock had just parted company at midnight, like a tall friend and a short one saying goodbye. As I reached to turn off the light, the telephone rang.

"Come quick. It's my dad."

When I reached the caller's house, I found the patient moribund. No pulse perceptible, blood pressure zero, breathing shallow. Skin covered with a layer of beady sweat. A faraway groan and features set in a mask of agony. It was one of the most severe cases of coronary occlusion I have personally observed.

I provided what is standard, routine treatment in such emergencies. After several hours of stimulation, and hoping, and the family's bedside prayers, life seemed slowly to return to the dying man's body. His blood pressure rose to about forty and his pulse became perceptible, although it was still weak and thready.

How long did this "near-corpse" survive? One day, one month, one year? Eighteen years is the answer. And if this were a fictional short story, the ending would be unbelievable. He died not of coronary disease, not of heart disease. It was cancer, in the late sixties, that finally stamped his case as "closed."

A number of years ago, one of my best friends, a man in his fifties, suffered a coronary attack. Four times, that first night, "specials" and floor nurses rushed into the nearby room in which I was resting, to say: "Your patient is going—or gone!"

These were not cries of wolf-wolf. Each time he had had a short attack of cardiac standstill followed by convulsions. Each attack seemed his last. But each time it was possible to relieve the attack with an injection of adrenalin.

The next day the storm had blown over. Convalescence was smooth. He is alive today.

The layman is understandably frightened about coronary occlusion. Yet it is reassuring to know that there are many cases like the two I have described, and many patients have survived their original attack by twenty-five years or more. A few patients (mentioned in medical literature) have even lived and worked with both coronary arteries shut off (their branches had formed sufficient collateral circulation to take over).

If these recoveries seem amazing, consider the following one— one I shall never forget. There was a little girl in diabetic coma in the hospital where I served my internship. "One hundred out of one hundred such cases die," was the medical opinion at that time. What about insulin? Few had heard of it. We physicians knew it was being developed by Doctors Best and Banting in their laboratory in Canada, but not that it was an actuality yet. When would it be available for a sweet little girl like this one—and for all the other diabetics who were dying in coma?

The time was then. Insulin had just become available. It was flown to the hospital. It was administered. Later, that girl walked out of the hospital, one of the first in a long series of miracles that insulin has produced.

For the last twenty years, I have been taking care of a man— now about sixty-eight—who developed a puzzling blood disease about six years ago. It seemed at first to be a simple anemia. But, as time went on, his weakness became more pronounced, his skin and inner eyelids as pale as inner lemon peel. His red-blood-cell count fell to a fraction of normal.

At first he had a blood transfusion every month or two. Later this became a necessary procedure weekly and biweekly. He had over sixty transfusions.

An eminent out-of-town authority on diseases of the blood, to whom I had referred him, had said: "It's a destructive anemia of some kind. Can't find the cause and haven't the cure. Keep transfusing him to keep him alive until something comes along that is more specific."

And something did come along as it had for the little girl in the diabetic coma. ACTH and cortisone were discovered. I sent him to the blood specialist again. The specialist decided to try these drugs. The result was remarkable. The patient's red-blood-cell count increased spectacularly. He has not required a thimbleful of blood in a year. All he takes is one cortisone pill a day. His cheeks are pink, he is strong and healthy.

Such are the cases that instill new vigor into the old phrase, "Where there's life, there's hope."

When I am asked: "What was your most dramatic experience in medicine?", I always answer: "Performing my first blood transfusion over twenty-five years ago."

In the beginning, I used to think that I answered this question too quickly; that I should have considered the multitude of tense situations that are part and parcel of the doctor's everyday routine. But as the years slide by, I can find nothing else as interesting and arresting. So I cling to my first impression.

The blood transfusion, a quarter of a century ago, was a special event. It was not used as frequently—and easily—as it is today. There were no blood banks. When a sudden emergency occurred, we had to search madly for donors: a son, a daughter, a wife, or a father whose blood matched the patient's. After transferring the blood, we waited tensely to see what would happen next. The technique was new and often we could not predict the outcome.

Yes, blood transfusion was drama in those days. For example, in about 1925, I was called to do an emergency transfusion. A woman of forty had just given birth to a baby. Everything had been going well when sudden hemorrhage occurred and her pulse shot up to about 200 per minute; she was in a dangerous state of shock.

Every treatment tried did no good; she seemed to be going fast. Death was at the foot of the stairs walking confidently up to the obstetrical room to take her away.

She was now cold, clammy, and restless (as all bled-out patients are). She was the ghostliest white I had ever seen anyone —except for the horror-stricken obstetrician who had just delivered her. He seemed about to faint.

The intern and I finished scrubbing our hands and arms. It doesn't hurt my conscience to say that in this case the scrubbing was as hurried as the behind-the-ear ministrations of some little boys when they are asked to wash up.

On one table lay the mother. She was now very still; the only movement detectable was the upward rolling of her eyeballs. Her face was now almost lost on the whiteness of the surface where her head rested. A few feet away on a parallel table lay a young girl in her early twenties—a daughter born to this woman when she was seventeen.

The daughter's cheeks were, by comparison, like red roses in full bloom. They were smooth, and flushed by anxiety and excitement. Mother and daughter were quickly draped. All you could see were two faces and two arms. The scalpel cut down on the mother's vein. It was like working on a corpse. A needle was soon in the daughter's vein. What we took from one we pumped into the other. After the tenth syringeful of blood, you could see the mother's eyelids flicker a little. Into the white of her face began to creep a distant pink tint.

The nurse, holding the patient's hand and searching for a pulse, began to smile. The beats were coming through. You could sense the relief in everyone—we all seemed to sigh together.

Man loves to cheat death. It is the greatest thrill in winning that any game or contest can offer. And when the victory is attained by the return, to a dying mother, of a quart of the blood she gave to her unborn daughter many years before, the sheer human joy of the triumph is overwhelming.

Such triumphs, such amazing cases of recovery are not exceptional in medical practice. Any doctor who digs deep into his files—or his memory—can recount dozens of remarkable recoveries like these. If they teach a doctor anything at all, they teach him never to despair. If we wait for miracles—and work for miracles—often they will come.

Chapter 49

If Hippocrates Returned

Aʙᴏᴜᴛ ᴛᴡᴇɴᴛʏ-ꜰɪᴠᴇ ʜᴜɴᴅʀᴇᴅ ʏᴇᴀʀꜱ ʙᴀᴄᴋ, in ancient Greece, there was a physician named Hippocrates. He healed the sick, and taught young men in Athens, Delos, and Larissa how to be doctors. He took up his primitive pen and wrote some of the first treatises we have on medicine, surgery, and health. Because he accomplished so much with so little, in such a remote age, we call him the Father of Medicine.

If you read the writings and teachings of Hippocrates, his associates and disciples, you will admire the consecration of these physicians to their work, their inventiveness, their good common sense. For we must remember they worked in darkness.

Given the searching light of our present knowledge, they would have been as skilled in medicine and surgery as we are today. The potential capacity of man's brain has changed little, if at all, since Hippocrates' time. We seem much smarter than our ancestors, but that is because we know more, not because we have greater intelligence.

If Hippocrates returned today, he would see that much on which he speculated has come true. He would see much that he never even dreamed of, now actual reality. And he would see many of his practical precepts and procedures still in use—for instance, blood-letting, bowel cleansing, immobilization of fractures, hydrotherapy, and psychosomatic approaches to the treatment of the patient. Had he returned some centuries ago instead of today he would still walk in semi-darkness. Until three hundred years ago, for example, we did not even understand the circulation of the blood. The greatest medical advances have come recently—as measured against the backdrop of thousands of years.

The person who is dissatisfied with what the medical profession can accomplish probably remembers the failures and forgets the triumphs. Hippocrates, returned from the grave, would not be displeased with our progress in medicine. He would see the dread scourges of the past safely shackled—typhoid, smallpox, diphtheria, yellow fever, and the others. He would watch, with amazed eyes, how we destroy tuberculosis. Pneumonia, the former Captain of the Men of Death (as Osler termed it) is not the fear-inspiring disease it was just a decade ago. Malaria can be controlled. Life has been prolonged for tens of years in formerly hopeless cardiacs. Cancer can be cured—if the patient reports early enough.

Philosopher though he was, Hippocrates would not be able to remain calm while he viewed our progress in surgery and medical treatment. He would see how doctors open the skull and remove brain tumors and operate outside and inside the heart. He would behold them removing an entire lung and then observe life going on practically as before. He would see insulin, metrazol, and electric shock treatment performing marvels for the mentally sick.

No end to the wonders Hippocrates would find—X rays diagnosing and treating, radium destroying new growths, radioactive isotopes (a by-product of uranium and other metals combined with substances like phosphorus and iodine) searching out and destroying previously inaccessible cancers. Syphilis and gonorrhea at the mercy of the sulfas and anti-biotics like penicillin, aureomycin and terramycin; subacute bacterial endocarditis no longer the infallible killer it used to be, now that these drugs have come into use. The diabetic living with insulin, as long as his healthy neighbor; the victim of pernicious anemia made hale and strong by liver extracts and specialized vitamins.

Hippocrates would be delighted by our medical gadgets, like the stethoscope, which was invented by a Frenchman only a few hundred years ago; he would be intrigued by our comparatively recent blood-pressure measuring apparatus. The electrocardiograph in heart diagnosis, the electro-encephalograph in brain diagnosis, the fluoroscope (to see the actual beating of the heart and the dome of the diaphragm as it moves up and down with each breath)—these would make him pinch himself to be sure he was awake, and not still dreaming of the medicine of the future.

He would peer through a microscope and wonder at the cocci and bacilli there. He would attend operations and see the surgeons scrubbing, scrubbing, scrubbing—arms later dipped up to the elbows into disinfecting fluids—rubber gloves pulled on—and the white garments coming out of the huge sterilizing machines. He would see the patient carefully prepared, the site of operation thoroughly cleaned and surrounded by sterile drapes. He would learn the reasons for this and the importance of the little streptococci, staphylococci, and bacilli he saw under the microscope. He would then know why mothers can bear children without dying from infections, as they did in his time.

Our dazzled Greek would ponder another miracle—modern anesthesia in all its forms: spinal, local, intravenous, and general. He would consider the modern physician incredibly fortunate in having any of these at his disposal, not to mention being able to choose between making the patient oblivious of his surroundings or allowing him to stay awake—to observe and hear what is being done to his body but not to feel pain in the observing. In Hippocrates' time, and almost up to our own, people suffered direly from the pain of operation, often died of shock.

Hippocrates, making the rounds with us, probably would be overcome by the impact of the total mass of new diagnoses, treatments and preventive aspects in modern medicine, of which I have mentioned only a small part. Though he might in many ways question our social progress (man's attitudes toward himself and society are still prescientific), he would have to bow mutely before our achievements in science.

Having seen our modern world, it is unlikely that Hippocrates could ever return to the past. Like many of us, he would doubtless wish to journey into the future. Fifty years from now, man will truly live in an age of miracles, unspeakable and inconceivable. Hippocrates would find the greatest accomplishments of our time very petty compared to our children's works and wonders.

New drugs will have been discovered to abolish the severest pain. There will be specific cures for the thousands of presently hopeless sufferers from schizophrenia and the manic-depressive psychoses. There will be few neuroses; a harmless drug will wash chronic anxiety out of the minds of men. (The individual and his environment will thus become friends rather than remain enemies.) The tribulations of male and female change of life will be a thing of the past. Future Eddie Cantors and Bing Crosbys will have one joke less—the "all-girl" or "all-boy" families; there will be simple methods for selecting the sex of our children. There will be fewer childless marriages.

There will be sure-acting, harmless drugs to melt excess fat, or promote a good night's sleep. There will be anti-worry and anti-prolonged-grief drugs. There will be magnetic teeth—better than the originals.

Arteriosclerosis will be delayed. Coronary artery disease will not come until the last of life. Life will be lived vigorously to eighty and prolonged on the average to ninety or one hundred years. High blood pressure will be nonexistent because the specific cause will have been found and the proper antidote administered.

A simple routine test will discover cancer at its earliest inception. The disease will be localized quickly and exterminated by new methods which do not require operation.

It will be possible to replace bad hearts with good ones, bad kidneys with sound ones. Diseases of the blood will not be a complete mystery. No child (or adult) will be struck down by poliomyelitis. Normal sex life will be prolonged in all its early virility.

There will be earlier retirement. Parents will not live with their children; they will prefer ultra-modern villages with special conveniences for oldsters, which will become a necessity as medicine lengthens life.

Allergies of all kinds will be prevented and easily cured. And the common cold (I hear your sigh of relief) will be wiped out the moment it appears.

Only death will not have been conquered. That will only be because fifty years is such a brief span of time. I believe it was Hippocrates who commented, over two thousand years ago, that art—the art of medicine—is long.

Epilogue:

Away with the Calendar

Calendar, calendar,
Tell me the day.
Seems so funny
You can tell me the day
When you are only papers
With numbers on you.

(An unsigned poem by a lad of seven; from
the book section of the New York Times)

Man would be happier if he lost all track of time. But life
does not let him forget. The doctor asks, invariably: "How old
are you?" The vote registrar asks: "How old are you?" You want
a passport: "Your age, please." You want a marriage license:
"And your age?" You are admitted to a hospital: "How old
were you on your last birthday?" Birth certificate, college admission certificate, army discharge certificate—all ask: How old?
How old? They even are curious about your age when you die,
but somebody else answers then.

And so it goes; I was going to say ad infinitum—but it isn't
quite so long as that. Only a matter of seventy or eighty years.

Have you ever been at a party which you enjoyed so much that
you and the other guests forgot to refer to your watches? Then,
at about 2 or 3 A.M. one of the convivial gathering gasps, "God—
do you know what *time* it is?"

Everybody begins to chatter at once and make excuses to the
host for overstaying his welcome. But the host says: "Forget it"—
and means it. And you know he means it because everybody has
had such a good time.

Deep down, you say to yourself you're glad you did not look
for the time around midnight, because you might have missed

two more of the best hours of the evening.

Or, having looked and having stayed, your joy would have been diluted by the overhanging, ever-present realization that "it's getting late." If you have had the feelings I have described—and who hasn't had at least one such experience when visiting—you will know what I mean when I say that being calendar-conscious is like being clock-conscious, only worse.

If it were possible to devise some other, less joy-spoiling device than the calendar to prevent the workaday world from bogging down, it would be an earth-shaking discovery. Man could then go about his business without feeling that time and life are slipping from him.

Many young-old people I know have not been willing to wait for such a contribution to the welfare of the human race. They have taken matters into their own hands. They have become oblivious to the passage of time. And it isn't a pose! It is something, a belief, that they have woven into the very daily fabric of living.

I remember many such spiritful people. Two stand out. They are cousins. One is ninety-five, the other eighty-eight.

Merely to be in their presence is a process of rejuvenation of the body and mind. The man or woman of forty, fifty, or sixty who has convinced himself that the sweetest part of life has fled, has only to hear them and see them to be influenced for the better.

You might say: "It's easy for them. They have been blessed with good health and good fortune. Their brain arteries are soft and elastic; they have no advanced arteriosclerosis, which, depriving the mind of proper circulation, projects many oldsters into the senile second childhood which Shakespeare described so well."

But recall. How many crotchety healthy old persons have you met in your life who bewailed age long before their dotage? They were difficult and obtuse and stubborn and gloomy in their forties and fifties or even earlier. Old age, I've suggested, is but the extension of youth and middle age. You don't find the trunk of an apple tree branching off into one limb giving forth cherries and another, peaches.

I have known these wonderful women for twenty-five years. They look the same and act the same now as when I first met them. The younger sculpts, paints, and writes poems and short stories. The other day, in a local paper, I read a long poem she wrote describing the wonders of an automobile trip to Canada. The words love, sunset, sunrise, beauty, flowers, sweetness were there in abundance, modified by a profusion of exuberant adjectives. Had you not known the author, you would have guessed her to be a teen-ager, overcome by love and wonder at the beauty of nature.

It would have been hard for you to believe that the author was eighty-eight. This poem was no sudden, effusive last gasp by an oldster who had been privileged suddenly to see the sun of her youth through a parting of the clouds. No. She has been writing poetry all her life. Her secret is that she never stopped writing it. She never considered herself "too old for such nonsense!"

And why? Because she saw years ago that growing old need not mar the enjoyment of living, and tore her personal calendar into shreds. Had she decided otherwise, her spirit would not be so contagious and refreshing. Words would no longer spill from her in rivulets and torrents of enthusiasm. Her sense of loss would have sapped her natural vitality.

But it hasn't, in any sense. She will ask you what you think of Shostakovitch; or Stravinsky's latest. Being a co-spirit, she will tell you how much she enjoys Grandma Moses and her painting. Why doesn't the Administration do this? And why did the Governor do that? And after commenting on the sad state of the world today, she invariably brightens and says: "But this is today. Wait until you see tomorrow. The world is bound to improve. It always has."

And the ninety-five-year-old? She is the leader of the two, having been accustomed to giving orders all her life. She is the practical one. She reads a local paper and the New York *Times* every day.

"I couldn't possibly go on without my *Times*," she says. On her night table you will see *Harper's*, *The Atlantic Monthly*, *Time* and *Reader's Digest*. "Doctor," she will say, "I've just read the most stimulating piece. Here. You must take the magazine along with you." And there is no saying no. Her eyes are young-bright, and her ears readily catch the singing of the birds in the morning. Her phone keeps her busy. Many persons, her juniors by decades, call her for advice in business and personal affairs. She is a leader in community drives and many other charitable enterprises.

When you meet her for the first time, she will appraise you in a glance that takes you in from head to foot. Thereafter she rarely looks you in the eye. "I size up a person by his voice," she says. "When I look into a person's eyes I often am thrown off the right track. Eyes can fool me. A voice never can."

Mention her age to her and she really becomes provoked. "Why should people send me flowers and other gifts simply because I'm ninety-five? They're being nice, but I don't see the reason for it.

"Birthdays are all right when you're a growing infant. Personally, I'd rather cut a piece of juicy applepie than the most beautiful birthday cake in the world."

A few months ago I was called to her home because she had a cold. *She* never calls. Her cousin of eighty-eight, who hovers over her like a mother hen, always does the telephoning. "Doctor, come over this morning. But *please* don't say I called. She'll *never* forgive me."

This ritual has been performed many times over the last quarter-century. I was amused by it when I was a young doctor; the years have only intensified my pleasure in playing my part.

I ring the bell and the younger one opens the door a crack. She sees me and her face lights up. She closes the door, but not quietly enough; "Who's that?" a shrill voice asks from the upper bedroom. Then all is quiet.

The two of us start up the stairs—she behind me. "You go first Doctor, I don't want her to see me. Remember to tell her you were just passing by and dropped in to say hello!"

I reach the door, knock and walk in. She is propped up in bed on three or four pillows, studiously examining her morning paper. She looks as intent and absorbed as a fourth-grader reading a favorite story. "Good morning," I say.

She looks up startled as a deer caught in a car's headlights. "Why, Doctor! Oh! *I* know who's been up to her tricks again. Well, you may as well stay as long as you're here. But I look a mess. Better wait in the other room until I have time to get presentable."

The younger cousin walks in, and while she is hearing protestations, helps freshen her companion.

"Come in, Doctor."

And I find what I have expected—and what I have seen so many years. The bed is covered with a gaily designed bedspread. Our ninety-five-year-old sits there in a pale blue bedjacket, her hair hidden by a frilly headdress. She is all smiles. It becomes a friendly visit. All her distress at the sudden intrusion has dissipated.

There's no better way that I know to begin a day than by a visit with these two gentle ladies who refuse to accept the calendar as a necessary and established institution.

Once I said to the ninety-five-year-old (I think she was ninety-three at the time): "Take this prescription as directed. One teaspoonful before each meal." She looked at the prescription, looked up at me seriously and said: "I have complete confidence in you, Doctor. But tell me—how will this medicine affect me in *later life?*"

Some time ago, at the Berkshire Festival, I sat only a few feet from Fritz Kreisler at a performance of the Boston Symphony Orchestra. Although I enjoyed Dr. Munch's interpretation that evening, most of my visual attention was devoted to watching this wonderful man, Kreisler. He wore an earpiece, which seemed to intensify his own absorption in the concert.

I watched him as the music enveloped the music-shed. He looked ecstatic. Such rapture, such joy, such enthusiasm you can only find in the artist who himself has dispensed those emotional gifts.

Kreisler, too, is ageless. I know now why I used to leave his recitals, when I was a student of the violin as a boy, and spend a sleepless night—waiting for the daylight so I could practice without disturbing the neighbors and my family. The spirit which I saw here was but an extension of what he had infused into me when he himself held the center of the stage. There's no calendar in Kreisler's life.

Is there a calendar in Einstein's life as he walks the Princeton campus eating an ice cream cone? Is there a calendar in Bernard Baruch's life as he sits on his park bench and benignly holds court with the press? It's not necessary to remind you of the ancient great who were ageless. And many now living remember the Fords, Edisons and Firestones. And of course, there is Toscanini.

Once, I sat next to Robert Frost—when he was in his early seventies. He was waiting to be called upon to read his poetry. It was at a large informal gathering near his home in Vermont. Having finished his readings, he walked out into the garden. The applause had seemed to make him feel ill at ease.

As I was near the door, the program chairman gestured to me to invite Mr. Frost back. I was almost overcome by the poet's humility. When I asked him if he would acknowledge the applause, he turned to me and said, like a little boy: "Do they really want me?"

So you see, not only the small, but the great, may be ageless. They go on, doing as they did when they were more youthful. Their youth is of the spirit. It is something divorced from the body.

Such are the ones who seem to have realization that life does not go on forever—yet are not dismayed or prematurely broken down by this knowledge. Instead they go about their living intent on squeezing the most out of each day. They are jealous of their youth and will not be called old. Still, they do not clutch at youth; they hold on gracefully and firmly.

To another eighty-year-old lady who asked me: "Am I well enough to continue riding my horse three times a week, Doctor?", I answered: "Ride." To a seventy-five-year-old great-grandmother who insisted on "not only swimming but diving" (her blood pressure had been over 200 for years) my answer was: "Dive." I could not allow even a thin shadow of old age to fall on one of the ageless.

I have never seen a young-old person who did not have many interests. People may be born with the gift for remaining youthful; but I think most of us can remain youthful if we will learn—early—to live with bright eyes and attentive ears, a warm heart and an inquiring, curious mind.

There is only one way to thumb your nose at death: Don't spend your years waiting for him to carry you off. Treat him as though he didn't exist—he doesn't, really, for those who are truly alive. And remember that your youthfulness will die, if you allow yourself to be vulnerable to the sharp lunges of the calendar when another birthday comes around. Age is something that you must learn *early* to take on the chin. Away with the calendar if you want to learn how to live!

Further, young or old, you need a working philosophy that will satisfy your inner craving for a happy, fulfilled way of life. The core of your thinking, whether you are conscious of it or not, must rest on the realization that human beings—as all living things —tread a one-way street. Therefore, you must make the most of life as you live it day by day.

Marcus Aurelius gave us more than a hint when he wrote: "Do not act as if thou wert going to live ten thousand years." In modern dress: *You only live once*.

Never have I read a more beautiful—yet practical—formula for living than that written by Helen Keller: "I who am blind can give one hint to those who see—one admonition to those who would make full use of the gift of sight: Use your eyes as if tomorrow you would be stricken blind. And the same method can be applied to the other senses. Hear the music of voices, the song of a bird, the mighty strains of an orchestra as if you would be stricken deaf tomorrow. Touch each object you want to touch as if tomorrow your tactile senses would fail. Smell the perfume of flowers, taste with relish each morsel, as if tomorrow you could never smell and taste again. Make the most of every sense. Glory in all the facets of pleasure and beauty which the world reveals to you through the several means of contact which Nature provides."